2 —

This book belongs to
Dr K R C Mamander
108 coover Hall
Iowa State

Power System Stability:

SYNCHRONOUS
MACHINES

Power System Stability:

SYNCHRONOUS
MACHINES

By

Edward Wilson Kimbark

Head, Network Analog Group, Branch of
Bonneville Power Administration System Engineering,
Fellow I. E. E. E.

DOVER PUBLICATIONS, INC., NEW YORK

Published in Canada by General Publishing Company, Ltd., 30 Lesmill Road, Don Mills, Toronto, Ontario.
Published in the United Kingdom by Constable and Company, Ltd., 10 Orange Street, London WC 2.

This Dover edition, first published in 1968, is an unabridged republication of the work published in 1956 by John Wiley & Sons, Inc., New York.

Library of Congress Catalog Card Number: 68-12937

Manufactured in the United States of America
Dover Publications, Inc.
180 Varick Street
New York, N.Y. 10014

To my wife

RUTH MERRICK KIMBARK

PREFACE

This is the third volume of a three-volume work on power-system stability intended for use by power-system engineers and by graduate students. It grew out of lectures given by the author at Northwestern University in graduate evening courses.

Volume I, which appeared in 1948, covers the elements of the stability problem, the principal factors affecting stability, the ordinary simplified methods of making stability calculations, and illustrations of the application of these methods in studies which have been made on actual power systems.

Volume II, which appeared in 1950, covers power circuit breakers and protective relays and the influence of these devices on power-system stability.

Volume III, the present one, deals with the theory of synchronous machines and their excitation systems, an understanding of which is necessary for the justification of the simplifying assumptions ordinarily used in stability calculations and for carrying out calculations for the extraordinary cases in which greater accuracy is desired than that afforded by the simplified methods. This volume discusses such effects as saliency, damping, saturation, and high-speed excitation. It thus endeavors to give the reader a deeper understanding of power-system stability than that afforded by Volume I alone. Steady-state stability, which was discussed very sketchily in Volume I, is treated more fully in the present volume.

Volume I should be considered to be a prerequisite to the present volume, but Volume II should not.

I wish to acknowledge my indebtedness in connection with this volume, as well as with the preceding ones, to the following persons:

To my wife, Ruth Merrick Kimbark, for typing the entire manuscript and for her advice and inspiration.

To J. E. Hobson, W. A. Lewis, and E. T. B. Gross for reviewing the manuscript in its earlier form and for making many suggestions for its improvement. (They did not, however, review recent changes and additions and thus cannot be blamed for any shortcomings which this volume may now have.)

To manufacturers, authors, and publishers who supplied illustrations or gave permission for the use of material previously published elsewhere. Credit for such material is given at the place where it appears.

EDWARD WILSON KIMBARK

Seattle, Washington
November, 1955

CONTENTS

Power System Stability:

SYNCHRONOUS MACHINES

CHAPTER XII

SYNCHRONOUS MACHINES

Since the problem of power-system stability is to determine whether or not the various synchronous machines on the system will remain in synchronism with one another, the characteristics of those synchronous machines obviously play an important part in the problem.

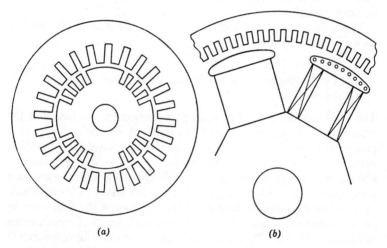

FIG. 1. Cross sections of synchronous machines, (a) round-rotor type, (b) salient-pole type.

Synchronous machines are classified into two principal types — round-rotor machines and salient-pole machines (Fig. 1). Generators driven by steam turbines (turbogenerators) have cylindrical (round) rotors with slots in which distributed field windings are placed. Most cylindrical rotors are made of solid steel forgings, though a few of them are built up from thick steel disks. The number of poles is two, four, or six. Most new machines are two-pole. Generators driven by water wheels (hydraulic turbines) have laminated salient-pole rotors with concentrated field windings and, usually, a large number of poles. Some water-wheel generators are provided with amortisseur windings

1

or damper windings; others are not. Synchronous motors and condensers have salient-pole rotors with amortisseur windings. Synchronous converters have rotating armatures and salient-pole stationary fields with amortisseurs.

In the foregoing chapters it was assumed that each synchronous machine could be represented by a constant reactance in series with a constant voltage, and, furthermore, that the mechanical angle of the rotor of each machine coincided with the electrical phase of that constant voltage of the machine. In view of the importance of synchronous machines in the stability problem, these assumptions require further investigation, both to justify the use of the assumptions in the ordinary case and to provide more rigorous methods of calculation in those extraordinary cases where the usual assumptions do not give accurate enough results.

The usual assumptions may be in error because of three phenomena, each of which requires consideration:

1. Saliency.
2. Field decrement and voltage-regulator action.
3. Saturation.

The word *saliency* is used as a short expression for the fact that the rotor of a synchronous machine has different electric and magnetic properties on two axes 90 elec. deg. apart — the *direct axis*, or axis of symmetry of a field pole, and the *quadrature axis*, or axis of symmetry midway between two field poles. This difference between the two axes is present not only in salient-pole machines but also, to a lesser extent, in round-rotor machines, because of the presence of the field winding on the direct axis only. In this respect both kinds of synchronous machines differ from induction machines. The effect of saliency will be considered first while the effects of field decrement, voltage-regulator action, and magnetic saturation are disregarded; later, these other effects will also be taken into account. A knowledge of synchronous-machine reactances, resistances, time constants, and vector diagrams is necessary to the understanding of all these effects.

REACTANCES, RESISTANCES, AND TIME CONSTANTS

As has already been noted, a synchronous machine is often represented in a circuit diagram (the positive-sequence network) by a constant reactance in series with a constant voltage. What reactance should be used for that purpose? A great many synchronous-machine reactances have been defined; for example, direct- and quadrature-axis synchronous, transient, and subtransient reactances. Before proceeding to define these reactances we may profitably review the fundamental concepts of inductance and of inductive reactance.

Fundamental concepts of inductance. The concepts of electric current and of lines of magnetic flux are familiar to all students of electricity. Since a line of flux is always a closed curve and an electric circuit is likewise a closed path,* a given flux line either does not link a given electric circuit at all or it does link it one or more times. Thus

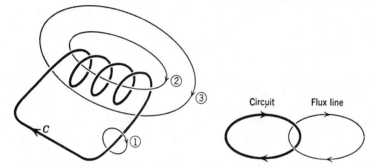

FIG. 2. Illustrating flux linkages.

FIG. 3. A line of magnetic flux constitutes a positive flux linkage with an electric circuit if it is related to the circuit according to the right-hand rule. A diagram similar to this one appears on the emblem of the A.I.E.E.

in Fig. 2 flux line 1 links circuit C once, line 2 links it four times, and line 3 does not link it at all. The *flux linkage ψ* of a circuit is defined as the algebraic sum of the numbers of linkages of all the lines of flux linking the circuit, the positive direction of linkage being taken according to Fig. 3. Thus in Fig. 2, if there were no flux lines linking the circuit except those shown, and if each line represented one weber of flux, the flux linkage of the circuit would be $-1 + 4 + 0 = 3$ weber-turns. In general, the flux should be divided into infinitesimal parts $d\phi$, each represented by a line or tube linking the circuit n times; the flux linkage of the circuit is then given by

$$\psi = \int n \, d\phi \quad \text{weber-turns} \qquad [1]$$

*The flux linkage of a *part* of a circuit, such as a winding of a machine, which is not a closed path, can be defined as the linkage of the closed path formed by the winding and a short line from one terminal of the winding to the other.

According to *Faraday's law of electromagnetic induction*, any change in the flux linkage of a circuit induces an electromotive force e, the sign and magnitude of which are given by

$$e = - \frac{d\psi}{dt} \quad \text{volts} \tag{2}$$

where t is time in seconds. A positive e.m.f. tends to set up a positive current (that is, a current in the direction of the circuit, Fig. 3). The applied e.m.f. required to overcome the induced e.m.f. is of opposite sign from the latter. Faraday's law is perfectly general: it holds whether the change of flux is caused by a change of current in the circuit considered, by a change of current in another circuit, by a deformation of the circuit, by relative motion of one circuit with respect to another, or by relative motion of magnetic materials or permanent magnets with respect to the circuit.

There are some circuits the flux linkages of which are substantially proportional to the current:

$$\psi = Li \quad \text{weber-turns} \tag{3}$$

where L is the *self-inductance* of the circuit in henrys and i is the current of the circuit in amperes. The self-inductance of such a circuit may be regarded as the flux linkage per ampere:

$$L = \frac{\psi}{i} \quad \text{henrys} \tag{4}$$

It is always a positive quantity, because, according to the right-hand rule and the sign convention of Fig. 3, a positive current sets up a positive linkage, and a negative current, a negative linkage.

Substitution of eq. 3 into eq. 2 yields, for the e.m.f. of self-induction,

$$e = - \frac{d}{dt}(Li) \quad \text{volts} \tag{5}$$

If the self-inductance L does not vary with time, this equation may be put in the customary form,

$$e = -L\frac{di}{dt} \quad \text{volts} \tag{6}$$

It would be decidedly unwise to assume constant self-inductance for the windings of rotating machines, where iron parts of the magnetic circuit are in motion relative to the windings. For such windings the more general equations 2 or 5 should be used. In cases where eq. 6

holds, however, the self-inductance can be defined by

$$L = -\frac{e}{di/dt} \qquad [7]$$

This relation is ordinarily used in defining the unit of inductance, the henry, as the inductance of a coil in which an e.m.f. of 1 volt is induced by a current changing at the rate of 1 amp. per second.

There are some circuits in which the flux linkage depends only upon the current in the same circuit, but is not directly proportional to the current because of the presence of saturating iron (see Fig. 4). The self-inductance of such a circuit can be defined by

$$L = \frac{d\psi}{di} \qquad [8]$$

Then, since

$$\frac{d\psi}{dt} = \frac{d\psi}{di} \cdot \frac{di}{dt} = L\frac{di}{dt} \qquad [9]$$

eq. 6 is still valid. However, the concept of inductance is useful chiefly where the linear relation of eq. 3 holds.

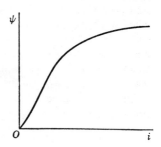

FIG. 4. Relation between flux linkage and current of a winding on a closed iron core.

Mutual inductance. There are some groups of inductively coupled circuits where the flux linkage of any circuit is a linear function of the currents in all the circuits, thus:

$$\psi_1 = L_{11}i_1 + L_{12}i_2 + L_{13}i_3 \cdots \qquad [10a]$$

$$\psi_2 = L_{21}i_1 + L_{22}i_2 + L_{23}i_3 \cdots \qquad [10b]$$

$$\psi_3 = L_{31}i_1 + L_{32}i_2 + L_{33}i_3 \cdots \qquad [10c]$$

$$\cdot$$
$$\cdot$$
$$\cdot$$

Here L_{11}, L_{22}, L_{33} are the self-inductances of circuits 1, 2, 3; L_{12} is the mutual inductance between circuits 1 and 2; L_{13} is the mutual inductance between circuits 1 and 3, and so on. Although the numerical values of self-inductance are always positive, those of mutual inductance may be either positive or negative, depending on the positive directions chosen arbitrarily for each of two coupled circuits as well as on their geometrical arrangement. The mutual inductance between any two circuits is the same in both directions; that is, $L_{12} = L_{21}$, and so on.*

From eqs. 10 the self- and mutual inductances can be defined by

$$L_{11} = \frac{\partial \psi_1}{\partial i_1} \qquad [11a]$$

$$L_{12} = \frac{\partial \psi_1}{\partial i_2} \qquad [11b]$$

and so on. The definition of self-inductance, eq. 11a, is more general than that of eq. 4 for the single linear circuit and that of eq. 8 for the single nonlinear circuit, and yet it is entirely consistent with them both.

Relation of inductance to the magnetic circuit. The magnetomotive force of a current i_1 amperes flowing in n_1 turns of a conductor surrounding a magnetic circuit is $n_1 i_1$ ampere-turns, and the flux ϕ_{11} due to this m.m.f. is

$$\phi_{11} = \mathcal{P}_{11} n_1 i_1 \quad \text{webers} \qquad [12]$$

where $\mathcal{P}_{11}$ is the permeance of the magnetic circuit in m.k.s. units (webers per ampere-turn, or henrys per turn-squared). The flux linkage of the same electric circuit is

$$\psi_1 = n_1 \phi_{11} = \mathcal{P}_{11} n_1{}^2 i_1 \quad \text{weber-turns} \qquad [13]$$

and the self-inductance of the circuit is

$$L_{11} = \frac{\partial \psi_1}{\partial i_1} = \mathcal{P}_{11} n_1{}^2 \quad \text{henrys} \qquad [14]$$

The flux linking a second electric circuit of n_2 turns due to current i_1 in the first circuit is

$$\phi_{21} = \mathcal{P}_{21} n_1 i_1 \quad \text{webers} \qquad [15]$$

where $\mathcal{P}_{21}$ is the permeance of the mutual flux paths. The flux linkage of circuit 2 due to the current in circuit 1 is

$$\psi_2 = n_2 \phi_{21} = \mathcal{P}_{21} n_2 n_1 i_1 \quad \text{weber-turns} \qquad [16]$$

and the mutual inductance of circuits 1 and 2 is

$$L_{21} = \frac{\partial \psi_2}{\partial i_1} = \mathcal{P}_{21} n_2 n_1 \quad \text{henrys} \qquad [17]$$

*This relation can be proved by deriving and comparing expressions for the energy put into two coupled circuits in order to build up the same magnetic field by each of two different procedures: (1) first establishing current I_1 in circuit 1 while the current in circuit 2 is zero, and then maintaining I_1 constant while current I_2 is established in circuit 2; (2) establishing currents I_2 and I_1 in the opposite order.

Thus both self- and mutual inductance are directly proportional to the permeance, or reciprocal of reluctance, of the associated magnetic circuits and the product of the numbers of turns of the two electric circuits (or square of the number of turns in case of self-inductance).

The permeance $\mathcal{P}$ and reluctance $\mathcal{R}$ of a magnetic circuit depend upon the permeability and dimensions of the circuit, and are given by

$$\frac{1}{\mathcal{P}} = \mathcal{R} = \oint \frac{dl}{\mu A} \qquad [18]$$

where μ is the permeability, A is the cross-sectional area, and l is the length of the magnetic circuit. If μ and A do not vary along the path,

$$\mathcal{P} = \frac{\mu A}{l} \qquad [19]$$

It is often useful to compare inductances of various circuits by comparing the permeabilities, lengths, and cross-sectional areas of the associated magnetic circuits.

Inductive reactance in ohms of a circuit of inductance L is given by

$$X = \omega L = 2\pi f L \qquad [20]$$

where f is the frequency in cycles per second. There are self- and mutual inductive reactances corresponding to self- and mutual inductances. Mutual inductive reactance has the same algebraic sign as the corresponding mutual inductance.

The reactance of a circuit can be determined by circulating in it sinusoidal alternating current, finding the fundamental-frequency component of terminal voltage in quadrature with the current, and taking the ratio of this voltage to the current. The reactance is positive if the voltage leads the current.

$$X = \frac{V \sin \theta}{I} = Z \sin \theta \qquad [21]$$

where I is the current in amperes, V is the fundamental-frequency component of voltage drop in volts, and θ is the angle by which V leads I. V and I may be expressed in either peak or effective values.

Summary of concepts of inductance and inductive reactance. The concept of inductance has been presented from the following viewpoints:

1. Flux linkage per unit current.
2. Induced voltage per unit rate of change of current.

3. Derivative of flux linkage with respect to current.

4. Permeance of the associated magnetic circuit multiplied by the square of the number of turns.

The concept of inductive reactance has been presented from the following viewpoints:

1. Product of angular frequency and inductance.
2. Quadrature voltage per unit current.

Inductances of two coupled circuits (the transformer). Consider two inductively coupled circuits having constant resistances, self-inductances, and mutual inductance, and variable currents and termi-

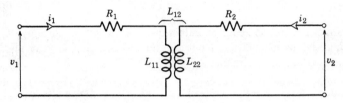

Fig. 5.   Two inductively coupled circuits.

nal voltages, as marked in Fig. 5.   The instantaneous terminal voltages are given in terms of the instantaneous currents and circuit constants by the following equations:

$$v_1 = R_1 i_1 + \frac{d\psi_1}{dt} = R_1 i_1 + L_{11} \frac{di_1}{dt} + L_{12} \frac{di_2}{dt} \qquad [22a]$$

$$v_2 = R_2 i_2 + \frac{d\psi_2}{dt} = R_2 i_2 + L_{22} \frac{di_2}{dt} + L_{12} \frac{di_1}{dt} \qquad [22b]$$

In the steady state, with sinusoidal alternating currents and voltages, the complex terminal voltages are:

$$\mathbf{V}_1 = R_1 \mathbf{I}_1 + j\omega(L_{11}\mathbf{I}_1 + L_{12}\mathbf{I}_2) \qquad [23a]$$

$$\mathbf{V}_2 = R_2 \mathbf{I}_2 + j\omega(L_{22}\mathbf{I}_2 + L_{12}\mathbf{I}_1) \qquad [23b]$$

or

$$\mathbf{V}_1 = \mathbf{Z}_{11}\mathbf{I}_1 + \mathbf{Z}_{12}\mathbf{I}_2 \qquad [24a]$$

$$\mathbf{V}_2 = \mathbf{Z}_{12}\mathbf{I}_1 + \mathbf{Z}_{22}\mathbf{I}_2 \qquad [24b]$$

where

$$\mathbf{Z}_{11} = R_1 + j\omega L_{11} \qquad [25a]$$

$$\mathbf{Z}_{22} = R_2 + j\omega L_{22} \qquad [25b]$$

$$\mathbf{Z}_{12} = \quad 0 + j\omega L_{12} \qquad [25c]$$

Short-circuit impedance and inductance. If the secondary circuit is short-circuited, $V_2 = 0$, and eq. 24b gives the following relation between primary and secondary currents:

$$I_2 = -\frac{Z_{12}}{Z_{22}} I_1 \tag{26}$$

If this value of I_2 is substituted into eq. 24a, the primary voltage is

$$V_1 = \left(Z_{11} - \frac{Z_{12}^2}{Z_{22}} \right) I_1 \tag{27}$$

and the driving-point impedance of the primary circuit with the secondary winding short-circuited is

$$Z_{sc} = \frac{V_1}{I_1} = Z_{11} - \frac{Z_{12}^2}{Z_{22}} \tag{28}$$

The first term of this expression, Z_{11}, is the self-impedance of the primary circuit, which is equal to the ratio V_1/I_1 when the secondary circuit is open or absent; and the second term is called the *reflected impedance* of the secondary circuit. By use of eqs. 25b and 25c, the reflected resistance and reactance may be found as the real and imaginary parts, respectively, of this term.

$$-\frac{Z_{12}^2}{Z_{22}} = -\frac{(j\omega L_{12})^2}{R_2 + j\omega L_{22}} = \frac{\omega^2 L_{12}^2 R_2 - j\omega^3 L_{12}^2 L_{22}}{R_2^2 + \omega^2 L_{22}^2} \tag{29}$$

Since ω, R_2, L_{22}, and L_{12}^2 are all positive numbers (whether L_{12} is positive or negative), the reflected resistance is positive, but the reflected reactance is negative. Therefore the presence of a closed secondary circuit *increases the apparent resistance* of the primary circuit and *decreases its apparent reactance*. The short-circuit reactance of an iron-core transformer may be as low as 1/500th of its open-circuit reactance.

If $R_2^2 \ll \omega^2 L_{22}^2$, then the driving-point impedance becomes

$$Z_{sc} \approx R_1 + \left(\frac{L_{12}}{L_{22}}\right)^2 R_2 + j\omega \left(L_{11} - \frac{L_{12}^2}{L_{22}} \right) \tag{30}$$

The driving-point inductance is

$$L_{sc} \approx L_{11} - \frac{L_{12}^2}{L_{22}} \tag{31}$$

and the driving-point reactance is

$$X_{sc} \approx X_{11} - \frac{X_{12}^2}{X_{22}} \tag{32}$$

The last two equations are similar in form to eq. 28.

Coefficient of coupling and leakage coefficient. Consider two inductively coupled coils 1 and 2 having n_1 and n_2 turns, respectively. Suppose that there is a current i_1 in coil 1 but no current in coil 2. If, under these circumstances, all the flux ϕ_1 due to the current in coil 1 should link all the turns of both coils, the self-inductance of coil 1 would be

$$L_{11} = \frac{n_1 \phi_1}{i_1} \qquad [33]$$

and the mutual inductance of coils 1 and 2 would be

$$L_{12} = \frac{n_2 \phi_1}{i_1} \qquad [34]$$

The ratio would be

$$\frac{L_{12}}{L_{11}} = \frac{n_2}{n_1} \qquad [35]$$

Similarly, with current i_2 in coil 2 and no current in coil 1, if the flux ϕ_2 should link all the turns of both coils, the self-inductance of coil 2 would be

$$L_{22} = \frac{n_2 \phi_2}{i_2} \qquad [36]$$

and the mutual inductance would be

$$L_{12} = \frac{n_1 \phi_2}{i_2} \qquad [37]$$

The ratio would be

$$\frac{L_{12}}{L_{22}} = \frac{n_1}{n_2} \qquad [38]$$

By elimination of n_1/n_2 from eqs. 35 and 38, the value of mutual inductance would be

$$L_{12} = \sqrt{L_{11}L_{22}} \qquad [39]$$

which is the greatest value that L_{12} could possibly have.

Actually, all the flux will not link all the turns of both coils. With current in coil 1 only, the linkages of both coils will be less than that given by eqs. 33 and 34, but, because of leakage flux, the linkage of coil 2 will be reduced more than that of coil 1. Hence

$$\frac{L_{12}}{L_{11}} = k_1 \frac{n_2}{n_1} \qquad [40]$$

where $k_1 < 1$. Similarly, with current in coil 2 only, the linkage of coil 1 is reduced more than that of coil 2, and

$$\frac{L_{12}}{L_{22}} = k_2 \frac{n_1}{n_2} \qquad [41]$$

where $k_2 < 1$. Elimination of n_1/n_2 between eqs. 40 and 41 gives

$$L_{12} = \sqrt{k_1 k_2 L_{11} L_{22}} = k \sqrt{L_{11} L_{22}} \qquad [42]$$

where

$$k = \sqrt{k_1 k_2} = \frac{L_{12}}{\sqrt{L_{11} L_{22}}} < 1 \qquad [43]$$

is the *coefficient of coupling*.

The *leakage coefficient* is defined as

$$\sigma = 1 - k^2 \qquad [44]$$

The short-circuit inductance given by eq. 31 may then be written

$$L_{sc} \approx \sigma L_{11} \qquad [45]$$

Thus the leakage coefficient is the ratio of the apparent inductance of the primary circuit when the secondary winding is short-circuited to that when the secondary circuit is open. This ratio is the same no matter which of the two windings is the primary. The tighter the coupling, the smaller is the leakage coefficient.

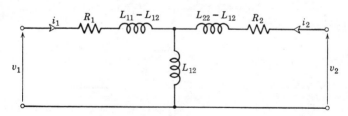

FIG. 6. Equivalent T circuit of the inductively coupled circuits of Fig. 5.

Equivalent T circuits. Equations 22, 23, and 24, which were written for the inductively coupled circuits of Fig. 5, are equally valid for the T circuit of Fig. 6. Therefore, the two circuits are equivalent. The T circuit is not always physically realizable because one of the series inductances, $L_{11} - L_{12}$ or $L_{22} - L_{12}$, may be negative. Although a negative self-inductance may be replaced by a capacitance in the steady state at a single fixed frequency, this substitution is not valid under transient conditions.

The T circuit of Fig. 7 differs from that of Fig. 6 in that the mutual inductance or impedance is multiplied by an arbitrary constant a (usually taken as a positive real number), and the secondary resistance, self-inductance, and impedance are multiplied by a^2. This circuit gives the same primary current and voltage as Figs. 5 and 6 do,

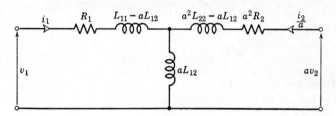

FIG. 7. T circuit that gives the same primary current and voltage as the circuits of Figs. 5 and 6, but different secondary current and voltage.

provided that the secondary current be divided by a and the voltage multiplied by a, as indicated in the figure. The power is correct on both primary and secondary sides. This circuit shows that it would be possible to substitute one closed secondary winding for another without making any difference in the primary current and voltage.

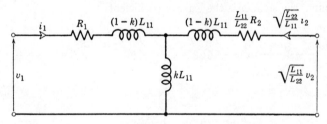

FIG. 8. The circuit of Fig. 7 with $a = \sqrt{L_{11}/L_{22}}$. The inductances of the two series arms are equal.

For example, if the number of secondary turns were doubled and their cross-sectional area halved, and if the winding occupied the same space as before, the mutual inductance and secondary e.m.f. would be doubled, the secondary resistance and self-inductance quadrupled, and the secondary current halved. In this case $a = 2$.

By choice of a in the range

$$k_2 \frac{n_1}{n_2} = \frac{L_{12}}{L_{22}} < a < \frac{L_{11}}{L_{12}} = \frac{1}{k_1} \frac{n_1}{n_2} \qquad [46]$$

both the series inductances of Fig. 7 are rendered positive. The greater is the coefficient of coupling, the narrower is this range. If $a = \sqrt{L_{11}/L_{22}}$, these two inductances become equal, and the equivalent T circuit is as shown in Fig. 8. If a is given one of the limiting values, then one of the series inductances becomes zero, as illustrated in Fig. 9 for $a = L_{12}/L_{22}$. (Compare this figure with eqs. 30 and 45

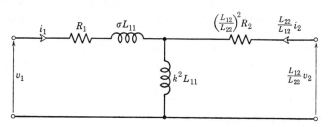

FIG. 9. The circuit of Fig. 7 with $a = L_{12}/L_{22}$. The inductance of the secondary series arm is zero.

for short-circuit impedance.) For iron-core transformers, it is customary to take a as the turns ratio n_1/n_2. The two series inductances (known as the primary and secondary *leakage inductances*) are then positive but not necessarily equal. For rotating machines having windings on opposite sides of an air gap, a may be taken as the ratio of currents which separately produce equal fluxes crossing the air gap per pole. The leakage fluxes are then fluxes which do not cross the air gap. Since a is arbitrary, however, the leakage inductances are arbitrary.

The theorem of constant flux linkage.[2,12] One of the most useful principles for analyzing transient phenomena in inductive electric circuits is the theorem of constant flux linkages, which will now be derived. Consider any closed circuit, or mesh, of an electric network, having finite resistance, flux linkage due to any cause whatever, and e.m.f.'s not due to change of linkage, but no series capacitance. The sum of the potential differences around such a path is

$$\sum Ri + \frac{d\psi}{dt} = \sum e \qquad [47]$$

Here the letters R, i, ψ, t, and e have their usual meanings. The summation sign $\sum$ is used because the mesh under consideration may consist of several branches, each having different resistance, current, and e.m.f. The flux linkage, on the other hand, is that of the entire mesh, as defined earlier in this chapter. Now integrate eq. 47 with respect to t from 0 to Δt.

$$\sum R \int_0^{\Delta t} i \, dt + \Delta\psi = \sum \int_0^{\Delta t} e \, dt \qquad [48]$$

If R and e are finite, then as Δt approaches zero the definite integrals approach zero, and therefore $\Delta\psi$ also approaches zero. This result may be stated as follows: *The flux linkage of any closed circuit of finite resistance and e.m.f. cannot change instantly.*

In the special case in which the resistance and e.m.f. are zero, eq. 47 becomes simply

$$\frac{d\psi}{dt} = 0 \qquad [49]$$

which integrates to

$$\psi = \text{constant} \qquad [50]$$

The flux linkage of any closed circuit having no resistance or e.m.f. remains constant.

Actually every circuit has some resistance, and therefore the flux linkage of the circuit changes at a rate $\sum(e - Ri)$ (eq. 47). In a linear network having no e.m.f.'s, the rate of change of flux linkage may be expressed in terms of the *time constants* of the network (discussed in the next section of this chapter).

The theorem of constant flux linkage is most useful in situations where the self-inductance of a circuit or the mutual inductance between it and another circuit change because of relative motion of parts of the circuit, or of two circuits, or of magnetic materials. If these changes occur in a time which is short compared with the time constant of the circuit, the flux linkages remain substantially constant during the change, and this fact may be used to calculate the currents after the change in terms of the currents before the change.

A few examples of applications of the theorem will now be given.

1. Suppose that a copper ring carrying no current is situated at first so that it surrounds a permanent bar magnet. Suppose further that the ring is then suddenly removed from the magnet. The current in the ring immediately after removal will be of such magnitude and in such direction that the magnetic flux passing through the ring is equal to its previous value; namely, the flux of the permanent magnet. This current is therefore equal to the flux of the magnet divided by the inductance of the ring. Ultimately, of course, the current decays to zero.

2. Next consider a relay having a hinged iron armature and a winding connected to a battery. Initially the armature is in contact with the magnet pole, and the current in the winding has its steady-state value, equal to the battery voltage divided by the resistance of the circuit. Suppose now that the armature is suddenly drawn away from the magnet. This action causes the current in the relay coil suddenly to increase to a value which maintains the same flux through the coil in spite of the decreased permeance of the magnetic circuit. (See Fig. 10.) While the armature is held away from the magnet, the cur-

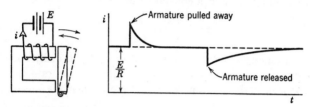

FIG. 10. Changes of current in relay coil when armature is suddenly drawn away from magnet and later is allowed to fall back.

rent slowly decreases to its steady-state value, and the flux also decreases. If now the armature is released, allowing it to be drawn back to the magnet, the current suddenly decreases to a value which holds the flux at the reduced value in spite of the increased permeance. Thereafter the current builds up slowly to its steady-state value and the flux builds up with it.

3. For the next example, consider a transformer having primary self-inductance L_{11}, secondary self-inductance L_{22}, and mutual inductance L_{12}. Initially the secondary winding is short-circuited, the primary winding is open, and the currents are zero. Suddenly a direct voltage E is applied to the primary terminals and is maintained constant. What are the currents if resistance is neglected? The initial flux linkage of the closed secondary circuit is zero and, in the absence of resistance, this value is maintained.

$$\psi_2 = L_{12}i_1 + L_{22}i_2 = 0 \qquad [51]$$

This requires a constant ratio of secondary current to primary current:

$$i_2 = -\frac{L_{12}}{L_{22}} i_1 \qquad [52]$$

The primary flux linkage is

$$\psi_1 = L_{11}i_1 + L_{12}i_2 \qquad [53]$$

which, by use of eq. 52, becomes

$$\psi_1 = \left(L_{11} - \frac{L_{12}^{2}}{L_{22}}\right) i_1 = L_{\text{sc}} i_1 \qquad [54]$$

The apparent inductance of the primary winding with the secondary winding short-circuited is thus seen to be the same when a direct voltage is suddenly applied to the primary terminals as when a steady alternating voltage is applied (eq. 31). With no resistance in the windings and voltage E applied to the primary terminals, the primary current would build up at a constant rate

$$\frac{di_1}{dt} = \frac{E}{L_{\text{sc}}} \qquad [55]$$

and the secondary current would build up proportionally to the primary current (eq. 52). With resistance present, the rate of increase of current is initially the same as with no resistance but falls off thereafter.

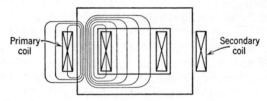

Fig. 11. Flux paths in a short-circuited iron-core transformer with coils on opposite legs.

If the transformer has a closed secondary winding with no resistance, no flux can be forced through it; therefore the flux caused by the primary current is forced into leakage paths, as illustrated in Fig. 11 for an iron-core transformer with primary and secondary coils on opposite legs of the core. The leakage paths have a higher reluctance than the path through the core which the flux could follow if the secondary winding were open. Therefore more primary current is required to produce a given amount of flux with the secondary winding closed than with the secondary winding open, and consequently the primary inductance (linkage per unit current) is lower on short circuit than on open circuit. This is true not only for alternating voltage but also, initially, for suddenly applied direct voltage.

After the steady state has been reached, however, following the application of direct voltage, the currents and linkages of both windings become the same as if the secondary circuit were open, and the driving-point inductance, which is the primary flux linkage per ampere of primary current, becomes the same as the open-circuit inductance. Thus, when direct voltage is suddenly applied to a linear transformer with short-circuited secondary winding, the inductance gradually increases from the short-circuit value to the open-circuit value.

4. Now consider the same transformer under different operating conditions. Initially the secondary winding is open and the primary winding is excited in the steady state with alternating current. Then the secondary winding is suddenly short-circuited. What are the currents?

Before application of the short circuit, the secondary flux linkage varies sinusoidally, and, in general, this linkage will not be zero at the instant of short circuit. If the linkage is not zero, some flux is "trapped" in the secondary winding by the short circuit and must remain constant thereafter, provided that the secondary resistance is negligible. At the same time, the primary linkage must continue to vary sinusoidally in order to give a countervoltage equal and opposite to the applied voltage. The maintenance of constant secondary linkage requires a direct component of secondary current. The sudden appearance of this component of secondary current would alter the primary linkage did not a direct component of primary current appear simultaneously. The production of the sinusoidal alternating primary linkage requires an alternating component of primary current. This would produce an alternating secondary linkage if it were not opposed by an alternating component of secondary current. The alternating components of current are sustained by the applied voltage and are the steady-state currents. The direct components of current are transient. Their initial values depend on the trapped flux, which, in turn, depends on the instant of the cycle at which the short circuit occurs. Thus the offset of the current waves depends upon the instant of switching.

The principle of constant flux linkage has been applied very effectively by R. E. Doherty in determining the short-circuit currents of rotating machines.[2,6,11] A qualitative discussion of three-phase short circuits of synchronous machines is given later in this chapter.

Before leaving the subject of the theorem of constant flux linkage, the reader may be interested to note that the theorem is analogous to the principle of *conservation of momentum* in mechanics. In the usual analogy between electricity and mechanics, inductance is analogous to mass, and current to velocity; accordingly, the product of inductance and current, which is flux linkage, is analogous to the product of mass and velocity, which is momentum.

Fundamental concepts of time constant. Although the theorem of constant flux linkage is useful for finding the initial values of transient currents, it does not give their rates of decay. In linear static circuits

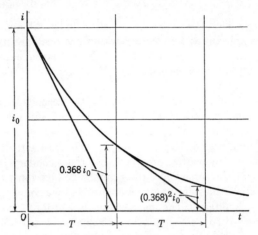

FIG. 12. Exponential decay of current.

with no capacitance the transient currents consist of components each of which decays exponentially. The rate of decay of each component can be expressed in terms of a time constant, thus:

$$i_t = i_{t0}\epsilon^{-t/T} \qquad [56]$$

Here i_t is the transient current at any time t, i_{t0} is the initial value of i_t, and T is the *time constant*. At time $t = T$, the transient current has decreased to $\epsilon^{-1} = 0.368$ of its initial value. The rate of decay at any time is

$$\frac{di_t}{dt} = -\frac{i_{t0}\epsilon^{-t/T}}{T} = -\frac{i_t}{T} \qquad [57]$$

If this rate continued without change, the current would decay to zero in a time interval T.

The time constant of an exponential curve may be defined in either of two equivalent ways. It is either

1. The time in which the variable decreases to 0.368 of its initial value, or
2. The time in which the variable would decrease to zero if it continued to decrease at its initial rate.

Both these definitions are illustrated in Fig. 12. At time T the curve itself has decreased to 0.368 of its initial value and at the same time the tangent to the curve at the initial point intersects the horizontal axis. In the interpretation of these statements, any point on the curve may be taken as the initial point.

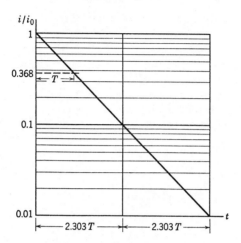

FIG. 13.   Plot of exponential on semilog paper.

If $\log i$ is plotted against t, or — what amounts to the same thing — if i is plotted against t on semilog paper, the exponential curve becomes a straight line (Fig. 13).

Simple R-L circuit. In a series circuit of resistance R ohms and inductance L henrys, the transient current i is given by the solution of the differential equation

$$Ri + L\frac{di}{dt} = 0 \qquad [58]$$

which, as may be verified by substitution, is

$$i = i_0\epsilon^{-Rt/L} \qquad [59]$$

Here the time constant is

$$T = \frac{L}{R} \quad \text{seconds} \qquad [60]$$

The time constant may be regarded also as

$$T = \frac{Li}{Ri} = \frac{\psi}{Ri} \qquad [61]$$

If the circuit contains a *constant e.m.f.* E volts, the steady-state current is $I_s = E/R$, and the actual current i is the sum of the steady-state and transient components.

$$i = I_s + (I_0 - I_s)\epsilon^{-Rt/L} \qquad [62]$$

where I_0 is the initial value of total current (steady-state plus transient).

If the circuit contains a *sinusoidal e.m.f.*, the steady-state current is found from well-known methods, and again the actual current is the sum of the steady-state and the transient components.

If the circuit contains a *varying e.m.f.* which is any known function of time $e(t)$, the current can be found either graphically or by a point-by-point calculation. The differential equation is

$$Ri + L\frac{di}{dt} = e(t) \qquad [63]$$

whence

$$\frac{di}{dt} = \frac{e(t) - Ri}{L} = \frac{[e(t)/R] - i}{L/R}$$

$$\frac{di}{dt} = \frac{i_s(t) - i}{T} = -\frac{i_t}{T} \qquad [64]$$

At every instant the rate of change of current is equal to the difference i_t between the steady-state current $i_s(t)$ which would be reached if the e.m.f. remained at its instantaneous value and the actual current i, divided by the time constant T.

Wagner[41] has given a simple graphical solution of eq. 64, which he calls the *follow-up method*: The coordinates of the desired curve are current i and time t. On the same coordinates a curve of $i_s(t) = e(t)/R$ is first plotted against t, which curve, however, is shifted to the right by a distance T (see Fig. 14). From a point representing the initial current I_0 at $t = 0$, a straight line is drawn to the point on the curve of $e(t)/R$ representing $e(0)/R$, which point, as already mentioned, is at a distance T to the right of the origin. The slope of this line is therefore that given by eq. 64 and represents the initial slope of the desired curve of i against t. The slope of the curve is assumed to be constant for a short time interval Δt. At the point on the straight line at $t = \Delta t$, a new value of slope is determined by drawing a second straight line from this point to a point on the curve of i_s at $t = T + \Delta t$. The new value of slope is assumed to be constant during a second interval Δt, and so on. The process is illustrated in Fig. 14, with a modification which will now be described.

EXAMPLE 1   21

Some cumulative error enters this process if, as described above, the slope di/dt at the *beginning* of a time interval Δt is assumed equal to the average slope throughout the interval. A much more accurate value of average slope during an interval is obtained if the straight

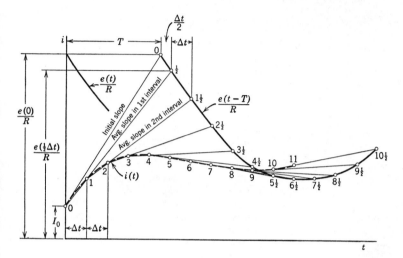

Fig. 14. The "follow-up method" for graphical determination of current in an *R-L* circuit with varying e.m.f.

line is drawn to a point on the curve of $e(t)/R$ at the *middle*, instead of at the *beginning*, of the interval. See, for example, the line in Fig. 14 labelled "Avg. slope in 1st interval." This construction is equivalent to using a time constant $T + \frac{1}{2}\Delta t$ instead of T.

In *point-by-point calculation* of the current, the time constant is modified as just described, so that eq. 64 becomes:

$$\frac{\Delta i}{\Delta t} = \frac{[e(t + \frac{1}{2}\Delta t)/R] - i}{T + \frac{1}{2}\Delta t} \qquad [65]$$

Example 1

To illustrate the accuracy of point-by-point calculations of transient current, compute the decaying current in a circuit having a resistance of 1 ohm, an inductance of 1 henry, and no e.m.f., if the initial current is 1 ampere.

Exact solution. The time constant is

$$L/R = 1/1 = 1 \text{ sec.}$$

The exact solution for the current is

$$i = \epsilon^{-t} \qquad (a)$$

Values, read from a table of exponential functions, are tabulated in the last column of Table 1.

TABLE 1

POINT-BY-POINT COMPUTATION OF EXPONENTIAL CURVE
(EXAMPLE 1)

t	i	Δi	e^{-t}
0	1.000	−0.182	1.000
0.2	0.818	−0.149	0.819
0.4	0.669	−0.122	0.670
0.6	0.547	−0.100	0.549
0.8	0.447	−0.081	0.449
1.0	0.366	−0.067	0.368
1.2	0.299	−0.054	0.301
1.4	0.245	−0.045	0.247
1.6	0.200	−0.036	0.202
1.8	0.164	−0.030	0.165
2.0	0.134		0.135

Point-by-point solution. Let $\Delta t = 0.2$ sec. Then $T + \Delta t/2 = 1.1$ sec. Equation 65 becomes

$$\frac{\Delta i}{\Delta t} = - \frac{i}{1.1} \qquad (b)$$

$$\Delta i = - \frac{i \, \Delta t}{1.1} = - \frac{0.2}{1.1} i = - \frac{i}{5.5} \qquad (c)$$

and

$$i_n = i_{n-1} + (\Delta i)_n \qquad (d)$$

The computation is shown in Table 1.

The accuracy is very good with as few as five points per time constant. The maximum error in i is −0.002. If, however, the uncorrected value $T = 1$ had been used instead of 1.1 in eq. b, the maximum error in i with $\Delta t = 0.2$ would have been −0.038, or 19 times as large.

The point-by-point calculation of transients in circuits with saturated iron will be illustrated in Chapter XIII.

Two coupled circuits. Consider two linear, inductively coupled circuits having resistances R_1 and R_2, self-inductances L_{11} and L_{22}, and mutual inductance L_{12}. The transient currents i_{t1} and i_{t2} satisfy the differential equations

$$R_1 i_{t1} + L_{11} \frac{di_{t1}}{dt} + L_{12} \frac{di_{t2}}{dt} = 0 \qquad [66a]$$

$$R_2 i_{t2} + L_{22} \frac{di_{t2}}{dt} + L_{12} \frac{di_{t1}}{dt} = 0 \qquad [66b]$$

and are of the form

$$i_{t1} = I_{1a} \epsilon^{p_a t} + I_{1b} \epsilon^{p_b t} \qquad [67a]$$

$$i_{t2} = I_{2a} \epsilon^{p_a t} + I_{2b} \epsilon^{p_b t} \qquad [67b]$$

where p_a and p_b are the roots of the determinantal equation

$$\begin{vmatrix} R_1 + L_{11}p & L_{12}p \\ L_{12}p & R_2 + L_{22}p \end{vmatrix} = 0 \qquad [68]$$

or

$$(R_1 + L_{11}p)(R_2 + L_{22}p) - L_{12}{}^2 p^2 = 0 \qquad [69]$$

$$(L_{11}L_{22} - L_{12}{}^2)p^2 + (R_1 L_{22} + R_2 L_{11})p + R_1 R_2 = 0 \qquad [70]$$

The roots are readily found, for given numerical values of R_1, R_2, L_{11}, L_{22}, and L_{12}, through use of the formula for the roots of a quadratic equation. The coefficients I_{1a}, I_{1b}, I_{2a}, and I_{2b} can be determined from a knowledge of the initial values of i_{t1}, i_{t2}, and their derivatives, which can be found as if there were no resistance.

The flux linkages of the two circuits, being linear functions of the two currents, consist of exponential components having the same values of p that the currents have. The initial values of the linkages can often be found from the theorem of constant flux linkage.

The time constants of the transient current components of eqs. 67 are

$$T_a = -\frac{1}{p_a} \qquad \text{and} \qquad T_b = -\frac{1}{p_b} \qquad [71]$$

These time constants of the coupled circuits can be found in terms of the time constants of the two separate circuits,

$$T_1 = \frac{L_{11}}{R_1} \qquad \text{and} \qquad T_2 = \frac{L_{22}}{R_2} \qquad [72]$$

as roots of the quadratic equation[40]

$$T^2 - T(T_1 + T_2) + \sigma T_1 T_2 = 0 \qquad [73]$$

where σ is the leakage coefficient defined by eqs. 43 and 44. Equation 73 follows directly from eq. 70 and the substitutions indicated by eqs. 71 and 72.

The roots of eq. 73 can be found when the values of T_1, T_2, and σ are given.   If σ is small, the roots are approximately

$$T_a \approx T_1 + T_2 \qquad\qquad [74a]$$

and

$$T_b \approx \frac{\sigma T_1 T_2}{T_1 + T_2} \qquad\qquad [74b]$$

EXAMPLE 2

What are the time constants of two coupled R-L circuits if the leakage coefficient is 0.15 and the time constants of the two separate circuits are 5 sec. and 1 sec.?

Solution.   Given: $T_1 = 5$ sec., $T_2 = 1$ sec., $\sigma = 0.15$.   Equation 73 becomes

$$T^2 - 6T + 0.75 = 0 \qquad\qquad (a)$$

By the quadratic formula, the roots are

$$T_a = 3 + \sqrt{9 - 0.75} = 5.872 \text{ sec.} \qquad\qquad (b)$$

and

$$T_b = \frac{0.75}{3 + \sqrt{9 - 0.75}} = 0.128 \text{ sec.} \qquad\qquad (c)$$

By the approximate equations (74), the time constants are

$$T_a \approx 5 + 1 = 6 \text{ sec.} \qquad\qquad (d)$$

and

$$T_b \approx \frac{0.15 \times 5 \times 1}{5 + 1} = 0.125 \text{ sec.} \qquad\qquad (e)$$

The errors of the approximate formulas are seen to be small if σ is as small as 0.15.

Reactances of synchronous machines.   The concepts of inductive reactance and time constant, which have been developed for static circuits, will now be extended to synchronous machines, where some circuits move with respect to others.   The reactances discussed initially will be specifically those of a three-phase, salient-pole rotating-field machine without saturation or iron loss.   At the same time, the differences between salient-pole and round-rotor machines will be pointed out.   Later, the effects of saturation will be discussed.

The impedances of three-phase machines are classified, according to the method of symmetrical components, into positive-sequence, negative-sequence, and zero-sequence impedances.   In the determination of any of these, the rotor circuits are closed but not excited, the rotor is turned forward at synchronous speed, current of the proper sequence is applied to the armature windings, and the armature terminal voltage of the same phase sequence as the current is found. The ratio of the voltage to the current is, of course, the impedance. The reactance is by far the most important component of every synchronous-machine impedance, and the resistance is negligible for most purposes.

Any one machine has only one zero-sequence reactance and one negative-sequence reactance,* but it has several different positive-sequence reactances, depending upon the angular position of the rotor and upon whether the positive-sequence armature currents are steady or are suddenly applied.

Direct-axis synchronous reactance x_d. It is well known that positive-sequence armature currents in a polyphase armature winding set up a rotating magnetic field in the air gap. More accurately described, this field consists of waves of m.m.f. and of flux, including both the space fundamental and various space harmonics, some rotating forward and some backward at various speeds; but the most important of these waves are the space fundamentals which rotate forward at synchronous speed with respect to the armature and are therefore stationary with respect to the field structure (rotor). Given armature currents produce the same fundamental m.m.f. wave, regardless of the angular position of the rotor; but the fundamental flux wave varies greatly with the rotor position. If the rotor is so rotated that the direct, or pole, axis stays in line with the crest of the rotating m.m.f. wave, a path of high permeance is offered (the flux paths are approximately as shown in Fig. 15a), and the fundamental flux wave has its greatest possible magnitude for a given armature current. Accordingly, the total flux linkage of each phase winding of the armature (including both the flux which crosses the air gap and that which does not) has the greatest possible value for a given current in the winding, and the armature inductance and inductive reactance are greater than they would be for any other position of the rotor. The flux linkage of an armature phase per ampere of armature current under these conditions is the *direct-axis synchronous inductance* L_d. The *direct-axis synchronous reactance* is $x_d = \omega L_d$.

Note that, under the stipulated conditions, the flux is stationary with respect to the field structure, and that, therefore, it makes no

---

*As brought out on pp. 67–69, the negative-sequence reactance varies somewhat with the harmonic content of the current.

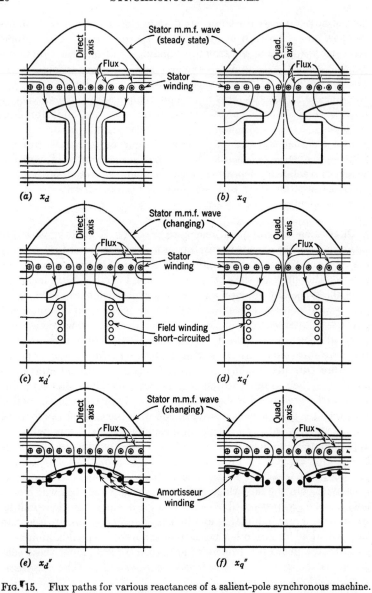

FIG. 15. Flux paths for various reactances of a salient-pole synchronous machine. (a) Direct-axis synchronous reactance. (b) Quadrature-axis synchronous reactance. (c) Direct-axis transient reactance. (d) Quadrature-axis transient reactance. (e) Direct-axis subtransient reactance. (f) Quadrature-axis subtransient reactance. (From Ref. 34 by permission.)

difference whether the field winding is open or closed — the field flux linkage is constant in either case. With respect to the armature, however, the flux is moving at synchronous speed. Consequently the flux linkage of each armature phase winding varies sinusoidally with time. The time variation of flux linkage is in phase with the time variation of armature current because the space-fundamental flux wave is in phase with the space-fundamental m.m.f. wave. Therefore the ratio of flux to current is the same regardless of whether instantaneous, maximum, or effective values are used. The armature voltage induced by change of flux linkage is in quadrature with the flux and current. The ratio of this voltage to the current, under the stipulated conditions, is the direct-axis synchronous reactance x_d.

One method of *measuring* x_d has already been suggested: Apply sustained positive-sequence currents to the armature, drive the rotor forward at synchronous speed, in such position that its direct axis coincides with the crest of the space-fundamental forward-rotating m.m.f. wave, and measure the sustained positive-sequence armature voltage in quadrature with the current.

There is another method of measuring x_d, which is easier to carry out than the method just described. The rotor is driven at rated speed with the field winding excited, and the open-circuit armature voltage is measured. Then a three-phase short circuit is applied to the armature terminals and the sustained armature current is measured, the field current being the same as before. The ratio of open-circuit voltage* to short-circuit current is x_d. This method does not require a separate source of three-phase power, and the armature m.m.f. is automatically aligned with the direct axis of the rotor.

That the second method gives the same result as the first in an unsaturated machine can be shown by the principle of superposition, which is valid for linear circuits. In Fig. 16a the field winding of the generator is excited by application of a direct voltage, producing a positive-sequence alternating voltage E at the open-circuited armature terminals. If now an external alternating e.m.f. E is applied to the armature, exactly balancing the open-circuit voltage, no armature currents flow. This subterfuge is necessary because the principle of superposition is valid only when the impedances of the circuit are constant: we cannot have an open circuit at one time and a short circuit at another time. Any current (or voltage) in Fig. 16a, resulting from the application of field and armature e.m.f.'s together, is equal to the

---

*If the machine is saturated, the voltage read from the air-gap line should be used instead of the open-circuit voltage read from the no-load saturation curve. The result is then the unsaturated value of x_d.

sum of the currents (or voltages) at the same place resulting from the application of the field and armature e.m.f.'s separately (Figs. 16b and 16c). In Fig. 16a the armature currents are zero; therefore the armature currents in Fig. 16b must be equal and opposite to the corresponding armature currents in Fig. 16c. The armature voltage E in Fig. 16a is likewise the sum of the armature voltages in Figs. 16b and c, which

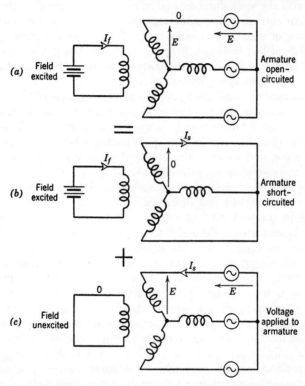

FIG. 16. Application of the principle of superposition to show the equivalence of two different methods of measuring x_d: first, open-circuit and sustained short-circuit tests, shown in (a) and (b), respectively; second, sustained application of armature voltage to unexcited machine, shown in (c).

are zero and E, respectively. The field current I_f in Fig. 16a is the sum of the field currents in Figs. 16b and c, which are I_f and zero, respectively. Therefore, the reactance x_d determined from the scalar ratio of the voltage E in Fig. 16a to the current I_s in Fig. 16b is the same as the value of x_d determined from the same voltage E and current I_s in Fig. 16c, the field currents being equal in Figs. 16a and b.

Figure 16c embodies the conditions used in defining x_d; Figs. 16a and b portray the alternative method of measuring x_d by means of open-circuit and short-circuit tests, which is the usual test method.

Quadrature-axis synchronous reactance x_q. It has already been noted that the magnitude of the space-fundamental wave of air-gap flux depends on the position of the rotor with respect to the space-fundamental wave of m.m.f. and is greatest when the direct axis of the rotor coincides with the crest of the m.m.f. wave. On the other hand, the flux wave is smallest when the quadrature, or interpolar, axis of the rotor coincides with the crest of the m.m.f. wave. The flux paths for this condition are shown in Fig. 15b. Under this condition the armature flux linkage per armature ampere is the quadrature-axis synchronous inductance L_q. The quadrature-axis synchronous reactance is $x_{q'} = \omega L_q$. This reactance is also equal to the component of armature voltage in quadrature with the armature current, divided by the current.

In round-rotor machines x_d and x_q are almost equal. However, x_q is slightly less than x_d because of the effect of the rotor slots.

Note that both x_d and x_q are defined with the field pole cores in a symmetrical position with respect to the rotating m.m.f. wave. Therefore, in neither case is there any magnetic torque tending to pull the rotor into a different position. No mechanical power is developed in either case, and the voltage is purely reactive in both cases. With the rotor in any intermediate position, the flux wave would not be in space phase with the m.m.f. wave, and therefore the voltage would not be in quadrature with the current. Motor or generator action would then occur. A torque, called a reluctance torque, would be developed, tending to move the rotor into the position in which its direct axis coincides with the m.m.f. wave. (See "Power-angle curves of a salient-pole machine," p. 80.)

For the measurement of x_q, a procedure suggests itself similar to the first one for measuring x_d. Positive-sequence currents would be applied to the armature, and the rotor would be driven forward at synchronous speed with the quadrature axis in line with the crest of the rotating m.m.f. wave. Under these conditions, the sustained positive-sequence armature voltage would be measured, and the ratio of armature voltage to armature current would be x_q.

The procedure just described is very difficult to carry out because, on account of reluctance torque, the rotor is in unstable equilibrium when the quadrature axis coincides with the crest of the m.m.f. wave. A more feasible procedure is the *slip test*, in which the rotor is driven at a speed differing slightly from synchronous speed as determined from the frequency of the applied armature currents. These currents are modulated at slip frequency by the machine; they have maximum amplitude when the quadrature axis is in line with the m.m.f. wave and minimum amplitude when the direct axis is in line with the m.m.f. wave. Because of impedance in the supply line, the armature voltage

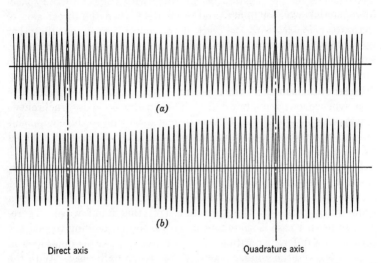

Direct axis   Quadrature axis

FIG. 17. Oscillogram for determination of x_d and x_q by the "slip test." (a) Armature voltage, (b) armature current.

$$x_d = \frac{\text{max. voltage}}{\text{min. current}} \qquad x_q = \frac{\text{min. voltage}}{\text{max. current}}$$

is usually modulated at slip frequency too, being greatest when the current is least and vice versa. Figure 17 represents an oscillogram showing these variations of current and voltage. If the slip is small, the maximum and minimum values of voltage and current can be read from an indicating voltmeter and ammeter. Quadrature-axis synchronous reactance is the ratio of minimum voltage to maximum current. From this same test the direct-axis synchronous reactance is found as the ratio of maximum voltage to minimum current.

In the slip test the field winding should be open so that slip-frequency current is not induced in it.

Armature leakage reactance x_l is the reactance resulting from the difference between the total flux produced by the armature current acting alone and the space fundamental of the flux in the air gap. It consists of three parts, due to the following fluxes:

1. Slot-leakage flux.
2. End-winding flux.
3. Differential-leakage flux, which comprises space harmonics of air-gap flux that induce fundamental-frequency armature voltage.

Armature leakage reactance is a calculated quantity and cannot be measured. It forms a part of the direct-axis and quadrature-axis synchronous reactances, as well as of all other positive- and negative-sequence reactances.

Potier reactance x_p is discussed on p. 122.

Direct-axis transient reactance x_d'. The conditions used in defining direct-axis transient reactance are the same as those used in defining direct-axis synchronous reactance except that the positive-sequence armature currents are suddenly applied and the positive-sequence armature voltage is measured immediately after application of the current instead of after the voltage has reached its steady-state value. In both cases the rotor is rotated forward at synchronous speed, with its direct axis in line with the crest of the armature-m.m.f. wave and with the field winding closed but not excited. (For the time being, assume that there are no other rotor circuits.) Abrupt application of the armature currents causes the sudden appearance of a m.m.f. opposite each field pole, tending to establish flux through the pole core. Such flux would link the field winding and is opposed by induced field current, tending to maintain the flux linkage of the field winding constant at zero value. By the theorem of constant flux linkage, at the instant immediately after application of the armature currents the field linkage is still zero. Therefore the only flux that can be established immediately is that which does not link the field winding but rather passes through low-permeance leakage paths, largely in air, as shown in Fig. 15c. Under these conditions the flux per ampere is small and is defined as the *direct-axis transient inductance* L_d'. The direct-axis transient reactance is $x_d' = \omega L_d'$. It is always less than the direct-axis synchronous reactance: $x_d' < x_d$.

The synchronous machine, under the conditions described, is analogous to a transformer with a short-circuited secondary winding and with direct current suddenly applied to the primary winding. The armature winding is the primary; the field winding, the secondary.

The direct-axis synchronous reactance x_d is analogous to the primary self-reactance, or open-circuit reactance, x_{11}; and the direct-axis transient reactance x_d' corresponds to the primary short-circuit reactance $x_{sc} = \sigma x_{11} = x_{11} - (x_{12}^2/x_{22})$. Hence $x_d' = \sigma x_d$. There is a difference between the transformer and the synchronous machine, however: in the transformer, the frequency is the same in both windings; whereas, in the machine, positive-sequence fundamental-frequency alternating current in the armature corresponds to direct current in the field winding; that is, both produce forward-rotating magnetic fields. Suddenly applied armature currents induce unidirectional field current which opposes change of the field flux linkage. As time passes, however, unidirectional flux linkage of the field winding slowly builds up, ultimately reaching a steady value, and, at the same time, the field current decays to zero. The steady condition that is finally reached if the amplitude of armature currents or voltages are held constant is the condition under which direct-axis synchronous reactance was defined, and under this condition it does not matter whether the field winding is open or closed because its linkage is constant in either case.

If positive-sequence armature current I is suddenly applied, the positive-sequence armature voltage is initially $x_d'I$, but gradually increases to x_dI. If positive-sequence voltage V is suddenly applied, the positive-sequence current is initially V/x_d', but gradually decreases to V/x_d. The change is exponential with a time constant of the order of several seconds (discussed later in this chapter under the heading "Time constants of synchronous machines").

Direct-axis transient reactance, like direct-axis synchronous reactance, can be measured by means of open-circuit and short-circuit tests with the field winding excited. This topic will be discussed more fully under the heading "Sudden Three-Phase Short Circuit."

Direct-axis subtransient reactance x_d''. In defining x_d' we assumed that there were no rotor circuits except the main field winding. There may be additional rotor circuits on both axes, however. Many salient-pole machines have amortisseur (damper) windings, shown in Figs. 15e and 15f. A few salient-pole machines have field collars. In round-rotor machines the solid steel rotor core furnishes significant paths for eddy currents.

If positive-sequence armature currents are suddenly applied in such time phase that the crest of the rotating m.m.f. wave is in line with the direct axis of the rotor, transient currents are induced in the additional direct-axis rotor circuits as well as in the main field winding.

These transient currents oppose the armature m.m.f., and initially they are strong enough to keep the flux linkage of every rotor circuit constant at zero value. The additional rotor circuits are situated nearer the air gap than the field winding is. Consequently, the flux set up by the armature current is initially forced into leakage paths of smaller cross-sectional area and lower permeance than would be the case if the only rotor circuit were the field winding (see Fig. 15e). Under these conditions the armature flux linkage per armature ampere is the *direct-axis subtransient inductance* L_d''. The *direct-axis subtransient reactance* is $x_d'' = \omega L_d''$. The subtransient inductance and reactance are always smaller than the corresponding transient quantities. Even in water-wheel generators without amortisseur windings x_d'' is about 15% smaller than x_d' because of the effects of saturation* and of such closed circuits as those through the pole rivets.

Invariably the decrement of the currents in the additional rotor circuits is very rapid compared with that of the field current, so that after a few cycles all rotor currents except the field current have become negligibly small. The effective armature reactance has then increased from the subtransient to the transient value. The term *subtransient* is intended to convey the idea of a transient of very short duration.

The transient reactance of machines having amortisseur windings is practically equal to that which would exist if the amortisseur windings were removed. It can be found, however, without removing the amortisseurs, by plotting a curve of reactance against time (or current against time after sudden application of a short circuit) and extrapolating the slowly changing part of this curve (which does not include the first few cycles) back to the instant at which current or voltage was applied. The procedure is explained in more detail under the heading "Sudden Three-Phase Short Circuit." The same procedure is applicable to round-rotor machines, the additional rotor circuits of which obviously cannot be removed.

Quadrature-axis transient reactance x_q' and subtransient reactance x_q''. These quantities are defined in a manner similar to x_d' and x_d'', respectively, except that the suddenly applied positive-sequence armature current is in such time phase that the crest of the space-funda-

---

*Rüdenberg[40] has shown that, even if there is no direct-axis rotor circuit except the main field winding, the effect of saturation is to produce a more rapid decay of armature current in the early part of the transient than in the following part, which is practically exponential. The whole transient can be approximated by the sum of two exponentials with different time constants just as in the case of two rotor circuits.

mental m.m.f. wave is in line with the quadrature axis of the rotor instead of the direct axis.

In a machine having laminated salient poles and no amortisseurs, the changing flux can pass sideways through the field coils without linking them and inducing field current. The flux paths (Fig. 15d) are the same as those for a steady flux (Fig. 15b). This is true also of a machine with amortisseurs after the current in them has become negligible. Consequently, for salient-pole machines, x_q' is equal to x_q. Because field current is induced by a changing direct-axis flux, though not by a changing quadrature-axis flux, x_d' is less than x_q'. Amortisseur windings restrict the quadrature-axis flux initially to low-permeance paths, as shown in Fig. 15f, thereby making the quadrature-axis subtransient reactance x_q'' much less than the transient reactance x_q'. However, x_q'' is usually slightly greater than x_d''. In a salient-pole machine without amortisseur windings, x_q'' is equal to x_q', which, as already stated, is equal to x_q.

In a machine with a solid round rotor, the changing reactance due to quadrature-axis eddy currents can be represented fairly well as the sum of two exponentials, one of which is rapid, the other slow. The slower transient, extrapolated back to zero time, gives x_q'; the initial total reactance is x_q''. In such machines the value of x_q' is between the values of x_d' and x_q, and x_q'' is slightly smaller than x_q'.

Negative-sequence reactance x_2. Let the unexcited field structure be rotated forward at synchronous speed with all rotor circuits closed while negative-sequence currents are applied to the armature winding. The negative-sequence currents produce a magnetomotive force rotating backward at synchronous speed with respect to the armature and hence backward at twice synchronous speed with respect to the rotor. Seen from the rotor, the m.m.f. alternates at twice the rated frequency of the machine. Currents of twice rated frequency are induced in all rotor circuits, keeping the flux linkages of those circuits almost constant at zero value. The flux due to the armature current is forced into paths of low permeance which do not link any rotor circuits. These paths are the same as those for subtransient reactance (shown in Figs. 15e and 15f). The armature flux linkage per armature ampere under these conditions is the negative-sequence inductance L_2. The negative-sequence reactance is $x_2 = \omega L_2$.

Since the m.m.f. wave moves at twice synchronous speed with respect to the rotor, it alternately meets permeances of the two rotor axes, corresponding to subtransient reactances x_d'' and x_q''. Hence the value of x_2 lies between x_d'' and x_q''. It is usually taken as the arithmetical mean,

$$x_2 = \frac{x_d'' + x_q''}{2} \qquad [75]$$

The test for measuring x_2 is obvious from the defining conditions.

Zero-sequence reactance x_0. If zero-sequence currents are applied to the armature, there is no space-fundamental m.m.f. Hence the reactance is small and is hardly affected by the motion of the rotor. There is, in general, a third space harmonic of air-gap m.m.f. which is stationary but pulsating. This m.m.f. is opposed by currents induced in the closed rotor circuits; therefore not much air-gap flux is produced. The zero-sequence currents produce slot-leakage, end-winding-leakage, and differential-leakage fluxes, but these are not the same as those produced by positive-sequence currents. Altogether very little flux is set up, and the zero-sequence reactance is the lowest of the synchronous-machine reactances — even lower than x_d''.

The actual value of x_0 varies through a wider range than that of the other reactances and depends upon the pitch of the armature coils. The reactance is least for a pitch of two-thirds because then each slot has two coil sides carrying equal and opposite currents.

Zero-sequence reactance is readily measured by connecting the three armature windings in series and sending single-phase current through them. The ratio of terminal voltage of one phase winding to the current is the zero-sequence impedance, which has very nearly the same magnitude as the zero-sequence reactance.

Resistances of synchronous machines. *Positive-sequence resistance r_1.* The positive-sequence resistance of a synchronous machine is its a-c. armature resistance r, which is greater than the d-c. armature resistance r_a because of nonuniform current density and local iron loss. The positive-sequence resistance is nearly always neglected in power-system studies, including both studies of normal operation and stability studies. The only exception is the case of a three-phase short circuit on or near the generator terminals. Neglecting resistance in this case leads to pessimistic conclusions regarding stability because the armature copper loss is large enough to make the accelerating power considerably less than the value calculated neglecting the loss.

Negative-sequence resistance r_2. Under negative-sequence conditions, currents are induced in all rotor circuits. The negative-sequence power input to the armature supplies half the copper losses of the rotor circuits, the other half being supplied mechanically.* As these losses are much greater than the armature copper loss, the negative-sequence resistance (which is negative-sequence armature power input per phase divided by the square of the negative-sequence armature current) is greater than the positive-sequence resistance. Its value depends largely upon the resistance of the amortisseur windings if such windings are present. Negative-sequence resistance is discussed more fully in Chapter XIV of this book.

Zero-sequence resistance r_0 is equal to or somewhat greater than the positive-sequence resistance, depending upon the rotor copper loss due to rotor currents induced by zero-sequence armature currents. It is usually neglected. If the neutral of a Y-connected armature winding is grounded through a resistor, three times the resistance of the resistor should be added to the zero-sequence resistance of the machine itself. Such external zero-sequence resistance is not negligible.

Time constants of synchronous machines. During transient conditions in synchronous machines, the currents and voltages have components the magnitudes of which change in accordance with one or more of the following time constants:

Direct-axis transient open-circuit time constant $T_{d0}{}'$. If the armature is open-circuited and if there is no amortisseur winding, the field circuit is not affected by any other circuit. Under these conditions the change of field current in response to sudden application, removal, or change of e.m.f. in the field circuit is governed by the field open-circuit time constant, or direct-axis transient open-circuit time constant, which is given by an expression similar to that of any simple R-L circuit, to wit:

$$T_{d0}{}' = \frac{L_{ff}}{R_f} \quad \text{seconds} \qquad [76]$$

where L_{ff} is the self-inductance of the field circuit in henrys and R_f is the resistance of the field circuit in ohms. The field circuit includes the field winding, the field rheostat (if one is used), the armature of the exciter, and the connecting wiring.

---

*The equivalent circuit of an induction motor (see Chapter XIV) is applicable to a synchronous machine under negative-sequence conditions, the slip being 2 per unit. The rotor branch of the equivalent circuit has resistance R_r/s, where R_r is the rotor resistance and s the slip. R_r/s may be split into two parts in series, one having resistance R_r, the other $R_r(1 - s)/s$. The loss in the resistances has the following significance: $I_r{}^2 R_r/s$ = electric power input of rotor, $I_r{}^2 R_r$ = rotor copper loss, and $I_r{}^2 R_r(1 - s)/s$ = mechanical power output of rotor. Putting $s = 2$ into these expressions proves the statement.

The amplitude of the open-circuit a-c. armature terminal voltage of an unsaturated machine is directly proportional to the field current and, therefore, changes with the same time constant as the field current.

This time constant is greater than any of the other time constants discussed below; it is of the order of 2 to 11 sec., with 6 sec. as an average value.

Direct-axis transient short-circuit time constant $T_d{'}$. If both field and armature circuits are closed, current in either circuit induces current in the other. Because of the rotation of one circuit with respect to the other, however, the two currents are not of the same frequency: direct current in the field winding is associated with positive-sequence alternating currents in the armature winding, and direct current in the armature is associated with alternating current in the field. Each set of currents has a different time constant. The one which governs the rate of change of the direct current in the field and of the *amplitude* of the alternating current in the armature is the *field*, or *direct-axis transient*, *time constant*; the one which governs the direct current in the armature and the alternating current in the field is the *armature time constant*.

The field time constant is the ratio of the apparent inductance of the field circuit when coupled to the closed armature circuits to the apparent resistance of the field circuit under the same conditions. Hence its value depends upon the impedance of the armature circuits. The field open-circuit time constant, discussed above, is a particular value of field time constant which is valid when the armature is open-circuited. At the other extreme is the field short-circuit time constant, which is valid when the armature is short-circuited. On short circuit the effective inductance of the field circuit is much less than on open circuit, for the same reason that the short-circuit inductance of a transformer is less than its open-circuit inductance. Furthermore, the fact that the ratio of short-circuit inductance to open-circuit inductance of a transformer is the same from both sides of the transformer (being equal to the leakage coefficient σ in both cases) enables us to find the ratio of field-circuit inductance with short-circuited armature to that with open-circuited armature. It is equal to the ratio of armature-circuit inductance with short-circuited field to that with open-circuited field for suddenly applied positive-sequence alternating armature current. From the discussion of positive-sequence armature reactances earlier in this chapter, it is clear that the ratio is $L_d{'}/L_d$ or $x_d{'}/x_d$.

The apparent resistance of the field winding, unlike its inductance, is practically the same whether the armature is open- or short-circuited. At first sight this statement appears to contradict the fact that, in the case of two coupled circuits at rest with respect to each other, the apparent resistance of the primary circuit depends on that of the secondary (see eqs. 29 and 30). Circumstances are different, however, in the rotating machine, where one winding carries direct current and the other, alternating current. Here the resistance of the d-c. winding is much more effective than that of the a-c. winding. Indeed, when the a-c. winding is short-circuited, its resistance has negligible effect. For in the a-c. winding the self- and mutual reactances are so much greater than the resistance that the latter has negligible effect upon the magnitude and phase of the current. In the d-c. winding, however, the current changes much more slowly than in the a-c. winding, with the result that the inductive drop is comparable with the resistive drop.*

Because the ratio of the short-circuit inductance of the field winding to its open-circuit inductance is x_d'/x_d, while its resistance is unchanged, the ratio of the short-circuit time constant to the open-circuit time constant is equal to the ratio of the corresponding inductances. Hence the direct-axis transient short-circuit time constant is

$$T_d' = \frac{x_d'}{x_d} T_{d0}' \qquad [77]$$

It is about one-fourth as large as the open-circuit time constant, or about 1.5 sec.

If the armature circuit is closed through finite balanced external impedances, then the field time constant has a value between T_d' and T_{d0}'. If the external impedances are purely reactive, the time constant is given by a modification of eq. 77 in which both x_d' and x_d are increased by the amount of external reactance per phase. If the external impedances have much resistance, or if the machine is connected to a network having other large synchronous machines (as is always true in a stability study), the situation is more complex, but it will be shown later in this chapter that in every case the field transient can be computed in terms of the *open-circuit time constant*.

Direct-axis subtransient time constants T_{d0}'' and T_d''. In a machine with amortisseurs, there are on the direct axis of the rotor two coupled

---

*In this connection the reader may recall that the apparent reactance of the rotor circuit of an induction motor, referred to the stator, is independent of the slip, but the apparent resistance varies inversely as the slip and hence becomes great at small slips.

circuits (the field and amortisseur windings) at rest with respect to one another but both in rotation with respect to the armature. The two coupled circuits have two time constants, as discussed earlier in this chapter. The longer one is the transient time constant; the shorter one, the subtransient time constant. Both time constants are affected by the impedance of the armature circuit. If the armature circuit is open, the time constants have their open-circuit values T_{d0}' and T_{d0}''. If the armature is short-circuited, the time constants have their short-circuit values T_d' and T_d''.

Typical open-circuit values, $T_{d0}' = 6$ sec. and $T_{d0}'' = 0.125$ sec. (7.5 cycles), were calculated in Example 2. Typical short-circuit values are $T_d' = 1.5$ sec., $T_d'' = 0.035$ sec. (2 cycles).

Quadrature-axis time constants T_{q0}', T_q', T_{q0}'', and T_q''. In a machine with a solid round rotor, the changing amplitude of the quadrature-axis component of alternating armature current or voltage can be represented fairly well by the sum of two exponentials, as stated previously in the discussion of x_q' and x_q''. The time constants of these exponentials are T_{q0}' and T_{q0}'' when the armature circuit is open; T_q' and T_q'' when the armature is short-circuited. The value of T_q' is about one-half that of T_d', or about 0.8 sec. The value of T_q'' is very nearly equal to T_d'', or about 0.035 sec. (2 cycles).

In a salient-pole machine T_q' is meaningless; but, if the machine has amortisseurs, T_q'' is significant and is approximately equal to T_d''.

Armature short-circuit time constant T_a. This time constant applies to direct current in the armature windings and to alternating currents in the field and amortisseur windings, both of which are closed. It is equal to the ratio of armature inductance to armature resistance under the stated conditions. The armature inductance under these conditions is equal to the negative-sequence inductance L_2 because, although the rotor currents are of fundamental frequency in the present case and twice fundamental frequency in the negative-sequence case, in both cases the flux linkages of the rotor circuits are constant and the flux created by the armature current is forced into low-permeance paths, as illustrated in Figs. 15e and f. The armature resistance is unaffected by the rotor circuits, for reasons already explained, and is the d-c. value r_a. Consequently the armature time constant is

$$T_a = \frac{L_2}{r_a} = \frac{x_2}{\omega r_a} \qquad [78]$$

It has a value of about 0.15 sec. with a short circuit on the armature terminals, but is greatly shortened by any external resistance in the armature circuit.

Typical values of reactances, resistances, and time constants of synchronous machines of various types are listed in Table 2.

TABLE 2

TYPICAL CONSTANTS OF THREE-PHASE SYNCHRONOUS MACHINES
(Adapted from Refs. 15, 34, and 41)

	Turbo-generators (solid rotor)			Water-Wheel Generators (with dampers)†			Synchronous Condensers			Synchronous Motors (general purpose)		
	Low	*Avg.*	*High*	*Low*	*Avg.*	*High*	*Low*	*Avg.*	*High*	*Low*	*Avg.*	*High*
Reactances in per unit												
x_d	0.95	1.10	1.45	0.60	1.15	1.45	1.50	1.80	2.20	0.80	1.20	1.50
x_q	0.92	1.08	1.42	0.40	0.75	1.00	0.95	1.15	1.40	0.60	0.90	1.10
x_d'	0.12	0.23	0.28	0.20	0.37	0.50‡	0.30	0.40	0.60	0.25	0.35	0.45
x_q'	0.12	0.23	0.28	0.40	0.75	1.00	0.95	1.15	1.40	0.60	0.90	1.10
x_d''	0.07	0.12	0.17	0.13	0.24	0.35	0.18	0.25	0.38	0.20	0.30	0.40
x_q''	0.10	0.15	0.20	0.23	0.34	0.45	0.23	0.30	0.43	0.30	0.40	0.50
x_p	0.07	0.14	0.21	0.17	0.32	0.40	0.23	0.34	0.45			
x_2	0.07	0.12	0.17	0.13	0.24	0.35	0.17	0.24	0.37	0.25	0.35	0.45
x_0*	0.01		0.10	0.02		0.21	0.03		0.15	0.04		0.27
Resistances in per unit												
r_a(d-c.)	0.0015		0.005	0.003		0.020	0.002		0.015			
r(a-c.)	0.003		0.008	0.003		0.015	0.004		0.010			
r_2	0.025		0.045	0.012		0.20	0.025		0.07			
Time constants in seconds												
T_{d0}'	2.8	5.6	9.2	1.5	5.6	9.5	6.0	9.0	11.5			
T_d'	0.4	1.1	1.8	0.5	1.8	3.3	1.2	2.0	2.8			
$T_d'' = T_q''$	0.02	0.035	0.05	0.01	0.035	0.05	0.02	0.035	0.05			
T_a	0.04	0.16	0.35	0.03	0.15	0.25	0.1	0.17	0.3			

*x_0 varies from about 0.15 to 0.60 of x_d'', depending upon winding pitch.

†For water-wheel generators without damper windings,

$$x_d'' \approx 0.85x_d', \qquad x_q'' = x_q' = x_q, \qquad x_2 = (x_d' + x_q)/2,$$

and x_0 is as listed.

‡For curves showing the normal value of x_d' of water-wheel-driven generators as a function of kilovolt-ampere rating and speed, see Ref. 54.

SUDDEN THREE-PHASE SHORT CIRCUIT

One important application of the reactances and time constants of synchronous machines is the prediction of short-circuit currents. Conversely, oscillograms of short-circuit current can be used to determine the values of some of the reactances and time constants.

A typical short-circuit oscillogram is shown in Fig. 18. A three-phase short circuit was suddenly applied to the armature terminals of an unloaded three-phase generator, and the currents of the three armature phases and the field circuit were recorded.

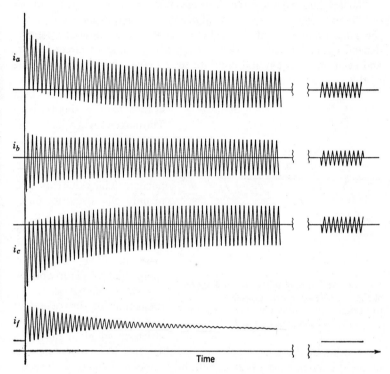

FIG. 18. Short-circuit currents of synchronous generator. Armature currents i_a, i_b, i_c; field current i_f.

Description of oscillogram. Armature currents. Each armature current consists of a symmetrical, or alternating, component and an asymmetrical, or direct, component. The *a-c. components* of all three armature currents have identical envelopes, though the sine waves bounded by the envelopes are 120° apart in phase, constituting a positive-sequence set of currents. The envelope of the a-c. component is high at the instant of short circuit, and decays ultimately to *the sustained value* I_s. If I_s is subtracted from the a-c. wave, the remainder is found to consist of two exponential components: the *transient component* I' with a long time constant T_d', and the *subtransient* *component* I'' with a very short time constant T_d''. Thus the amplitude of the a-c. component is given as a function of time t by

$$I_{ac} = I_s + I_0'\epsilon^{-t/T_d'} + I_0''\epsilon^{-t/T_d''} \qquad [79]$$

The *d-c. components* of the three armature currents are generally all of different magnitudes. They all decrease to zero exponentially with the same time constant T_a. The initial values of these components depend upon the point in the cycle at which the short circuit occurs and each one is equal and opposite to the initial instantaneous value of the a-c. component of the same phase, so that there are no discontinuities in the current waves at the instant of short circuit. The maximum possible initial value of the d-c. component is equal to the initial value of the envelope of the a-c. component. This value can occur in only one armature phase at a time. Thus, in Fig. 18, wave i_a is almost completely offset, while i_b is almost symmetrical. The initial d-c. components of all three phases can be found by taking the projections on the real axis of three vectors 120° apart and of length equal to the initial crest value of the a-c. component (see Fig. 19). The algebraic sum of the d-c. components is zero, both initially and thereafter, since the time constant is the same for all. The last two statements assume that the short circuit is applied simultaneously to all terminals, which is not always strictly true.

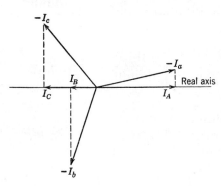

FIG. 19. Relation of initial d-c. components of short-circuit armature currents (I_A, I_B, I_C) to vectors representing initial crest values of the a-c. components (I_a, I_b, I_c).

If $x_d'' \neq x_q''$ there are also *second-harmonic components* of armature current, which are proportional to the d-c. components. The second-harmonic components do not show in Fig. 18 and are appreciable only in salient-pole machines without damper windings.

Field current. The field current, like the armature current, consists of d-c. and a-c. components. The *d-c. component* may be further subdivided into *sustained, transient,* and *subtransient components*. The sustained component, if no voltage regulator is used, is equal to the field current before occurrence of the short circuit, and is the quotient of the exciter voltage by the field-circuit resistance. The transient and subtransient d-c. components of field current decrease with the same time constants, T_d' and T_d'' respectively, as the corresponding a-c. components of armature current. The *a-c. component* of field current decays with time constant T_a, as do the d-c. components of the armature currents. The initial crest value of the a-c. component is equal to the initial value of the transient d-c. component.

Explanation of short-circuit currents. The reasons for the existence of the various components of armature and field currents just described can be explained by the principle of constant flux linkage.[2] Assume that before the occurrence of the short circuit the field winding is excited and the armature terminals are open-circuited. Then the flux linkage of the field circuit is constant, but the linkages of the armature windings vary sinusoidally with time with 120° phase difference between adjacent windings. The flux linking each armature winding at the instant of short circuit is "trapped" and must thereafter remain constant (to a degree of approximation depending upon the resistance of the windings). The trapped flux comprises a set of armature poles equal and opposite in strength to the field poles and located opposite the places where the field poles were at the instant of short circuit, just as if the field poles had stamped their images upon the armature. The armature poles are fixed with respect to the armature while the field poles are fixed with respect to the field and rotate with respect to the armature. The strength of both sets of poles remains constant during the rotation because of the requirement of constant flux linkages of both armature and field windings.

The maintenance of stationary armature poles requires d-c. components of armature current, the relative magnitudes of which in the three windings depend upon the position of the poles, hence upon the position of the field poles at the instant of short circuit. In addition to the d-c. components, a-c. components of armature currents are also required to maintain the armature poles, for the following reason:

The constant flux from the field poles would continue to produce three-phase positive-sequence fundamental-frequency flux linkages with the armature did not three-phase positive-sequence fundamental-frequency currents flow in the armature to oppose the field m.m.f. and to prevent any change of armature flux linkage. Therefore three-phase armature currents are induced. These currents, as is well known, produce a m.m.f. rotating forward at synchronous speed with respect to the armature but stationary with respect to the field and centered on the direct axis of the field. This armature m.m.f. opposes the field m.m.f. and tends to reduce the flux linkages of the field and damper windings. To prevent such changes of linkages, an increase of field current is induced and damper currents are also induced. Thus we have the transient and subtransient d-c. components in the rotor windings and the corresponding a-c. components in the armature windings.

The stationary armature poles would produce a fundamental-frequency alternating linkage of the field and damper windings if fundamental-frequency currents did not flow in these windings to prevent it. The alternating current in the field winding creates a pulsating m.m.f. which is stationary with respect to the field poles. This m.m.f. may be resolved into two waves of m.m.f., one rotating forward, the other backward, with respect to the field poles. The backward-rotating m.m.f. is stationary with respect to the armature and opposes the m.m.f. of the d-c. components of armature current. The forward-rotating m.m.f. travels at twice normal speed with respect to the armature and induces positive-sequence second-harmonic currents in the armature in order to prevent any change of armature flux linkage. However, if the machine has damper windings, currents are induced in them which almost prevent this field m.m.f. from inducing second-harmonic armature currents.

Decrements. If the flux linkages remained absolutely constant, the short-circuit currents would not decay. Actually they have decrements, which were explained in the section on "Time constants of synchronous machines." The direct-axis short-circuit time constants T_d' and T_d'' control the decrement of alternating armature currents and direct field currents; the armature short-circuit time constant T_a controls the decrement of the direct armature currents and alternating field current.

Amplitudes. The amplitudes of the various alternating components of armature current can be found in terms of the direct-axis reactances x_d, x_d', and x_d'' by use of the principle of superposition. This principle was invoked earlier in this chapter to justify the measurement of synchronous reactance x_d as the ratio of open-circuit armature voltage to sustained short-circuit armature current, as shown in Fig. 16. Here $x_d = E/I_s$, or $I_s = E/x_d$, where E is the open-circuit voltage and I_s is the sustained short-circuit armature current, both in effective values.

If the armature is *suddenly* short-circuited, the initial alternating armature current of a machine without amortisseurs is given by $I_s + I' = E/x_d'$; or the transient reactance is $x_d' = E/(I_s + I')$, the ratio of the open-circuit voltage to the initial short-circuit alternating armature current. This method of measuring x_d' is shown in Fig. 20 to be equivalent to the method used in defining x_d' (namely, the sudden application of armature voltage to an unexcited machine). In

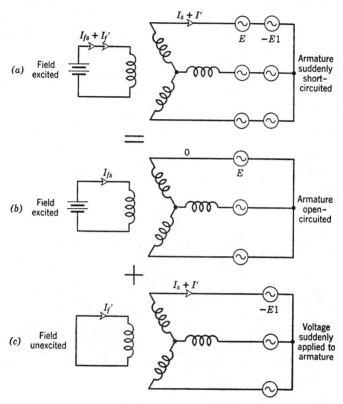

FIG. 20. Application of the principle of superposition to show the equivalence of two different methods of measuring x_d': first, open-circuit and sudden-short-circuit tests, shown in (b) and (a); second, sudden application of armature voltage to unexcited machine, shown in (c).

Fig. 20b the open-circuit condition is represented, as before, by the artifice of applied armature e.m.f.'s which balance the generated e.m.f.'s of the machine. The sudden application of a short circuit to the armature terminals is represented in Fig. 20a by the sudden connection of a second set of external e.m.f.'s in the armature circuit in series with the first set and equal and opposite to them, resulting in a net terminal voltage of zero. The combination of e.m.f.'s shown in Fig. 20a results in the same currents as the separate application of the two sets of e.m.f.'s in Figs. 20b and c. Since the armature currents are zero in Fig. 20b, the armature currents produced by sudden short circuit (Fig. 20a) are equal to those produced by sudden application of armature voltage to an unexcited machine (Fig. 20c), provided this applied voltage is equal and opposite to the open-circuit voltage of the excited machine (Fig. 20b).

If the machine has amortisseur windings, both methods give subtransient as well as transient components of armature current.

The initial values of the alternating components of armature current are given by

$$I_s = \frac{E}{x_d} \qquad [80]$$

$$I_s + I_0' = \frac{E}{x_d'} \qquad [81]$$

and

$$I_s + I_0' + I_0'' = \frac{E}{x_d''} \qquad [82]$$

Hence eq. 79 for the amplitude of the a-c. component of short-circuit armature current may be written in terms of reactances as

$$I_{ac} = E \left[\frac{1}{x_d} + \left(\frac{1}{x_d'} - \frac{1}{x_d} \right) \epsilon^{-t/T_d'} + \left(\frac{1}{x_d''} - \frac{1}{x_d'} \right) \epsilon^{-t/T_d''} \right] \qquad [83]$$

where E is the open-circuit voltage of an unsaturated machine, or the voltage read from the air-gap line of a saturated machine. Effective values are generally used for I_{ac} and E. The d-c. component of armature current is given by

$$I_{dc} = \frac{\sqrt{2}\, E \cos \alpha}{x_d''} \epsilon^{-t/T_a} \qquad [84]$$

where α is the switching angle. The effective value of armature current, including a-c. and d-c. components, is

$$I = \sqrt{I_{ac}^2 + I_{dc}^2} \qquad [85]$$

The greatest possible initial effective value of armature current, obtained with a fully offset wave, is composed of an a-c. component

$$I_{0\,ac} = \frac{E}{x_d''} \qquad [86]$$

EXAMPLE 3   47

and a d-c. component

$$I_{0\,\mathrm{dc\,max}} = \frac{\sqrt{2}\,E}{x_d''} \qquad [87]$$

and hence is

$$I_{0\,\mathrm{max}} = \sqrt{I_{0\,\mathrm{ac}}^2 + I_{0\,\mathrm{dc\,max}}^2} = \frac{\sqrt{3}\,E}{x_d''} \qquad [88]$$

This value, slightly decreased to allow for decrement in the first half-cycle, is used in figuring the required short-time momentary ratings of circuit breakers.

Analysis of oscillogram. The oscillogram of short-circuit armature currents can be separated into d-c. and a-c. components, and the a-c. components can be separated into sustained, transient, and subtransient components. From the open-circuit prefault armature voltage and the initial values of the several components of armature current, the values of the direct-axis reactances x_d, x_d', and x_d'' can be calculated. From logarithmic plots of the transient, subtransient, and d-c. components, the direct-axis short-circuit time constants T_d', T_d'', and T_a can be calculated.

Example 3

The short-circuit oscillogram of Fig. 18 was taken on a water-wheel generator rated as follows: 56 Mva., 13.8 kv., three-phase, 60 cycles, 112.5 r.p.m., 90% power factor. The field current was set at 128 amp., giving an open-circuit voltage of 4,600, and a three-phase short circuit was then applied to the armature terminals, giving the armature and field currents shown in the figure. The sustained short-circuit armature current was 800 amp. r.m.s. Find the values of reactances x_d, x_d', and x_d'' and time constants T_d', T_d'', and T_a. Plot the r.m.s. values of the a-c. and d-c. components and of the total armature current as functions of time, all in per unit, assuming that the d-c. component has the greatest possible value and that the internal voltage is equal to rated voltage.

Solution. *Currents and time constants.* The envelopes of the current waves were drawn and their ordinates were measured at times of 0, 1, 2, 3, 4, 5, 7, 10, 15, 20, 25, 30, 40, 50, 60, 80, 100, and 120 cycles after the instant of short circuit. The a-c. (crest value) and d-c. components were calculated as half the difference and half the sum, respectively, of the upper and lower envelopes, multiplied by the proper oscillograph scale factors. The a-c. components of the three armature currents were averaged. The resulting components of armature current are plotted in Fig. 21.

The crest value of sustained armature current ($\sqrt{2} \times 800 = 1,130$ amp.) was then subtracted from the envelope of the a-c. component, and the

remainder was plotted on semilog paper in Fig. 22. The points lie nearly on
a straight line except during the first few cycles. This straight line, extended
back to zero time, gives the initial value of the transient component I',
which is 2,190 amp. crest, or 1,550 amp. r.m.s. The time constant is found
as twice the time required for I' to drop to $1/\sqrt{\epsilon}$, or 0.606, times its initial
value, or 1,330 amp. crest. This time is 85.5 cycles, making the time constant $T_d' = 171$ cycles $= 2.85$ sec.

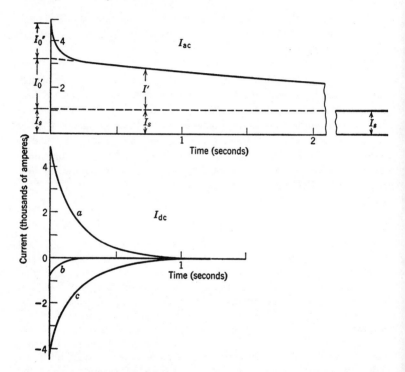

FIG. 21.   D-c., or unsymmetrical, components and amplitude (crest value) of a-c.,
or symmetrical, component of short-circuit armature currents.

The values of I', read from the straight line, are then subtracted from the
ordinates of the curve $I' + I''$ in the first few cycles and are replotted on
semilog paper in Fig. 23. These values lie on a straight line. The initial
value of I'' is 1,470 amp. crest, or 1,040 amp. r.m.s. The time constant T_d''
is the time taken for I'' to decrease to $1/\epsilon$ or 0.368 of its initial value, or to
537 amp. crest. This time is $T_d'' = 2.4$ cycles, or 0.04 sec.

An approximate check on T_d' is obtained by plotting the d-c. component
of field current less the sustained value in Fig. 24. This gives $T_d' = 160$
cycles, or 2.67 sec. This value is believed to be less accurate than that ob-

EXAMPLE 3   49

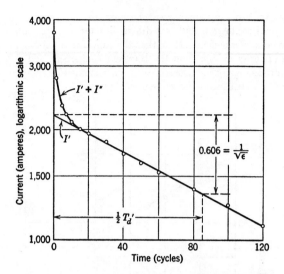

Fig. 22. Semilog plot of excess of a-c. component of short-circuit armature current over sustained current. The transient component is represented by the straight line, from which time constant T_d' is determined.

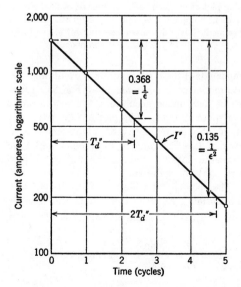

Fig. 23. Semilog plot of subtransient component I'' of short-circuit armature current for determination of time constant T_d''.

tained from the a-c. armature current, because the zero axis was not recorded on the original oscillogram but was drawn in later, possibly introducing an error in the d-c. component. Note that the subtransient component of field current is opposite in sign from the transient component and is small compared with the subtransient armature current. It must be opposed by a large subtransient current in the amortisseur windings.

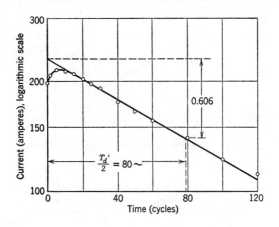

FIG. 24. Semilog plot of excess of d-c. component of field current over sustained value. The transient component is represented by the straight line, from which T_d' can be determined. The subtransient component is small and of opposite sign from the transient component.

The d-c. components of the three armature currents and the a-c. component of field current are plotted logarithmically in Fig. 25. Except for i_b, which is too small to be determined accurately, the plots of these currents are parallel but not quite straight. The plot of alternating field current i_f is the straightest, possibly for reasons stated above, and was therefore used in the determination of T_a. The value of T_a so found is 13.6 cycles, or 0.23 sec. Values found from the plots of i_a and i_c range from 10 to 15 cycles, depending upon how the straight line is drawn.

Reactances. The open-circuit voltage used in the test is 4,600/13,800, or only one-third of normal. At such a low voltage the machine is unsaturated. The line-to-neutral value of open-circuit voltage is $4,600/\sqrt{3} = 2,650$ volts.

By eq. 80,

$$x_d = \frac{E}{I_s} = \frac{2,650}{800} = 3.32 \text{ ohms}$$

By eq. 81,

$$x_d' = \frac{E}{I_s + I_0'} = \frac{2,650}{2,350} = 1.13 \text{ ohms}$$

EXAMPLE 3   51

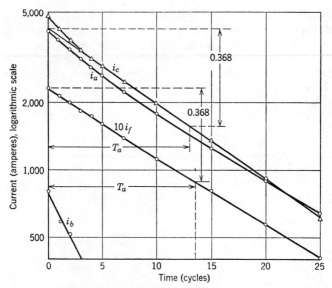

FIG. 25. Semilog plot of d-c. components of armature currents i_a, i_b, i_c and a-c. component (crest value) of field current i_f for determination of time constant T_a.

By eq. 82,

$$x_d'' = \frac{E}{I_s + I_0' + I_0''} = \frac{2,650}{3,390} = 0.783 \text{ ohm}$$

To convert the values of reactance into per unit, they must be divided by the base impedance, which, from the machine rating, is

$$\frac{(13.8 \times 10^3)^2}{56 \times 10^6} = 3.40 \text{ ohms}$$

TABLE 3

CONSTANTS OF A 56-MVA. WATER-WHEEL GENERATOR,
AS DETERMINED FROM SHORT-CIRCUIT OSCILLOGRAM

Reactances (per unit)	Time Constants (sec.)
$x_d = 0.98$	$T_d' = 2.85$
$x_d' = 0.332$	$T_d'' = 0.04$
$x_d'' = 0.230$	$T_a = 0.23$

The per-unit values of reactance and the time constants are summarized in Table 3. All these values lie within the limits given in Table 2 for water-wheel generators.

Substitution of these values and of $E = 1$ into eq. 83 gives, for the a-c. component,

$$I_{ac} = 1.02 + 2.00\epsilon^{-t/2.85} + 1.33\epsilon^{-t/0.04} \text{ per unit}$$

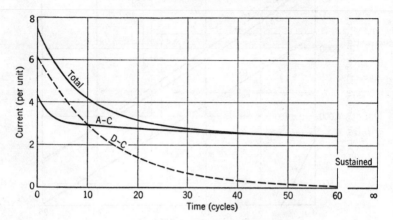

FIG. 26.   R.m.s. values of d-c. and a-c. components and of total short-circuit armature current, fully offset wave (Example 3).

Equation 84, with $E = 1$ and $\cos \alpha = 1$, gives the d-c. component of a fully offset wave as

$$I_{dc} = 6.14\epsilon^{-t/0.23} \text{ per unit}$$

The total current is given by eq. 85.   The a-c. and d-c. components and the total current are plotted in Fig. 26.

MATHEMATICAL THEORY

In the foregoing part of this chapter physical concepts of synchronous-machine reactances and time constants were set forth and applied to the determination of the three-phase short-circuit currents.   Before applying these concepts to stability calculations, it is desirable to have a more comprehensive mathematical theory of synchronous machines in the transient state than has been given.   The following theory is developed from the fundamental starting point that the machine consists of several inductively coupled circuits, the self- and mutual inductances of which vary periodically with the angular position of the rotor.

A three-phase salient-pole machine without amortisseur windings will be considered.   Iron loss and saturation will be neglected.   Such a machine has four windings: the field winding and three armature phase windings.

The instantaneous terminal voltage of any one of these windings may be written in the form

$$v = ri + \frac{d\psi}{dt} \qquad [89]$$

where r is the resistance of the winding, i is the current, and ψ is the flux linkage of the winding, which depends upon the self-inductance of the winding, the mutual inductances between it and other windings, and the currents in all the coupled windings; thus:

$$\psi = \sum Li \qquad [90]$$

Denoting the armature windings by subscripts a, b, c, and the field winding by f, eqs. 89 and 90 yield the following:

$$v_a = ri_a + \frac{d\psi_a}{dt} \qquad [91a]$$

$$v_b = ri_b + \frac{d\psi_b}{dt} \qquad [91b]$$

$$v_c = ri_c + \frac{d\psi_c}{dt} \qquad [91c]$$

$$v_f = r_f i_f + \frac{d\psi_f}{dt} \qquad [91d]$$

where

$$\psi_a = L_{aa}i_a + L_{ab}i_b + L_{ac}i_c + L_{af}i_f \qquad [92a]$$
$$\psi_b = L_{ba}i_a + L_{bb}i_b + L_{bc}i_c + L_{bf}i_f \qquad [92b]$$
$$\psi_c = L_{ca}i_a + L_{cb}i_b + L_{cc}i_c + L_{cf}i_f \qquad [92c]$$
$$\psi_f = L_{fa}i_a + L_{fb}i_b + L_{fc}i_c + L_{ff}i_f \qquad [92d]$$

In eqs. 91 r represents the resistance of each armature phase and r_f represents the field resistance.

Because many of the inductances vary with time, it is impossible to solve the differential equations 91 to find the currents for any given terminal voltages without knowing these inductances as functions of time. Therefore, they will be expressed in terms of the angular position of the rotor θ, which changes with time, thus:

$$\theta = \omega t + \theta_0 \qquad [93]$$

where ω is the angular speed, which for present purposes may be considered constant, and θ_0 is the initial value of θ.

Inductances of the windings as functions of the rotor position. The conventions for positive directions of currents and angle will be taken in accordance with Fig. 27. The magnetic axes of the three armature phases are 120 elec. deg. apart.

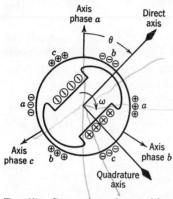

The direct and quadrature axes of the field are 90 elec. deg. apart, with the quadrature axis leading. The position of the rotor is given by the angle θ by which the direct axis of the field has turned beyond the axis of armature phase a.

The self-inductance of each armature phase is always positive but varies with the position of the rotor, being greatest when the direct axis of the field coincides with the axis of the armature phase and least when the quadrature axis coincides with it. The variation of the self-inductance between these two positions can be either calculated from design data or measured; by both methods it is found to be practically sinusoidal. See Fig. 28, for example. The variation of the self-inductance of phase a may be expressed by the following equation:

$$L_{aa} = L_s + L_m \cos 2\theta \qquad [94]$$

Fig. 27. Conventions for positive angle, currents, and m.m.f.'s. (From Ref. 34 by permission.)

where $L_s > L_m$. It has maximum values at $\theta = 0$ and $180°$, and minimum values at $\theta = 90°$ and $270°$. For phase b the variation of self-

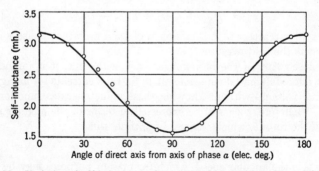

Fig. 28. Variation of self-inductance of armature phase a with position of the field. The test points, taken on a 4-pole 15-kva. 220-volt 1,800-rpm. synchronous motor, compare favorably with the curve showing the theoretical variation of an ideal machine: $L_{aa} = L_s + L_m \cos 2\theta = 2.36 + 0.796 \cos 2\theta$ mh. (From Ref. 34 by permission.)

inductance is similar, except that the maximum value occurs where the direct axis coincides with the axis of phase b, that is, at $\theta = 120°$ or $-60°$. Hence, the proper equation for phase b is obtained by replacing θ in eq. 94 by $\theta - 120°$.

$$L_{bb} = L_s + L_m \cos 2(\theta - 120°)$$
$$= L_s + L_m \cos (2\theta + 120°) \tag{95}$$

Similarly, for the self-inductance of phase c,

$$L_{cc} = L_s + L_m \cos 2(\theta + 120°)$$
$$= L_s + L_m \cos (2\theta - 120°) \tag{96}$$

The mutual inductance between two armature phases also varies with the position of the field. It is always negative, and its greatest absolute value occurs where the direct axis lies midway between the axis

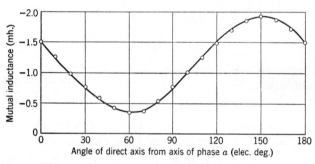

FIG. 29. Variation of mutual inductance between armature phases a and b with position of the field. The test points, taken on the same machine as in Fig. 28, are close to the curve which shows theoretical variation for an ideal machine: $L_{ab} = -M_s + L_m \cos (2\theta - 120°) = -1.14 + 0.796 \cos (2\theta - 120°)$ mh. (From Ref. 34 by permission.)

of one phase and the reversed axis of the other phase. Thus the maximum absolute value of the mutual inductance between phases a and b occurs at $\theta = -30°$ or $150°$; between phases a and c, at $\theta = -150°$ or $30°$; and between phases b and c, at $\theta = 90°$ or $270°$.

It is also found, both by calculation and by test, that the amplitude of variation of the mutual inductance between two stator phases is practically the same as the variation of the self-inductance of a stator phase. For example, see Fig. 29. Consequently, it will be denoted by the same symbol, L_m.

$$L_{ab} = L_{ba} = -[M_s + L_m \cos 2(\theta + 30°)]$$
$$= -M_s + L_m \cos (2\theta - 120°) \tag{97}$$

$$L_{bc} = L_{cb} = -[M_s + L_m \cos 2(\theta - 90°)]$$
$$= -M_s + L_m \cos 2\theta \qquad [98]$$

$$L_{ca} = L_{ac} = -[M_s + L_m \cos 2(\theta + 150°)]$$
$$= -M_s + L_m \cos (2\theta + 120°) \qquad [99]$$

The mutual inductance between the field winding and any armature phase is greatest when the direct axis coincides with the axis of that phase. After the field turns 180° from this position the mutual inductance is equal and opposite to its original value. The variation is sinusoidal: it may be shown that sinusoidal variation of this mutual inductance is necessary to give a sinusoidal open-circuit voltage, which is usually attained closely in commercial machines.

$$L_{af} = L_{fa} = M_f \cos \theta \qquad [100]$$

$$L_{bf} = L_{fb} = M_f \cos (\theta - 120°) \qquad [101]$$

$$L_{cf} = L_{fc} = M_f \cos (\theta + 120°) \qquad [102]$$

The self-inductance of the field winding L_{ff} is constant.

On substituting the values of the inductances (eqs. 94 through 102) into eqs. 92, we obtain the following expressions for the flux linkages:

$$\psi_a = (L_s + L_m \cos 2\theta)i_a + [-M_s + L_m \cos (2\theta - 120°)]i_b$$
$$+ [-M_s + L_m \cos (2\theta + 120°)]i_c + (M_f \cos \theta)i_f \qquad [103a]$$

$$\psi_b = [-M_s + L_m \cos (2\theta - 120°)]i_a + [L_s + L_m \cos (2\theta + 120°)]i_b$$
$$+ (-M_s + L_m \cos 2\theta)i_c + [M_f \cos (\theta - 120°)]i_f \qquad [103b]$$

$$\psi_c = [-M_s + L_m \cos (2\theta + 120°)]i_a + (-M_s + L_m \cos 2\theta)i_b$$
$$+ [L_s + L_m \cos (2\theta - 120°)]i_c + [M_f \cos (\theta + 120°)]i_f \qquad [103c]$$

$$\psi_f = (M_f \cos \theta)i_a + [M_f \cos (\theta - 120°)]i_b + [M_f \cos (\theta + 120°)]i_c$$
$$+ L_{ff}i_f \qquad [103d]$$

Now assume that the voltages impressed on the four windings (three armature phases and the field) are known as functions of time and that expressions are wanted for the currents as functions of time. Four differential equations are needed which have no unknowns except the four currents and their time derivatives. To obtain such equations, put $\theta = \omega t + \theta_0$ in eqs. 103, and, assuming that ω is constant, take the time derivative of these equations and substitute the result into eqs. 91. The resulting equations are very complicated; for example, the equation for v_a is:

$$v_a = [r - 2\omega L_m \sin 2(\omega t + \theta_0)]i_a - [2\omega L_m \sin (2\omega t + 2\theta_0 - 120°)]i_b$$
$$- [2\omega L_m \sin (2\omega t + 2\theta_0 + 120°)]i_c - [\omega M_f \sin (\omega t + \theta_0)]i_f$$
$$+ [L_s + L_m \cos 2(\omega t + \theta_0)]\frac{di_a}{dt} + [M_s + L_m \cos (2\omega t + 2\theta_0 - 120°)]\frac{di_b}{dt}$$
$$+ [M_s + L_m \cos (2\omega t + 2\theta_0 + 120°)]\frac{di_c}{dt} + [M_f \cos (\omega t + \theta_0)]\frac{di_f}{dt} \quad [104]$$

While the solution of four simultaneous differential equations of this kind is theoretically possible, it would not be feasible as they stand.

Park's transformation. The equations of the synchronous machine may be greatly simplified by a proper substitution (transformation) of variables. That is, a set of fictitious currents, voltages, and flux linkages will be defined as functions of the actual currents, voltages, and flux linkages, and the equations will be put into terms of the new variables. The equations may then be solved for the new variables as functions of time. From the results, the actual electrical quantities can be found as functions of time. The substitution could be regarded as a purely mathematical one, and from this point of view it would not be necessary to give any physical interpretation to the fictitious or substituted quantities. They could merely be chosen in such a way that the equations would be simplified by the substitution. Actually, the particular substitution used is based on physical reasoning and the substituted variables can be given physical interpretations.

The reader has already encountered the use of substitute variables in the method of symmetrical components. The particular substitution that we are about to use is from R. H. Park.[10] It is therefore fitting to call it "Park's transformation" and to call the substitute variables "Park's variables."

Let the actual armature phase currents i_a, i_b, and i_c be replaced by new fictitious currents i_d, i_q, and i_0 in accordance with the following equations:

$$i_a = i_d \cos \theta - i_q \sin \theta + i_0 \quad [105a]$$

$$i_b = i_d \cos (\theta - 120°) - i_q \sin (\theta - 120°) + i_0 \quad [105b]$$

$$i_c = i_d \cos (\theta + 120°) - i_q \sin (\theta + 120°) + i_0 \quad [105c]$$

No substitution will be made for the field current i_f. Similar substitutions are made for armature voltages and for armature flux linkages.

The inverse transformation is:

$$i_d = \tfrac{2}{3}[i_a \cos\theta + i_b \cos(\theta - 120°) + i_c \cos(\theta + 120°)] \qquad [106a]$$

$$i_q = -\tfrac{2}{3}[i_a \sin\theta + i_b \sin(\theta - 120°) + i_c \sin(\theta + 120°)] \qquad [106b]$$

$$i_0 = \tfrac{1}{3}(i_a + i_b + i_c) \qquad [106c]$$

for armature currents and similarly for armature voltages and armature flux linkages. Equations 106 may be obtained from eqs. 105 as follows: To obtain i_d, multiply the first, second, and third equations by $\cos\theta$, $\cos(\theta - 120°)$, and $\cos(\theta + 120°)$, respectively, and add. To obtain i_q, multiply them by $\sin\theta$, $\sin(\theta - 120°)$, and $\sin(\theta + 120°)$, respectively. To obtain i_0, simply add the three equations together. The following identities are needed:

$$\cos^2\theta + \cos^2(\theta - 120°) + \cos^2(\theta + 120°) = \tfrac{3}{2} \qquad [107]$$

$$\sin^2\theta + \sin^2(\theta - 120°) + \sin^2(\theta + 120°) = \tfrac{3}{2} \qquad [108]$$

$$\sin\theta\cos\theta + \sin(\theta - 120°)\cos(\theta - 120°)$$
$$+ \sin(\theta + 120°)\cos(\theta + 120°) = 0 \qquad [109]$$

$$\cos\theta + \cos(\theta - 120°) + \cos(\theta + 120°) = 0 \qquad [110]$$

$$\sin\theta + \sin(\theta - 120°) + \sin(\theta + 120°) = 0 \qquad [111]$$

These identities may be proved by writing the sines and cosines in terms of exponentials.

Flux linkages in terms of Park's variables. Now we will proceed with the change of variables. Before obtaining differential equations of voltage in the new system, analogous to eqs. 91, let us obtain the equations for flux linkages as functions of the currents, analogous to eqs. 103. To accomplish this, first write equations similar to 106 for ψ_d, ψ_q, and ψ_0 in terms of ψ_a, ψ_b, and ψ_c. Then substitute eqs. 103 into them, and eqs. 105 into the result. The amount of algebraic and trigonometric work required is formidable, but if the reader persists he will find that the multiple products of trigonometric functions can be reduced to simple constants, some of which were given in eqs. 107 through 111, and the following simple equations are finally obtained:

$$\psi_d = (L_s + M_s + \tfrac{3}{2}L_m)i_d + M_f i_f \qquad [112a]$$

$$\psi_q = (L_s + M_s - \tfrac{3}{2}L_m)i_q \qquad [112b]$$

$$\psi_0 = (L_s - 2M_s)i_0 \qquad [112c]$$

$$\psi_f = \tfrac{3}{2}M_f i_d + L_{ff}i_f \qquad [112d]$$

These equations are simpler than eqs. 103 in two ways: first, in that all the coefficients are constants, independent of the rotor position θ; second, in that there is almost a complete separation of variables. The quantities in parentheses are the ratios of flux linkage to current; obviously, they are the *inductances* in the new system of variables. Furthermore, it may be suspected that they are identical with some of the synchronous-machine inductances which were previously defined, and this will be proved a little later.

$$L_s + M_s + \tfrac{3}{2}L_m = L_d = \text{direct-axis synchronous inductance} \qquad [113]$$

$$L_s + M_s - \tfrac{3}{2}L_m = L_q = \text{quadrature-axis synchronous inductance} \qquad [114]$$

$$L_s - 2M_s = L_0 = \text{zero-sequence inductance} \qquad [115]$$

Thus, eqs. 112 may be written

$$\psi_d = L_d i_d + M_f i_f \qquad [116a]$$

$$\psi_q = L_q i_q \qquad [116b]$$

$$\psi_0 = L_0 i_0 \qquad [116c]$$

$$\psi_f = \tfrac{3}{2}M_f i_d + L_{ff} i_f \qquad [116d]$$

Physical interpretation of Park's variables. A physical interpretation of the new variables is now in order. The m.m.f. of each armature phase, being sinusoidally distributed in space, may be represented by a vector the direction of which is that of the phase axis and the magnitude of which is proportional to the instantaneous phase current. The combined m.m.f. of the three phases may likewise be represented by a vector which is the vector sum of the phase-m.m.f. vectors. The projections of the combined-m.m.f. vector on the direct and quadrature axes of the field are equal to the sums of the projections of the phase-m.m.f. vectors on the respective axes as given by the expressions for i_d and i_q, eqs. 106. The constant $\tfrac{2}{3}$ is arbitrary. Thus i_d may be interpreted as the instantaneous current in a fictitious armature winding which rotates at the same speed as the field winding and remains in such position that its axis always coincides with the direct axis of the field, the value of the current in this winding being such that it gives the same m.m.f. on this axis as do the actual three instantaneous armature phase currents flowing in the actual armature windings. The interpretation of i_q is similar to that of i_d except that it acts in the quadrature axis instead of in the direct axis. The i_0 of the new variables is identical with the usual zero-sequence current, except that it is an instantaneous value and is defined in terms of the instantaneous phase currents. This current gives no space-fundamental air-gap flux.

The flux linkages of the fictitious armature windings in which i_d and i_q flow are ψ_d and ψ_q, respectively.

In view of the foregoing interpretation of i_d and i_q, it is apparent that their m.m.f.'s are stationary with respect to the rotor and therefore act on paths of constant permeance. Hence the corresponding inductances L_d and L_q are independent of rotor position.

The fictitious direct-axis stator winding and the field winding are inductively coupled. Each has a self-inductance (L_d and L_{ff}), and there is a mutual inductance between them. It should be noted that the mutual inductance has different values in eqs. 116a and d, being M_f in one and $\frac{3}{2}M_f$ in the other. The difference could have been avoided by a different choice of the constant coefficients in eqs. 105 and 106; however, we will retain the form of the variables given by Park.

Circuit equations in terms of Park's variables. Now that the equations of the form $\psi = \sum Li$ have been transformed from their original form (eqs. 103) to equations in the new variables (eqs. 116), it remains to make a similar transformation on eqs. 91, which have the form

$$v = ri + \frac{d\psi}{dt}$$

The Park voltages are given by equations similar to eqs. 106 for currents, to wit:*

$$v_d = \frac{2}{3}[v_a \cos \theta + v_b \cos (\theta - 120°) + v_c \cos (\theta + 120°)] \qquad [117a]$$

$$v_q = -\frac{2}{3}[v_a \sin \theta + v_b \sin (\theta - 120°) + v_c \sin (\theta + 120°)] \qquad [117b]$$

$$v_0 = \frac{1}{3}(v_a + v_b + v_c) \qquad [117c]$$

Substitute into eqs. 117 the expressions for phase voltages, eqs. 91,

---

*A different convention on the application of subscripts d and q to voltages was used by Doherty and Nickle [3,4,6,11] and others. A speed voltage generated by direct-axis flux ψ_d they called a direct-axis voltage (e_d), and one generated by quadrature-axis flux ψ_q they called a quadrature-axis voltage (e_q). Both Park's and Doherty and Nickle's voltage notations have been widely used in the literature, but Park's is deemed preferable and is used in this book.

obtaining from eq. 117a:

$$v_d = \frac{2}{3}\left[\left(ri_a + \frac{d\psi_a}{dt}\right)\cos\theta + \left(ri_b + \frac{d\psi_b}{dt}\right)\cos(\theta - 120°)\right.$$

$$\left. + \left(ri_c + \frac{d\psi_c}{dt}\right)\cos(\theta + 120°)\right]$$

$$= r\frac{2}{3}[i_a\cos\theta + i_b\cos(\theta - 120°) + i_c\cos(\theta + 120°)]$$

$$+ \frac{2}{3}\left[\frac{d\psi_a}{dt}\cos\theta + \frac{d\psi_b}{dt}\cos(\theta - 120°) + \frac{d\psi_c}{dt}\cos(\theta + 120°)\right]$$

$$= ri_d + \left(\frac{d\psi}{dt}\right)_d \qquad [118]$$

where $(d\psi/dt)_d$, which is introduced as an abbreviation for the second bracketed expression, should not be confused with $d\psi_d/dt$. Indeed, the latter, found by taking the time derivative of

$$\psi_d = \frac{2}{3}[\psi_a\cos\theta + \psi_b\cos(\theta - 120°) + \psi_c\cos(\theta + 120°)] \qquad [119]$$

where $\theta = \omega t + \theta_0$, is

$$\frac{d\psi_d}{dt} = \frac{2}{3}\left[\frac{d\psi_a}{dt}\cos\theta + \frac{d\psi_b}{dt}\cos(\theta - 120°) + \frac{d\psi_c}{dt}\cos(\theta + 120°)\right]$$

$$- \omega\frac{2}{3}[\psi_a\sin\theta + \psi_b\sin(\theta - 120°) + \psi_c\sin(\theta + 120°)]$$

$$= \left(\frac{d\psi}{dt}\right)_d + \omega\psi_q \qquad [120]$$

Substituting the value of $(d\psi/dt)_d$ from eq. 120 into eq. 118, we obtain

$$v_d = ri_d + \frac{d\psi_d}{dt} - \omega\psi_q \qquad [121]$$

Proceeding in the same manner with v_q, we obtain

$$v_q = ri_q + \frac{d\psi_q}{dt} + \omega\psi_d \qquad [122]$$

Also

$$v_0 = ri_0 + \frac{d\psi_0}{dt} \qquad [123]$$

Equation 123 has the usual form, like eq. 89, but eqs. 121 and 122 are unusual because of the extra terms $-\omega\psi_q$ and $\omega\psi_d$, respectively. The presence of these terms demands a physical interpretation.

In the interpretation of eqs. 116, it was suggested that i_d and i_q were the currents in fictitious *rotating* stator windings — if that paradoxical expression may be used — which gave the same m.m.f.'s as did the actual armature currents in the actual armature windings. But it is not necessary to have the fictitious windings rotate. The same effect can be achieved by conceiving the armature winding to be stationary (as it actually is) and to be a closed-circuit winding with a commutator on which rest brushes which rotate with the field. The magnetic axis of the stator will always coincide with the brush axis. Thus i_d may be interpreted as the current entering and leaving the armature through a pair of brushes which are aligned with the direct axis of the field. Similarly, i_q may be regarded as the current entering and leaving the armature through a second pair of brushes, aligned with the quadrature axis of the field. In other words, the armature may be thought of as like that of a synchronous converter, having both commutator and slip rings, but having brushes in both axes instead of in the quadrature axis only. The actual phase currents, entering the slip rings, give the same m.m.f.'s as do the substitute currents i_d and i_q entering the commutator brushes.

This physical picture is also correct with respect to the voltages. The terms $-\omega\psi_q$ and $\omega\psi_d$ occurring in eqs. 121 and 122 may be regarded as components of applied voltage required to balance the *speed voltages*. The speed voltage across each pair of brushes is proportional to the flux on the axis 90° ahead of the brush axis.

We may now substitute eqs. 116 for the flux linkages into eqs. 121, 122, 123, and 91d in order to obtain differential equations of the voltages in terms of the currents. The results are as follows:

$$v_d = ri_d + L_d \frac{di_d}{dt} - \omega L_q i_q + M_f \frac{di_f}{dt} \qquad [124a]$$

$$v_q = ri_q + L_q \frac{di_q}{dt} + \omega(L_d i_d + M_f i_f) \qquad [124b]$$

$$v_0 = ri_0 + L_0 \frac{di_0}{dt} \qquad [124c]$$

$$v_f = r_f i_f + L_{ff} \frac{di_f}{dt} + \frac{3}{2} M_f \frac{di_d}{dt} \qquad [124d]$$

These equations correspond with those like eq. 104 but are much simpler than the latter as there are only two, three, or four terms per equation instead of eight and as the currents and their derivatives have constant coefficients.

Proof of expressions for Park inductances. When the $\psi = \sum Li$ equations (eqs. 116) were obtained in terms of Park's variables, the inductances were suspected to be identical with some of the synchronous-machine inductances previously defined. This will now be proved.

Direct-axis synchronous inductance L_d. The conditions previously specified in the definition of this inductance were:

1. Steady-state positive-sequence currents applied to the armature:

$$i_a = I \cos \omega t \qquad [125a]$$

$$i_b = I \cos (\omega t - 120°) \qquad [125b]$$

$$i_c = I \cos (\omega t + 120°) \qquad [125c]$$

2. Field circuit open:*

$$i_f = 0 \qquad [126]$$

3. Field rotated at synchronous speed with the direct axis in line with the axis of the armature m.m.f. wave:

$$\theta = \omega t \qquad [127]$$

Under these conditions the flux linkage per armature ampere is equal to the direct-axis synchronous inductance L_d. Consider phase a, the linkage of which is given by eq. 103a. Substitute the specified conditions (eqs. 125 through 127) into it, obtaining:

$$\psi_a = (L_s + L_m \cos 2\omega t)I \cos \omega t + [-M_s + L_m \cos (2\omega t - 120°)]$$
$$\times I \cos (\omega t - 120°) + [-M_s + L_m \cos (2\omega t + 120°)]I \cos (\omega t + 120°)$$
$$= \{L_s \cos \omega t - M_s [\cos (\omega t - 120°) + \cos (\omega t + 120°)]$$
$$+ L_m [\cos 2\omega t \cos \omega t + \cos (2\omega t - 120°) \cos (\omega t - 120°)$$
$$+ \cos (2\omega t + 120°) \cos (\omega t + 120°)]\} I \qquad [128]$$

Through use of the identities

$$\cos (\omega t - 120°) + \cos (\omega t + 120°) = -\cos \omega t \qquad [129]$$

and

$$\cos 2\omega t \cos \omega t + \cos (2\omega t - 120°) \cos (\omega t - 120°)$$
$$+ \cos (2\omega t + 120°) \cos (\omega t + 120°) = \tfrac{3}{2} \cos \omega t \qquad [130]$$

---

*As stated previously, the field current is zero under the specified conditions regardless of whether the field circuit is open or not.

eq. 128 reduces to

$$\psi_a = (L_s + M_s + \tfrac{3}{2}L_m)I \cos \omega t$$
$$= (L_s + M_s + \tfrac{3}{2}L_m)i_a \qquad [131]$$

$$L_d = \frac{\psi_a}{i_a} = L_s + M_s + \tfrac{3}{2}L_m \qquad [132]$$

which agrees with eq. 113. The same result can be obtained for phase b or for phase c.

Quadrature-axis synchronous inductance L_q. The conditions specified in the definition of L_q are the same as those for L_d except that the field is rotated with the quadrature axis in line with the axis of the armature m.m.f. wave:

$$\theta = \omega t - 90°* \qquad [133]$$

For these conditions, eq. 103a becomes

$$\psi_a = [L_s + L_m \cos 2(\omega t - 90°)]I \cos \omega t$$
$$+ \{-M_s + L_m \cos [2(\omega t - 90°) - 120°]\}I \cos (\omega t - 120°)$$
$$+ \{-M_s + L_m \cos [2(\omega t - 90°) + 120°]\}I \cos (\omega t + 120°)$$
$$= \{L_s \cos \omega t - M_s [\cos (\omega t - 120°) + \cos (\omega t + 120°)]$$
$$+ L_m [\cos (2\omega t - 180°) \cos \omega t + \cos (2\omega t + 60°) \cos (\omega t - 120°)$$
$$+ \cos (2\omega t - 60°) \cos (\omega t + 120°)]\}I$$
$$= (L_s + M_s - \tfrac{3}{2}L_m)I \cos \omega t$$
$$= (L_s + M_s - \tfrac{3}{2}L_m)i_a \qquad [134]$$

$$L_q = \frac{\psi_a}{i_a} = L_s + M_s - \tfrac{3}{2}L_m \qquad [135]$$

which agrees with eq. 114.

Zero-sequence inductance L_0. The conditions specified in the definition of L_0 are:

1. Steady-state zero-sequence currents applied to the armature:

$$i_a = i_b = i_c = I \cos \omega t \qquad [136]$$

2. Field circuit open:

$$i_f = 0 \qquad [137]$$

3. Motion of field not specified:

$$\theta = \theta \qquad [138]$$

*The same result could be obtained by letting $\theta = \omega t$ as before and advancing the phase of the armature currents 90°.

Equation 103a becomes:

$$\psi_a = (L_s - 2M_s)I \cos \omega t + L_m [\cos 2\theta + \cos (2\theta - 120°)$$
$$+ \cos (2\theta + 120°)]I \cos \omega t$$
$$= (L_s - 2M_s)i_a \qquad [139]$$

$$L_0 = \frac{\psi_a}{i_a} = L_s - 2M_s \qquad [140]$$

which agrees with eq. 115.

Direct-axis transient inductance $L_d{}'$. This inductance is the initial armature flux linkage per unit armature current (ψ_a/i_a) under the following conditions:

1. Positive-sequence currents suddenly applied to the armature:

$$i_a = I \cos \omega t \ \mathbf{1} \qquad [141a]$$

$$i_b = I \cos (\omega t - 120°) \ \mathbf{1} \qquad [141b]$$

$$i_c = I \cos (\omega t + 120°) \ \mathbf{1} \qquad [141c]$$

2. Field circuit closed but not excited:

$$v_f = 0 \qquad [142]$$

3. Field rotated as specified under direct-axis synchronous inductance:

$$\theta = \omega t \qquad [143]$$

Condition 1, substituted in eqs. 106, yields:

$$i_d = I\mathbf{1} \qquad [144a]$$

$$i_q = 0 \qquad [144b]$$

$$i_0 = 0 \qquad [144c]$$

Condition 2 and the law of constant flux linkage show that initially

$$\psi_f = 0 \qquad [145]$$

and from eq. 116d,

$$\tfrac{3}{2}M_f i_d + L_{ff}i_f = 0$$

or

$$i_f = -\frac{3}{2}\frac{M_f}{L_{ff}}i_d \qquad [146]$$

Substitution of the values of the currents (eqs. 146 and 144b and c) into eqs. 116 yields:

$$\psi_d = \left(L_d - \frac{3}{2} \frac{M_f{}^2}{L_{ff}} \right) i_d \qquad [147a]$$

$$\psi_q = 0 \qquad [147b]$$

$$\psi_0 = 0 \qquad [147c]$$

Since, according to eqs. 144, $i_q = i_0 = 0$, from eq. 105a we have

$$i_a = i_d \cos \theta \qquad [148]$$

and similarly, since, according to eqs. 147, $\psi_q = \psi_0 = 0$,

$$\psi_a = \psi_d \cos \theta \qquad [149]$$

Therefore, upon dividing eq. 149 by eq. 148 and then using eq. 147a,

$$\frac{\psi_a}{i_a} = \frac{\psi_d}{i_d} = L_d - \frac{3}{2} \frac{M_f{}^2}{L_{ff}} = L_d{}' \qquad [150]$$

This is the direct-axis transient inductance. Since L_{ff} is a positive quantity,

$$L_d{}' < L_d \qquad [151]$$

Equation 150 should be compared with eq. 31 for the equivalent inductance of a transformer with short-circuited secondary winding. L_d corresponds to the self-inductance of the primary winding, L_{ff} to that of the secondary winding, and M_f to the mutual inductance between the two windings. The only difference between the two equations is the presence of the factor $\frac{3}{2}$ in eq. 150, which appears in consequence of the coefficients arbitrarily chosen in Park's transformation.

Quadrature-axis transient inductance $L_q{}'$ and subtransient inductances $L_d{}''$ and $L_q{}''$. It was assumed in the development of the mathematical theory that the only circuit on the rotor was the field winding in the direct axis. Under this assumption the direct-axis subtransient inductance is equal to the direct-axis transient inductance, and the quadrature-axis transient and subtransient inductances are equal to the quadrature-axis synchronous inductance. The addition of a damper winding in the direct axis would make the direct-axis subtransient inductance less than the transient inductance. A damper winding in the quadrature axis would make the quadrature-axis subtransient inductance less than the transient and synchronous inductances although the last two would still be equal unless there were a field winding in the quadrature axis (a very unusual condition) or some other circuit of similar time constant, for example, the solid rotor of a turbogenerator.

Negative-sequence inductance L_2. The negative-sequence inductance of a three-phase synchronous machine is the flux linkage of an armature phase per ampere of armature current under the following conditions:

1. Steady-state negative-sequence currents applied to the armature windings:

$$i_a = I \cos \omega t \qquad [152a]$$

$$i_b = I \cos (\omega t + 120°) \qquad [152b]$$

$$i_c = I \cos (\omega t - 120°) \qquad [152c]$$

2. Field circuit closed, not excited:

$$v_f = 0 \qquad [153]$$

3. Field rotated at synchronous speed, in any position:

$$\theta = \omega t + \alpha \qquad [154]$$

The Park currents corresponding to eqs. 152 are:

$$i_d = I \cos (2\omega t + \alpha) \qquad [155a]$$

$$i_q = -I \sin (2\omega t + \alpha) \qquad [155b]$$

$$i_0 = 0 \qquad [155c]$$

Note that i_d and i_q are of twice the applied frequency. Current i_d induces a field current of the same frequency. At this frequency the resistance of the field circuit is usually negligible compared with its reactance and may therefore be neglected.

$$v_f = r_f i_f + \frac{d\psi_f}{dt} \approx \frac{d\psi_f}{dt} = 0 \qquad [156]$$

Hence

$$\psi_f = \text{constant}$$

and, in the steady state,

$$\psi_f = 0$$

Therefore, as shown before (eqs. 145, 146, 147a, and 150),

$$i_f = -\frac{3}{2} \frac{M_f}{L_{ff}} i_d \qquad [157]$$

$$\psi_d = L_d i_d + M_f i_f = \left(L_d - \frac{3}{2} \frac{M_f{}^2}{L_{ff}} \right) i_d$$

$$= L_d{}' i_d \qquad [158]$$

Also, by eqs. 116b and c,

$$\psi_q = L_q i_q \qquad\qquad [159]$$

$$\psi_0 = 0 \qquad\qquad [160]$$

The flux linkage of phase a is (compare eq. 105a):

$$
\begin{aligned}
\psi_a &= \psi_d \cos\theta - \psi_q \sin\theta + \psi_0 \\
&= L_d' i_d \cos\theta - L_q i_q \sin\theta \\
&= [L_d'\cos(2\omega t + \alpha)\cos(\omega t + \alpha) + L_q \sin(2\omega t + \alpha)\sin(\omega t + \alpha)]I \\
&= \left\{ \frac{L_d' + L_q}{2}[\cos(2\omega t + \alpha)\cos(\omega t + \alpha) + \sin(2\omega t + \alpha)\sin(\omega t + \alpha)] \right. \\
&\quad \left. + \frac{L_d' - L_q}{2}[\cos(2\omega t + \alpha)\cos(\omega t + \alpha) - \sin(2\omega t + \alpha)\sin(\omega t + \alpha)] \right\} I \\
&= \left[\frac{L_d' + L_q}{2}\cos\omega t + \frac{L_d' - L_q}{2}\cos(3\omega t + 2\alpha)\right] I \qquad [161]
\end{aligned}
$$

It may be seen from this result that, although the applied currents are exclusively of fundamental frequency, the armature flux linkage, and consequently also the armature voltage, consists of a fundamental and a third harmonic. For this reason the instantaneous value of ψ_a/i_a is not constant. It would be discreet now to modify the definition of negative-sequence inductance to: fundamental-frequency armature flux linkage per fundamental-frequency armature ampere. Then

$$L_a = \frac{\psi_{a(\text{fundamental})}}{i_a} = \frac{L_d' + L_q}{2} \qquad [162]$$

That is, negative-sequence inductance is the arithmetical average of direct-axis transient inductance and quadrature-axis synchronous inductance. But this result is valid only if there are no rotor circuits save the field winding.

If there are low-resistance damper windings in both axes, the Park flux linkages are

$$\psi_d = L_d'' i_d \qquad\qquad [163]$$

$$\psi_q = L_q'' i_q \qquad\qquad [164]$$

and the negative-sequence inductance becomes

$$L_2 = \frac{L_d'' + L_q''}{2} \qquad\qquad [165]$$

Likewise, the negative-sequence reactance is

$$x_2 = \frac{x_d'' + x_q''}{2} \qquad\qquad [166]$$

If the resistances of the damper windings should be appreciable compared with their self-reactances at double frequency, then the negative-sequence reactance would depend somewhat upon the resistances as well as upon the reactances of the windings.

It is of academic interest to note that if fundamental-frequency negative-sequence voltages (or flux linkages) are impressed upon the armature, the armature currents are not sinusoidal but contain a third harmonic in addition to the fundamental. In this case the negative-sequence inductance, defined again as the ratio of fundamental flux linkage per fundamental unit current, has a different value than before; it is now:

$$L_2 = \frac{2L_d'' L_q''}{L_d'' + L_q''} \tag{167}$$

This is the "harmonic mean" of L_d'' and L_q''. The harmonic mean gives the lower limit, and the arithmetic mean (eq. 165), the upper limit, of values of L_2. In practice there is little difference between the two values and the arithmetic mean, being simpler, is generally used. The proof of eq. 167 is left as an exercise.

VECTOR DIAGRAMS

Vector diagrams for positive-sequence steady state. Let the field be excited with constant current:

$$i_f = I_f \tag{168}$$

and let the armature currents be steady and of positive sequence:

$$i_a = \text{Re}(\mathbf{I}\underline{/\omega t}) = I \cos (\omega t + \beta) \tag{169a}$$

$$i_b = \text{Re}(\mathbf{a^2 I}\underline{/\omega t}) = I \cos (\omega t + \beta - 120°) \tag{169b}$$

$$i_c = \text{Re}(\mathbf{aI}\underline{/\omega t}) = I \cos (\omega t + \beta + 120°) \tag{169c}$$

where

$$\mathbf{I} = I\underline{/\beta} \tag{170}$$

Then the Park currents (eqs. 106) are:

$$i_d = I \cos \beta = \text{constant} = I_d \tag{171a}$$

$$i_q = I \sin \beta = \text{constant} = I_q \tag{171b}$$

$$i_0 = 0 \tag{171c}$$

The Park fluxes are:

$$\psi_d = L_d I_d + M_f I_f \tag{172a}$$

$$\psi_q = L_q I_q \tag{172b}$$

$$\psi_0 = 0 \qquad [172c]$$

$$\psi_f = \tfrac{3}{2}M_f I_d + L_{ff}I_f \qquad [172d]$$

all of which are constant. The Park voltages (eqs. 121 and 122) are:

$$v_d = rI_d - \omega\psi_q = rI_d - \omega L_q I_q = rI_d - x_q I_q$$
$$= V_d = \text{constant} \qquad [173]$$

and

$$v_q = rI_q + \omega\psi_d = rI_q + \omega L_d I_d + \omega M_f I_f$$
$$= rI_q + x_d I_d + E_q = V_q = \text{constant} \qquad [174]$$

where

$$E_q = \omega M_f I_f \qquad [175]$$

is the *excitation voltage,* the *voltage behind synchronous impedance,* or the *steady-state internal voltage.* It is directly proportional to the field current I_f.

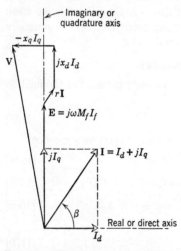

FIG. 30. Steady-state vector diagram of salient-pole synchronous motor with lagging (magnetizing) current. I_f, I_d, I_q, and β are positive. This diagram agrees with eq. 179.

The positive-sequence armature current is (by eqs. 170 and 171):

$$\mathbf{I} = I\,\underline{/\beta} = I\,(\cos\beta + j\sin\beta)$$
$$= I_d + jI_q \qquad [176]$$

and, similarly, the positive-sequence armature terminal voltage is:

$$\mathbf{V} = V_d + jV_q \qquad [177]$$

and the positive-sequence excitation voltage is:

$$\mathbf{E} = 0 + jE_q = j\omega M_f I_f \quad [178]$$

Substituting eqs. 173 and 174 into eq. 177,

$$\mathbf{V} = \mathbf{E} + r\mathbf{I} + jx_d I_d - x_q I_q \quad [179]$$

The voltages, currents, and linkages in eqs. 172 to 179 are constants equal to the crest values of the corresponding positive-sequence quantities, as indicated in eqs. 169 for current I. However, the corresponding *effective values* can be used equally well in any except the equations involving field current I_f.

The *vector diagram* corresponding to eq. 179 is shown in Fig. 30. It is drawn for positive I_f, I_d, I_q, and β. These conditions correspond to *motor* operation with *lagging* (magnetizing) current, as may be seen from the following considerations: If I_f and I_d are both positive, eq. 172a shows that their effects are cumulative; hence I_d is *magnetizing*. The field and armature poles are as shown in Fig. 31a. Now if

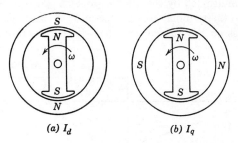

(a) I_d   *(b) I_q*

FIG. 31. Location of field and armature poles for positive I_f and (a) positive I_d only, (b) positive I_q only.

I_q is assumed to be positive and I_d to be zero, then, since the quadrature axis was taken 90° ahead of the direct axis, the poles will be located as shown in Fig. 31b, corresponding to *motor* operation (unlike poles attract). Negative I_d would be *demagnetizing*, and negative I_q would represent *generator* action.

Note that the original circuit equations (91) were set up with such conventions that positive power means power consumed (that is, motor operation). As a consequence, eq. 179, which was derived from the original equations, bears the same sign conventions and is of the form

$$V = E + ZI \qquad [180]$$

In dealing with generators the conventions on signs are usually taken so that eq. 180 becomes

$$V = E - ZI \qquad [181]$$

or

$$E = V + ZI \qquad [182]$$

requiring that either the sign of I or the signs of V and E be changed. If the sign of I (that is, of both I_d and I_q) is changed without changing the sign of I_f, then positive I_d is demagnetizing and positive I_q represents generator action. *This changed sign of I_d and I_q (including instantaneous values i_d and i_q) is in effect in the rest of this book and is in general use elsewhere.*

The vector diagram for generator action with lagging current is shown in Fig. 32. In this diagram the quadrature axis is drawn horizontally, as is customary, and resistance is neglected.

In both vector diagrams the excitation voltage $\mathbf{E}$ lies along the positive quadrature axis. If the vector $jx_q\mathbf{I}$ — that is, the *total* armature current multiplied by the quadrature-axis synchronous reactance — is added to the terminal-voltage vector $\mathbf{V}$, a vector $\mathbf{E}_{qd}$ is obtained which also lies on the quadrature axis. If the generator is operated

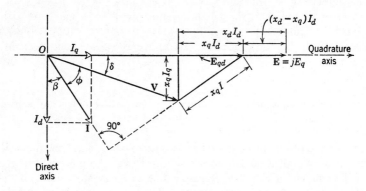

FIG. 32. Steady-state vector diagram of salient-pole synchronous generator with lagging (demagnetizing) current; resistance neglected.

with constant field current I_f but with slowly changing load or power factor, then $\mathbf{E}$ will be constant; and $\mathbf{E}_{qd}$, though not constant, will nevertheless remain in phase with $\mathbf{E}$. The phase of either $\mathbf{E}$ or $\mathbf{E}_{qd}$ is indicative of the mechanical position of the rotor, more specifically, the position of the quadrature axis of the rotor. Hence, when a steady-state stability study is being made on an a-c calculating board, each unsaturated salient-pole synchronous machine could be represented by an adjustable e.m.f. E_{qd} in series with reactance x_q. If this representation is used, the value of E_{qd} must be adjusted from time to time to correspond with the desired constant value of E, in accordance with the following relation:

$$E_{qd} = E - I_d(x_d - x_q) \qquad [183]$$

Because of the pronounced effect of saturation on steady-state stability, machines are seldom represented in this manner. (See Chapter XV.) A similar representation, suitable for transient stability studies, is described later in this chapter.

In a round-rotor machine x_d and x_q are very nearly equal and may be assumed equal without serious error. In this case $E_{qd} = E$.

Revised equations of a synchronous machine. Before proceeding with our consideration of vector diagrams of a synchronous machine, a résumé of the equations which have been derived will be given in which the algebraic signs of all armature currents (i_d and i_q) are reversed to conform with the usual practice in discussing generators, as explained in the last section. Consequently, positive i_q and i_d will now represent generator action with lagging (demagnetizing) current. The sign of the field current is not changed.

Moreover, to make the equations applicable to a machine with solid, round rotor, a circuit (denoted by subscript g) will be assumed present on the quadrature axis of the rotor. This new circuit is analogous to the main field winding (denoted by f) on the direct axis of the rotor.

The most important equations, modified in the two respects just described, are listed below:

Equation 116a becomes:

$$\psi_d = M_f i_f - L_d i_d \qquad [184]$$

116b,
$$\psi_q = M_g i_g - L_q i_q \qquad [185]$$

116d,
$$\psi_f = L_{ff} i_f - \tfrac{3}{2} M_f i_d \qquad [186]$$

Similarly,
$$\psi_g = L_{gg} i_g - \tfrac{3}{2} M_g i_q \qquad [187]$$

121,
$$v_d = -r i_d + \frac{d\psi_d}{dt} - \omega \psi_q \qquad [188]$$

122,
$$v_q = -r i_q + \frac{d\psi_q}{dt} + \omega \psi_d \qquad [189]$$

124a,
$$v_d = -r i_d + M_f \frac{di_f}{dt} - L_d \frac{di_d}{dt} - \omega M_g i_g + \omega L_q i_q \qquad [190]$$

124b,
$$v_q = -r i_q + M_g \frac{di_g}{dt} - L_q \frac{di_q}{dt} + \omega M_f i_f - \omega L_d i_d \qquad [191]$$

124d,
$$v_f = r_f i_f + L_{ff} \frac{di_f}{dt} - \tfrac{3}{2} M_f \frac{di_d}{dt} \qquad [192]$$

Similarly,
$$0 = r_g i_g + L_{gg} \frac{di_g}{dt} - \tfrac{3}{2} M_g \frac{di_q}{dt} \qquad [193]$$

173,
$$V_d = -r I_d + x_q I_q + E_d \qquad [194]$$

174,
$$V_q = -r I_q - x_d I_d + E_q \qquad [195]$$

175, unchanged $E_q = \omega M_f I_f$ [196]

Similarly to 175, $E_d = -\omega M_g I_g$ [197]

176, unchanged, $\mathbf{I} = I_d + jI_q$ [198]

177, unchanged, $\mathbf{V} = V_d + jV_q$ [199]

178, $\mathbf{E} = E_d + jE_q$ [200]

179, $\mathbf{V} = \mathbf{E} - r\mathbf{I} - jx_d I_d + x_q I_q$ [200a]

Vector diagram for the transient state. If the armature current $\mathbf{I}$ changes very slowly (compared with the transient decrement), then the field current I_f remains constant. The fictitious excitation voltage E_q, which by definition (eq. 196) is proportional to the field current, also remains constant. If there is a quadrature-axis rotor circuit, its current I_g remains at zero, and so does the fictitious armature voltage E_d (eq. 197). The terminal voltage $\mathbf{V}$ changes, however, for it differs from the constant voltage $\mathbf{E} = jE_q$ by a changing synchronous-impedance drop (see eq. 200a). The steady-state equations (194 to 200a) and vector diagram (Fig. 32) are valid for very slow changes, and I_f and E_q are constant during such changes.

Now consider a faster change of armature current (fast compared with the transient decrement, yet not faster than the subtransient decrement). Such a change may be due to the application or removal of a fault or to the swinging of the generator with respect to other machines of the power system. During such a change, the flux linkage ψ_f of the field winding remains substantially constant. A new fictitious internal armature voltage will be defined, proportional to the field flux linkage:

$$E_q' = \frac{\omega M_f}{L_{ff}} \psi_f \qquad [201]$$

Then this voltage will likewise remain constant during the change of armature current. It will be shown that the quadrature-axis terminal voltage V_q differs from E_q' by the quadrature-axis transient-impedance drop. The difference between E_q and E_q' is, by use of eqs. 196 and 201,

$$E_q - E_q' = \omega M_f i_f - \frac{\omega M_f}{L_{ff}} \psi_f \qquad [202]$$

which, upon substitution of eq. 186, becomes

$$E_q - E_q' = \frac{3\omega M_f^2}{2L_{ff}} i_d \qquad [203]$$

and, by use of eq. 150,

$$E_q - E_q' = \omega(L_d - L_d')i_d = (x_d - x_d')i_d \qquad [204]$$

This result may be arranged thus:

$$E_q - x_d i_d = E_q' - x_d' i_d \qquad [205]$$

The relation between the quadrature-axis components of excitation voltage and terminal voltage in the steady state is given by eq. 195, which was derived by setting the time derivatives in eq. 191 equal to zero. During changes of the rapidity which we are now considering, these derivatives are still negligible compared with the terms in ω;* therefore the steady-state equations (194, 195, and 200a) and the corresponding vector diagram are still valid. We shall denote the currents and voltages by capital letters, even though they are varying quantities, because they vary slowly and may be considered as the effective values of alternating currents and voltages. (Most writers, however, use lower-case e's and i's.) Granting that eq. 195 is still applicable, we can make the substitution of eq. 205 in it, obtaining:

$$V_q = -rI_q - x_d'I_d + E_q' \qquad [206]$$

Similarly, if there is a quadrature-axis rotor circuit, its flux linkage may be assumed constant and a voltage E_d' defined proportional to the linkage, thus:

$$E_d' = \frac{\omega M_g}{L_{gg}} \psi_g \qquad [207]$$

It follows, by analogy with eq. 204, that

$$-(E_d - E_d') = (x_q - x_q')i_q \qquad [208]$$

and, from eq. 194,

$$V_d = -rI_d + x_q'I_q + E_d' \qquad [209]$$

Combining eqs. 206 and 209 into an equation in complex numbers (analogous to eq. 200a), we get:

$$\mathbf{V} = \mathbf{E}' - r\mathbf{I} - jx_d'I_d + x_q'I_q \qquad [210]$$

where

$$\mathbf{E}' = E_d' + jE_q' \qquad [211]$$

may be called the *voltage behind the transient impedance* (or *reactance*)

*The relative sizes of the terms are approximately in the ratio of ω to $1/T$, where T is the time constant which expresses the rate of change of amplitude of the current. In a 60-cycle machine $\omega = 377$, while $1/T$ lies between the limits of about 30 for the subtransient short-circuit time constant and about 0.1 for the transient open-circuit time constant.

or the *transient internal voltage*. Its direct- and quadrature-axis components are E_d' and E_q', respectively. This voltage is constant on the assumption that the flux linkages of the rotor circuits, ψ_f and ψ_g, are constant. It is greater than the armature terminal voltage by

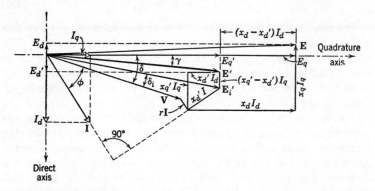

FIG. 33. Vector diagram of synchronous generator in the transient state. Vector **E′** remains constant during a rapid change of armature current **I**, but **V** and **E** change.

the amount of the transient-impedance drop, which consists of resistance and transient-reactance components. It is less than the excitation voltage by the difference of the synchronous-impedance and transient-impedance drops.

A vector diagram corresponding to eqs. 204, 206, 208, 209, and 210 is given in Fig. 33.

In the steady state preceding a change of armature current, the excitation-voltage vector **E** lies on the quadrature axis; that is, $E_d = 0$. The corresponding values of E_d' and E_q' may be computed, respectively, by adding $I_q(x_q - x_q')$ to 0 and by subtracting $I_d(x_d - x_d')$ from E_q. Then during a change of armature current **E′** remains constant; **E** varies and may depart from the quadrature axis unless $x_q = x_q'$.

Suppose that components I_d and I_q of the armature current undergo changes of ΔI_d and ΔI_q, respectively. The corresponding changes in other quantities are as follows:

$$\Delta\psi_f = 0 \qquad [212]$$

$$\Delta\psi_g = 0 \qquad [213]$$

$$\Delta\psi_d = -L_d' \, \Delta I_d \qquad [214]$$

$$\Delta\psi_q = -L_q' \, \Delta I_q \qquad [215]$$

$$\Delta I_f = \frac{3}{2} \frac{M_f}{L_{ff}} \Delta I_d = \frac{L_d - L_d{}'}{M_f} \Delta I_d \qquad [216]$$

$$\Delta I_g = \frac{3}{2} \frac{M_g}{L_{gg}} \Delta I_q = \frac{L_q - L_q{}'}{M_g} \Delta I_q \qquad [217]$$

$$\Delta E_q = (x_d - x_d{}') \Delta i_d \qquad [218]$$

$$\Delta E_d = -(x_q - x_q{}') \Delta i_q \qquad [219]$$

$$\Delta E_d{}' = 0 \qquad [220]$$

$$\Delta E_q{}' = 0 \qquad [221]$$

$$\Delta V_q = -r \Delta I_q - x_d{}' \Delta I_d \qquad [222]$$

$$\Delta V_d = -r \Delta I_d + x_q{}' \Delta I_q \qquad [223]$$

Salient-pole machine. Since a salient-pole machine has no quadra-ture-axis field circuit, $I_g = 0$ and $E_d = 0$, and the excitation voltage $\mathbf{E} = jE_q$ always lies on the quadrature axis in the transient state as

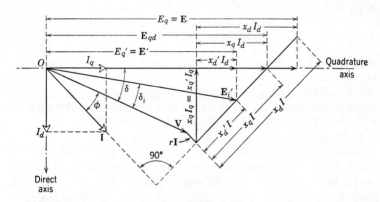

FIG. 34. Vector diagram of salient-pole synchronous machine ($x_q{}' = x_q$). Voltage vectors $\mathbf{E}$, $\mathbf{E}_{qd}$, and $\mathbf{E}'$ all lie on the quadrature axis, both in the transient state and in the steady state.

well as in the steady state. Furthermore, since $x_q{}' = x_q$, $E_d{}' = E_d = 0$, and the voltage behind transient reactance, $\mathbf{E}' = jE_q{}'$, also lies on the quadrature axis, as does E_{qd}, the voltage behind x_q. The vector dia-gram is shown in Fig. 34.

Turbogenerator. In the turbogenerator, which has a solid cylindrical rotor, $x_d{}'$ and $x_q{}'$ are very nearly equal, and x_d and x_q are almost equal. Consequently, the xI drops need not be split into direct- and quadrature-axis components. The vector diagram for the transient state is shown in Fig. 35.

Vector diagram for the subtransient state. In the preceding treatment of the transient state, amortisseur windings or their equivalent were assumed absent, because the equations that were used as a starting point were derived under that assumption. If, however, amortisseurs are present, their effect following a sudden change in circuit conditions dies away in a period of a few cycles, after which the relations just derived are valid.

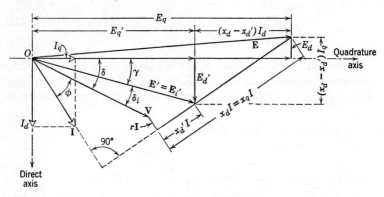

FIG. 35. Vector diagram of synchronous machine with solid, round rotor in the transient state. $x_d = x_q$ and $x_d' = x_q'$. In the steady state, $E_d = 0$ and $E = E_q$, but the same is not true in the transient state.

At the instant of a sudden change in circuit conditions, however, the flux linkages of the amortisseur windings, as well as of the field windings, are substantially constant. Under these conditions, the fictitious voltage, $\mathbf{E}'' = E_d'' + jE_q''$, known as the *voltage behind the subtransient impedance*, or the *subtransient internal voltage*, likewise remains constant. Equations similar to those derived for the transient state (205, 206, 208, 209, 210, and 212 through 223) can be written for the subtransient state by replacing E_d' by E_d'', E_q' by E_q'', $\mathbf{E}'$ by $\mathbf{E}''$, x_d' by x_d'', and x_q' by x_q''. The vector diagram for the subtransient state is similar to Fig. 33, with the changes just noted.

APPLICATIONS TO TRANSIENT STABILITY STUDIES

The period of mechanical oscillation of a machine during a disturbance is of the order of 1 sec., and the behavior of the machine during the first quarter-period often suffices to show whether the system is stable or unstable. The subtransient time constant of a machine is only about 0.03 to 0.04 sec., which is short compared with the period of mechanical oscillation. Therefore, in stability studies the subtransient phenomena are disregarded. The armature time constant is about 0.1 to 0.3 sec. for a short circuit at the armature terminals, but it is greatly diminished by external resistance. Therefore the d-c. component of armature current is ordinarily disregarded also, though its effect may be appreciable in case of a fault at or near the terminals of the machine.

The only electrical transient which need be considered in a stability study is the "transient component." Its time constant is from about 0.5 to 10 sec., usually being longer than the period of mechanical oscillation. Therefore the transient component cannot be ignored although its decrement is frequently ignored.

The transient component can be taken into account in a number of ways which differ as to the accuracy of the assumptions and the amount of calculation required. The following different assumptions can be made regarding a

Salient-pole machine:

1. The voltage behind direct-axis transient reactance may be assumed constant (constant E_i', Fig. 34); or

2. The flux linkage of the field winding may be assumed constant (constant E_q', Fig. 34); or

3. Field decrement and voltage-regulator action (if any) may be calculated (varying E_q').

These assumptions are listed in their order of increasing accuracy and decreasing simplicity of calculation. Method 1 was employed in earlier chapters of this book and is commonly used in practice. Methods 2 and 3 will be explained, illustrated, and compared with Method 1 in later sections of this chapter.

A machine with a solid cylindrical rotor has rotor circuits on both direct and quadrature axes concerning which assumptions must be made. Consequently, the following methods can be used for a

Round-rotor machine:

1. The voltage E_i' (Fig. 33 or 35) behind direct-axis transient reactance may be assumed constant; or

2. The flux linkages of the rotor circuits on both axes may be assumed constant (that is, constant E_d' and E_q', Fig. 33); or

3. The effect of decrement and voltage-regulator action on the flux linkage of the direct-axis rotor circuit (that is, on E_q') may be

calculated, while the quadrature-axis circuit is assumed open $(E_d' = 0)$; or

4. The decrement of the rotor flux linkages of both axes and the effect of voltage-regulator action, if any, on the direct-axis linkage may be calculated.

We will now consider Method 2 for a salient-pole machine. To do so we need the transient power-angle curve of the machine.

Power-angle curves of a salient-pole machine. *Steady state.* The electric power output of a salient-pole generator may be expressed in terms of the terminal voltage V, the excitation voltage E_q, the angle δ between these two voltages, and the components of the synchronous impedance r, x_d, and x_q. All these quantities are shown in the vector diagram, Fig. 34.

If eqs. 194 and 195 are solved for I_d and I_q, with E_d set equal to zero, the result is:

$$I_d = \frac{-V_d r + (E_q - V_q)x_q}{r^2 + x_d x_q} \qquad [224]$$

$$I_q = \frac{(E_q - V_q)r + V_d x_d}{r^2 + x_d x_q} \qquad [225]$$

The power output is

$$P = V_d I_d + V_q I_q \qquad [226]$$

Substitution of the values of I_q and I_d into this expression yields:

$$P = \frac{V_d(-V_d r + E_q x_q - V_q x_q) + V_q(E_q r - V_q r + V_d x_d)}{r^2 + x_d x_q}$$

$$= \frac{E_q(V_q r + V_d x_q) - (V_d^2 + V_q^2)r + V_d V_q(x_d - x_q)}{r^2 + x_d x_q} \qquad [227]$$

Now

$$V_q = V \cos \delta \qquad \text{and} \qquad V_d = V \sin \delta \qquad [228]$$

Hence

$$V_d^2 + V_q^2 = V^2 \qquad [229]$$

and

$$V_d V_q = V^2 \cos \delta \sin \delta = \tfrac{1}{2}V^2 \sin 2\delta \qquad [230]$$

Substitution of eqs. 228, 229, and 230 into eq. 227 gives:

$$P = \frac{E_q V(r \cos \delta + x_q \sin \delta) - V^2 r + \tfrac{1}{2}V^2(x_d - x_q)\sin 2\delta}{r^2 + x_d x_q} \qquad [231]$$

By introduction of the abbreviations

$$Z^2 = r^2 + x_d x_q \qquad [232]$$

$$Z_q{}^2 = r^2 + x_q{}^2 \qquad [233]$$

$$\gamma = \tan^{-1}\frac{r}{x_q} = \sin^{-1}\frac{r}{Z_q} = \cos^{-1}\frac{x_q}{Z_q} \qquad [234]$$

eq. 231 may be further simplified to

$$P = E_q V \frac{Z_q}{Z^2} \sin(\delta + \gamma) - V^2 \frac{r}{Z^2} + V^2 \frac{x_d - x_q}{2Z^2} \sin 2\delta \qquad [235]$$

If a synchronous machine is operated with constant field current and is connected to an infinite bus, both E_q and V are independent of δ. The graph of power P delivered to the infinite bus versus angle δ between the excitation voltage and the bus voltage then consists of a displaced sine wave (such as was previously found in the case of a machine represented by constant impedance and internal voltage) plus a second harmonic. The second-harmonic term represents the "reluctance power" due to saliency, and is present even when the excitation is removed. It depends upon the difference $x_d - x_q$ and thus disappears in a nonsalient-pole machine.

The internal electric power of the synchronous machine, which determines the torque, is

$$P_u = P + I^2 r = P + (I_d{}^2 + I_q{}^2)r \qquad [236]$$

This also, by substituting eqs. 224 and 225 in it, could be put in the form of the sum of a constant term and of first and second harmonics in δ. However, the resulting expression is very complicated.

If the synchronous machine is connected to the infinite bus through a series impedance, r includes the external resistance; likewise x_d and x_q include the external reactance. If the machine is connected to the infinite bus through a network having shunt branches, the network and the voltage of the infinite bus can be replaced by an equivalent e.m.f. and series impedance according to Thévenin's theorem.

If the series resistance is negligible compared with the reactance, the power-angle equation (235) simplifies to

$$P = \frac{E_q V}{x_d} \sin \delta + V^2 \frac{x_d - x_q}{2x_d x_q} \sin 2\delta \qquad [237]$$

The internal power, the output from the armature terminals, and the input to the infinite bus are all equal in the absence of resistance, all

being given by eq. 237. The power-angle curve is plotted in Fig. 36.
It will be observed that the effect of the reluctance power is to steepen
the curve in the stable region near the origin.

Transient. The electric power output of a salient-pole machine
may be expressed in terms of the quadrature-axis voltage $E_q{'}$ behind
transient reactance, the terminal voltage V, and the angle δ between

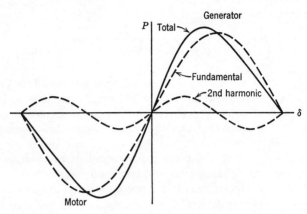

FIG. 36. Steady-state power-angle curve of salient-pole synchronous machine.

these two voltages. The expression is similar to eqs. 235 or 237 except
that E_q in these equations is replaced by $E_q{'}$, and x_d by $x_d{'}$. The angle
δ is the same in both cases because both E_q and $E_q{'}$ lie on the quadrature axis. Thus eq. 237 becomes

$$P = \frac{E_q{'}V}{x_d{'}} \sin \delta - V^2 \frac{x_q - x_d{'}}{2x_d{'}x_q} \sin 2\delta \qquad [238]$$

If both $E_q{'}$ and V are independent of δ, the power-angle curve has
fundamental and second-harmonic components, as shown in Fig. 37.
The second harmonic of the transient curve is reversed in sign from
that of the steady-state curve because $x_q > x_d{'}$. In other words, the
transient reluctance of the direct axis is greater than that of the
quadrature axis because of the presence of the closed field winding
whose flux linkage is constant; hence the transient "reluctance-power"
term is negative.

The effect of saliency. The knowledge of the transient power-angle
curve of a salient-pole synchronous machine enables us to use the
equal-area criterion to find either the critical switching angle or the

EXAMPLE 4 83

power limit of a system consisting of a salient-pole machine swinging with respect to an infinite bus. The results of such an analysis may then be compared with the corresponding results based upon the simpler round-rotor theory; that is, upon the assumption of constant voltage E_i' behind direct-axis transient reactance. The simplest case to analyze is that in which the machine is connected directly to the

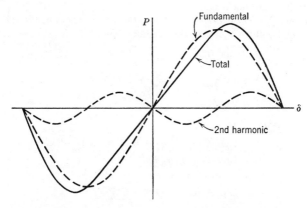

Fig. 37. Transient power-angle curve of salient-pole synchronous machine.

infinite bus and in which resistance is negligible. This case also constitutes a severe test of the validity of applying the usual round-rotor analysis to a salient-pole machine because the further the ratio x_d'/x_q departs from unity, the more the power-angle curve of a salient-pole machine departs from that of a round-rotor machine having the same value of x_d'. The addition of external reactance makes x_d'/x_q approach unity.

Two examples will now be given in which the results of a stability calculation where saliency is neglected are compared with the corresponding results where saliency is taken into account.

EXAMPLE 4

A salient-pole synchronous generator having the following per-unit reactances

$$x_d = 1.15 \qquad x_d' = 0.37$$

$$x_q = 0.75 \qquad x_q' = 0.75$$

is delivering current of 1.00 per unit at 0.91 power factor (lag) through a circuit breaker to an infinite bus having a voltage of 1.00 per unit. If the circuit breaker is then opened, how long may it be kept open before being reclosed without loss of synchronism? Find the answer by plotting the power-angle curve and using the equal-area criterion. Use each of the following power-angle curves and compare the results.

1. Power for constant E_q' versus δ.
2. Power for constant E_i' versus δ_i.

Additional data:

$H = 2.5$ kw-sec. per kva.

$f = 60$ cycles per second.

Solution. *Initial conditions.* Refer to the vector diagram, Fig. 34. Take the terminal voltage $\mathbf{V}$ as reference vector. Then

$$\mathbf{V} = 1.00 \underline{/0} \tag{a}$$

$$\mathbf{I} = 1.00 \underline{/-\cos^{-1} 0.91} = 1.00 \underline{/-24.5°} \tag{b}$$

$$\phi = 24.5° \tag{c}$$

$$\begin{aligned}
\mathbf{E}_{qd} &= \mathbf{V} + jx_q\mathbf{I} \\
&= 1.00 \underline{/0} + \underline{/90.0°} \times 0.75 \times 1.00 \underline{/-24.5°} \\
&= 1.00 \underline{/0} + 0.75 \underline{/65.5°} \\
&= 1.00 + 0.31 + j0.68 \\
&= 1.31 + j0.68 = 1.48 \underline{/27.5°}
\end{aligned} \tag{d}$$

$$\delta_0 = 27.5° \tag{e}$$

$$\begin{aligned}
I_q &= I \cos (\phi + \delta) = I \cos (24.5° + 27.5°) \\
&= 1.00 \cos 52.0° = 0.616
\end{aligned} \tag{f}$$

$$\begin{aligned}
I_d &= I \sin (\phi + \delta) \\
&= 1.00 \sin 52.0° = 0.788
\end{aligned} \tag{g}$$

$$\begin{aligned}
E_q' &= E_{qd} - (x_q - x_d')I_d \\
&= 1.48 - 0.38 \times 0.788 \\
&= 1.48 - 0.30 = 1.18
\end{aligned} \tag{h}$$

$$\begin{aligned}
\mathbf{E}_i' &= \mathbf{V} + jx_d'\mathbf{I} \\
&= 1.00 \underline{/0} + \underline{/90.0°} \times 0.37 \times 1.00 \underline{/-24.5°} \\
&= 1.00 \underline{/0} + 0.37 \underline{/65.5°} \\
&= 1.00 + 0.15 + j0.34 \\
&= 1.15 + j0.34 = 1.20 \underline{/16.3°}
\end{aligned} \tag{i}$$

$$\delta_{i0} = 16.3° \tag{j}$$

$$P = VI \cos \phi = 1.00 \times 1.00 \times 0.91 = 0.91 \tag{k}$$

Also

$$P = E_{qd}I_q = 1.48 \times 0.616 = 0.91 \; (Check) \tag{l}$$

EXAMPLE 4 85

and

$$P = E_i'I \cos (\phi + \delta_i) = 1.20 \times 1.00 \cos 40.8°$$
$$= 0.91 \; (Check) \qquad (m)$$

Power-angle curves. Assumption 1. By eq. 238

$$P_1 = \frac{E_q'V}{x_d'} \sin \delta - V^2 \frac{x_q - x_d'}{2x_d'x_q} \sin 2\delta \qquad (n)$$

$$= \frac{1.18 \times 1.00}{0.37} \sin \delta - \frac{(1.00)^2 \times 0.38}{2 \times 0.37 \times 0.75} \sin 2\delta$$

$$= 3.18 \sin \delta - 0.685 \sin 2\delta \qquad (o)$$

The computation of P_1 is given in Table 4.

TABLE 4

COMPUTATION OF P_1, ASSUMPTION 1 (EXAMPLE 4)

δ	2δ	$\sin \delta$	$\sin 2\delta$	$3.18 \sin \delta$	$-0.685 \sin 2\delta$	P_1
0	0	0	0	0	0	0
15°	30°	0.259	0.500	0.82	−0.34	0.48
30°	60°	0.500	0.866	1.59	−0.59	1.00
45°	90°	0.707	1.000	2.25	−0.68	1.57
60°	120°	0.866	0.866	2.76	−0.59	2.17
75°	150°	0.966	0.500	3.08	−0.34	2.74
90°	180°	1.000	0	3.18	0	3.18
105°	210°	0.966	−0.500	3.08	0.34	3.42
120°	240°	0.866	−0.866	2.76	0.59	3.35
135°	270°	0.707	−1.000	2.25	0.68	2.93
150°	300°	0.500	−0.866	1.59	0.59	2.18
165°	330°	0.259	−0.500	0.82	0.34	1.16
180°	360°	0	0	0	0	0
27.5°	55°	0.462	0.819	1.47	−0.56	0.91

Assumption 2. The power-angle curve is a sine.

$$P_2 = \frac{E_i'V}{x_d'} \sin \delta_i = \frac{1.20 \times 1.00}{0.37} \sin \delta_i = 3.24 \sin \delta_i \qquad (p)$$

Values of P_2 are computed in Table 5.

Both power-angle curves are plotted in Fig. 38. When the breaker is open the power output of the generator is zero; therefore the power-angle curve for this condition is the horizontal axis.

Critical switching angles. The critical angles at which the breaker must be closed are found graphically in Fig. 38 by use of the equal-area criterion. For assumption 1 the angle is 116°; for assumption 2 it is 104°. For assumption 2 the angle can be checked analytically, as follows:

TABLE 5

COMPUTATION OF P_2, ASSUMPTION 2 (EXAMPLE 4)

δ_i	$\sin \delta_i$	P_2
0 and 180°	0	0
15° " 165°	0.259	0.84
30° " 150°	0.500	1.62
45° " 135°	0.707	2.29
60° " 120°	0.866	2.80
75° " 105°	0.966	3.13
90°	1.000	3.24
16.3°	0.281	0.91

The net area is the area under the sine curve to the right of the critical angle less the area of the rectangle under the input line. Hence the area under the curve equals the area of the rectangle, or

$$\int_{\delta_c}^{180°-\delta_0} 3.24 \sin \delta_i \, d\delta_i = 0.91(180° - 2\delta_0) \qquad (q)$$

where δ_0 is the initial angle, which is 16.3°.

$$-3.24 \times 57.3° \cos \delta_i \Big]_{\delta_c}^{163.7°} = 0.91(180° - 32.6°) \qquad (r)$$

$$-185.4° (\cos 163.7° - \cos \delta_c) = 0.91 \times 147.4°$$

$$0.960 + \cos \delta_c = \frac{0.91 \times 147.4°}{185.4°} = 0.723$$

$$\cos \delta_c = 0.723 - 0.960 = -0.237$$
$$\delta_c = 104° \ (Check) \qquad (s)$$

As long as the breaker is open, $P_u = 0$, $P_i = 0.91$ per unit, and $P_a = P_i - P_u = 0.91$ per unit. The acceleration during this time is constant at the value

$$\frac{d^2\delta}{dt^2} = \frac{P_a}{M} \qquad (t)$$

The angular speed at the instant of opening the breaker is zero. After the breaker has been open for t seconds the speed is

$$\frac{d\delta}{dt} = \int_0^t \frac{P_a}{M} \, dt = \frac{P_a t}{M} \qquad (u)$$

and the angular displacement is

$$\delta = \delta_0 + \int_0^t \frac{P_a t}{M} = \delta_0 + \frac{P_a t^2}{2M} \qquad (v)$$

EXAMPLE 4   87

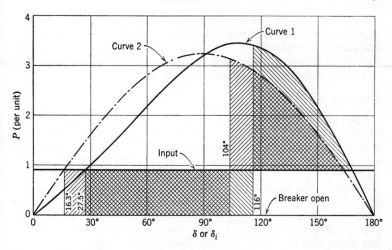

Fig. 38. Determination of critical switching angle by the equal-area criterion under two different assumptions. Curve 1 — saliency taken into account; P plotted against δ for constant E_q'. Curve 2 — saliency neglected; P plotted against δ_i for constant E_i'.

The critical angle δ_c corresponds to the critical time t_c.

$$\delta_c = \delta_0 + \frac{P_a t_c^2}{2M} \qquad (w)$$

$$t_c = \sqrt{\frac{2M(\delta_c - \delta_0)}{P_a}} \qquad (x)$$

The inertia constant is

$$M = \frac{GH}{180f} = \frac{1 \times 2.5}{180 \times 60} = 2.32 \times 10^{-4} \qquad (y)$$

Substitution of the values of M and P_a into eq. x gives

$$t_c = \sqrt{\frac{2 \times 2.32 \times 10^{-4}(\delta_c - \delta_0)}{0.91}} = \sqrt{\frac{\delta_c - \delta_0}{1,965}} \qquad (z)$$

For assumption 1, $\delta_c = 116°$, $\delta_0 = 27.5°$, and $\delta_c - \delta_0 = 88.5°$. The critical time is

$$t_c = \sqrt{\frac{88.5}{1,965}} = 0.212 \text{ sec.} \qquad (aa)$$

For assumption 2, $\delta_c = 104°$, $\delta_0 = 16.3°$, and $\delta_c - \delta_0 = 87.7°$. The critical time is

$$t_c = \sqrt{\frac{87.7}{1,965}} = 0.211 \text{ sec.} \qquad (bb)$$

Conclusion. In the present example the critical switching time computed on the basis of constant flux linkage of the field winding (taking saliency into account) agrees within the probable error of the graphical method with the value of critical switching time computed on the basis of constant voltage behind direct-axis transient reactance (saliency neglected).

EXAMPLE 5

If the salient-pole synchronous generator of the last example is initially operating as described in that example, to what value could the input power suddenly be increased without loss of synchronism? Work the problem on each of the two assumptions made in the last example and compare the results.

Solution. The power-angle curves are the same as in the last example (Fig. 38). They are copied in Figs. 39 and 40, and there the equal-area criterion is applied graphically to find the limiting values of power. The answer is 2.60 per unit by assumption 1 and 2.61 per unit by assumption 2. The discrepancy is less than the probable error of the graphical solution.

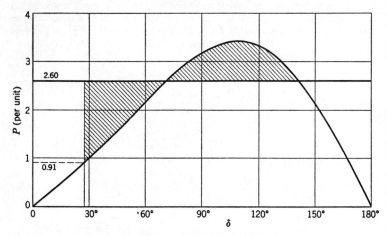

FIG. 39. Determination of power limit by the equal-area criterion, with saliency taken into account (Example 5).

Examples 4 and 5 plainly show that practically the same results are obtained through the use of the usual simple assumption of constant voltage E_i' behind direct-axis transient reactance as through use of the more rigorous salient-pole theory in which the flux linkage of the field winding is assumed constant.* It is reasonable to suppose that

*Concordia, in Ref. 59, p. 11, confirms the almost negligible effect of saliency by giving calculated curves of transient power limit of a 600-mile line with saliency first taken into account and then neglected.

an equally good agreement would be obtained in systems more complicated than the one considered, for example, in a system having several salient-pole machines. Therefore, of the two assumptions, it is natural to prefer the one which is simpler to use, namely, the assumption of constant E_i'.

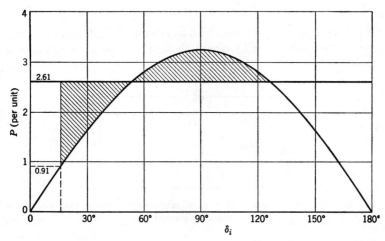

FIG. 40. Determination of power limit by the equal-area criterion, with saliency neglected (Example 5). The result agrees closely with that obtained in Fig. 39.

If, however, the assumption of constant flux linkage is not accurate enough and it is desired to include in the analysis the effect of change of linkage due to decrement or to decrement and voltage-regulator action, then saliency must be taken into account; that is, the two rotor axes must be considered separately. This is true for nonsalient-pole machines as well as for salient-pole machines, and is true even if $x_d' = x_q'$.

In the next few sections of this chapter the methods of taking change of rotor flux linkages into consideration will be set forth.

Representation of salient-pole machines. On a calculating board there is no reactor that presents different reactances to components of current I_d and I_q. A salient-pole machine can be represented, however, by a constant reactance* equal to the quadrature-axis synchronous reactance x_q, in series with a power source whose voltage is $\mathbf{E}_{qd}$ (Fig. 41). This representation has the advantage that the phase of voltage $\mathbf{E}_{qd}$ represents correctly the angular position of the field

---

*Armature resistance can be represented, if desired, but it is usually negligible.

structure. For, if the quantity $jx_q\mathbf{I}$ be added vectorially to the terminal voltage $\mathbf{V}$, the vector sum $\mathbf{E}_{qd}$ always lies on the quadrature axis (see the vector diagram, Fig. 34).

The magnitude of E_{qd} is not constant, however, even if $E_q{}'$ is constant. The relation between E_{qd} and $E_q{}'$ is:

$$E_{qd} = E_q{}' + (x_q - x_d{}')I_d \qquad [239]$$

If $E_q{}'$ is constant, E_{qd} changes with any change in I_d caused by swinging of the machines or by circuit changes, such as the clearing of a fault.

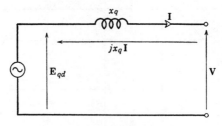

Fig. 41. Method of representing a salient-pole synchronous generator on a calculating board.

The power output of the machine is given correctly by the reading of a wattmeter taking voltage from either side of the reactor (that is, either E_{qd} or V). Usually the wattmeter is connected to the terminals of the power source (voltage E_{qd}). The power can be calculated as $E_{qd}I_q$.

The procedure during point-by-point computation of swing curves is as follows: Suppose that the adjustments have been made and that the power outputs of all machines have been read for one instant of time. The change of angular position of every machine is then computed as usual. The power sources are turned into their new angular positions, their voltage magnitudes (representing E_{qd}) being left unchanged for the moment. Then I_d of every machine is read.* On the assumption that $E_q{}'$ is constant, a new value of E_{qd} of every machine is calculated by eq. 239. The voltages of the power sources are adjusted to the new values of E_{qd}. This adjustment alters the values of I_d. Hence I_d of every machine should be measured again, and if any significant changes are found, the values of E_{qd} should be

---

*I_d can be found from the readings of a voltmeter (reading E_{qd}) and a varmeter the current coil of which carries I and the potential coil E_{qd}. The varmeter reading is $E_{qd}\,I \sin(\phi + \delta)$, which, divided by E_{qd}, gives $I \sin(\phi + \delta) = I_d$. On the Westinghouse network calculator I_d can be read directly from the vector meters.

recalculated and the voltages of the power sources readjusted accordingly. This procedure is repeated as many times as necessary, but one or two adjustments usually suffice. Then the power outputs of the machines may be read again for the next point.

The method just described for representing a salient-pole machine on a calculating board can be applied also to representation of the network on paper. However, the solution of the network on paper is more laborious than the solution on a calculating board, particularly since the network may need to be solved more than once for each point of the swing curves. The power output of each machine can be calculated as $E_{qd}I_q$.

If E_q' varies because of decrement or voltage-regulator action, the procedure is the same as that just described except that new values of E_q' must be calculated for each instant. The method of doing this is described in the next section.

Calculation of change of field flux linkage. Kirchhoff's voltage law, applied to the field circuit, gives the equation:

$$E_{ex}' = R_f i_f + \frac{d\psi_f}{dt} \qquad [240]$$

where E_{ex}' is the exciter armature e.m.f. in volts, R_f is the field-circuit resistance in ohms, i_f is the field current in amperes, and ψ_f is the field flux linkage in weber-turns. This equation may be put into terms of the armature circuit by multiplying it by $\omega M_f/R_f$ and making certain substitutions. Multiplication by $\omega M_f/R_f$ gives

$$\frac{\omega M_f E_{ex}'}{R_f} = \omega M_f i_f + \frac{\omega M_f}{R_f} \frac{d\psi_f}{dt} \qquad [241]$$

Here, by eq. 196,

$$\omega M_f i_f = E_q \qquad [242]$$

Also, by use of eqs. 76 and 201,

$$\frac{\omega M_f \psi_f}{R_f} = \frac{L_{ff}}{R_f} \frac{\omega M_f \psi_f}{L_{ff}} = T_{d0}' E_q' \qquad [243]$$

A new quantity, the exciter voltage referred to the armature circuit, is defined by

$$\frac{\omega M_f E_{ex}'}{R_f} = E_{ex} \qquad [244]$$

It is the open-circuit armature voltage which would be produced by exciter voltage E_{ex}' in the steady state. Substitution of eqs. 242, 243, and 244 into eq. 241 gives

$$E_{ex} = E_q + T_{d0}' \frac{dE_q'}{dt} \qquad [245]$$

or, solving for the derivative,

$$\frac{dE_q'}{dt} = \frac{E_{ex} - E_q}{T_{d0}'} \qquad [246]$$

Thus the rate of change of E_q' (which is proportional to the field flux linkage) is expressed in terms of the open-circuit transient time constant T_{d0}' even though the armature may not be open-circuited. In this equation E_{ex} either may be constant or may vary due to voltage-regulator action independently of the other variables in the equation. In either case it is assumed that E_{ex} is a known function of t. E_q depends upon E_q' and I_d, thus (eq. 204):

$$E_q = E_q' + (x_d - x_d')I_d \qquad [247]$$

and I_d depends upon the phase and magnitude of E_{qd} of every machine in the system. (The relation between E_{qd} and E_q' is given by eq. 239.)

Three-phase short circuit at terminals of machine. It is known from considerations stated in the section of this chapter entitled "Time constants of synchronous machines" that when a three-phase short circuit occurs on the armature terminals of a synchronous generator, the exciter voltage being constant, the transient a-c. component of armature current and the transient d-c. component of field current both decay exponentially with the transient short-circuit time constant

$$T_d' = \frac{x_d'}{x_d} T_{d0}' \qquad [248]$$

That this is consistent with eq. 246 will now be shown. During the short circuit the terminal voltage of the machine is zero and hence the short-circuit current is

$$I_d = \frac{E_q'}{x_d'} = \frac{E_q}{x_d} \qquad [249]$$

where E_q' has the same value just after the fault occurs as it had just before the fault occurred. From the last equation,

$$E_q' = E_q \frac{x_d'}{x_d} \qquad [250]$$

Substitute this into eq. 246, obtaining:

$$\frac{x_d'}{x_d}\frac{dE_q}{dt} = \frac{E_{ex} - E_q}{T_{d0}'} \qquad [251]$$

Dividing by x_d'/x_d,

$$\frac{dE_q}{dt} = \frac{E_{ex} - E_q}{\left(\dfrac{x_d'}{x_d}\right)T_{d0}'} = \frac{E_{ex} - E_q}{T_d'} \qquad [252]$$

The only dependent variable in the last equation is E_q, and its variation is controlled by the short-circuit time constant T_d'. The field current I_f is always proportional to E_q, by definition of E_q, and, as long as the short circuit is on, by eq. 249, E_q' and I_d are proportional to E_q. Hence E_q, E_q', I_d, and I_f all vary exponentially with time constant T_d', which was to be shown.

When the armature is open-circuited, eq. 249 does not hold, but, from eq. 247, since $I_d = 0$, $E_q = E_q'$. Then eq. 246 can be put in terms of either E_q or E_q' instead of both, and the equation shows that the variation of both E_q' and E_q (hence also of I_f) occurs with time constant T_{d0}'.

Point-by-point calculation. Earlier in this chapter it was stated that the accuracy of point-by-point calculation of transient current in an *R-L* circuit is improved if, in calculating the average rate of change of current during a time interval Δt, half a time interval ($\Delta t/2$) is added to the time constant and if the value of applied voltage at the middle of the interval is used. Obviously the result of adding $\Delta t/2$ to T_{d0}' in eq. 246 would not be the same as the result of adding $\Delta t/2$ to T_d' in eq. 252. The procedure is correct for the latter equation, whose form is similar to that of eq. 64, the solution of which was previously considered. What, then, should be the correction to T_{d0}' in order to produce a similar improvement of accuracy in solving eq. 246? Let numerator and denominator of the right-hand member of this equation be multiplied by E_q'/E_q. Then

$$\frac{dE_q'}{dt} = \frac{\left(\dfrac{E_q'}{E_q}\right)E_{ex} - E_q'}{\left(\dfrac{E_q'}{E_q}\right)T_{d0}'} \qquad [253]$$

For a fixed ratio E_q'/E_q, this equation shows that E_q' varies with a time constant $(E_q'/E_q)T_{d0}'$. (For the condition of short circuit, $E_q'/E_q = x_d'/x_d$ and hence the time constant is T_d'. But on open circuit $E_q'/E_q = 1$, and the time constant is T_{d0}'.) For improved accuracy, the denominator of eq. 253 should be increased by $\Delta t/2$, and the value of E_{ex} should be taken at time $t + \Delta t/2$; thus:

$$\frac{\Delta E_q'}{\Delta t} = \frac{\left(\dfrac{E_q'}{E_q}\right) E_{ex}(t + \Delta t/2) - E_q'}{\left(\dfrac{E_q'}{E_q}\right) T_{d0}' + \dfrac{\Delta t}{2}} \qquad [254]$$

Here the derivative has been replaced by the average slope. Now, after numerator and denominator have been divided by E_q'/E_q, eq. 254 becomes

$$\frac{\Delta E_q'}{\Delta t} = \frac{E_{ex}(t + \Delta t/2) - E_q}{T_{d0}' + \left(\dfrac{E_q}{E_q'}\right) \dfrac{\Delta t}{2}} \qquad [255]$$

which shows that the time constant T_{d0}' in eq. 246 should be increased by $(E_q/E_q')(\Delta t/2)$. Since the correction term is a minor one, its value need not be changed at every step of a point-by-point calculation even though the ratio E_q/E_q' varies somewhat.

Example 6

A three-phase short circuit occurs at the terminals of a salient-pole generator which is initially operating at no load and at rated terminal voltage. The constants of the generator are:

$$x_d = 1.05 \text{ per unit} \qquad x_q = x_q' = 0.69 \text{ per unit}$$

$$x_d' = 0.29 \text{ per unit} \qquad T_{d0}' = 5.0 \text{ sec.}$$

Calculate and plot excitation voltage E_q and quadrature-axis transient voltage E_q' as functions of time for each of the two following conditions:

(a) Constant exciter voltage E_{ex}.

(b) Linear exciter-voltage build-up of 2.5 units per second.

Solution. Before occurrence of the fault, at no load,

$$E_q' = E_q = V = E_{ex} = 1.00 \text{ unit} \qquad (a)$$

$$I_d = I_q = 0 \qquad (b)$$

Immediately after occurrence of the fault, by the law of constant flux linkage,

$$E_q' = 1.00 \text{ unit} \qquad (c)$$

Also

$$E_{ex} = 1.00 \text{ unit} \qquad (d)$$

$$V = 0 \qquad (e)$$

EXAMPLE 6　　　　　　　95

$$I_d = \frac{E_q'}{x_d'} = \frac{1.00}{0.29} = 3.45 \text{ units} \qquad (f)$$

$$I_q = 0 \qquad (g)$$

$$E_q = E_q' + (x_d - x_d')I_d = x_d'I_d + (x_d - x_d')I_d = x_dI_d$$
$$= 1.05 \times 3.45 = 3.62 \text{ units} \qquad (h)$$

$$\frac{E_q}{E_q'} = \frac{3.62}{1.00} = 3.62 \qquad (i)$$

This ratio remains constant while the fault is on. For the point-by-point calculation, take an interval $\Delta t = 0.2$ sec. The equation governing the change of E_q' is eq. 255:

$$\frac{\Delta E_q'}{\Delta t} = \frac{E_{ex}(t + \Delta t/2) - E_q}{T_{d0}' + (E_q/E_q')(\Delta t/2)} = \frac{E_{ex}(t + \Delta t/2) - E_q}{5.0 + 3.62 \times 0.1}$$
$$= \frac{E_{ex}(t + \Delta t/2) - E_q}{5.36} \qquad (j)$$

In condition a the exciter voltage has the constant value $E_{ex} = 1.00$ unit. During the first interval,

$$\frac{\Delta E_q'}{\Delta t} = \frac{1.00 - 3.62}{5.36} = \frac{-2.62}{5.36} = -0.489 \text{ unit per second} \qquad (k)$$

hence

$$\Delta E_q' = \frac{\Delta E_q'}{\Delta t} \Delta t = -0.489 \times 0.2 = -0.0978 \text{ unit} \qquad (l)$$

At the end of the first interval

$$E_q' = 1.00 - 0.098 = 0.902 \text{ unit} \qquad (m)$$

The computation is continued in Table 6.

In condition b the exciter voltage increases linearly according to the equation

$$E_{ex} = 1.00 + 2.50t \text{ units} \qquad (n)$$

During the first interval, the average value of E_{ex} is

$$E_{ex}(t + \Delta t/2) = 1.00 + 2.50 \times 0.1 = 1.25 \text{ units} \qquad (o)$$

and the average rate of change of E_q' is, by eq. j,

$$\frac{\Delta E_q'}{\Delta t} = \frac{1.25 - 3.62}{5.36} = \frac{-2.37}{5.36} = -0.441 \text{ unit per second} \qquad (p)$$

The computation is continued in Table 7.

Curves of E_q, E_q', and E_{ex} for the two cases are plotted in Fig. 42.

Conclusions. The assumption of constant flux linkage of the field winding appears at first sight to be a poor one because the flux linkage decreases in

TABLE 6

Point-by-Point Computation of E_q' and E_q
Condition a: Constant Exciter Voltage $E_{ex} = 1.00$ (Example 6)

t (sec.)	E_q' (p.u.)	I_d (p.u.)	E_q (p.u.)	E_{ex} (p.u.)	$E_{ex} - E_q$ (p.u.)	$\Delta E_q'$ (p.u.)
0+	1.000	3.45	3.62	1.00	-2.62	-0.098
0.2	0.902	3.11	3.26	1.00	-2.26	-0.084
0.4	0.818	2.82	2.96	1.00	-1.96	-0.073
0.6	0.745	2.57	2.70	1.00	-1.70	-0.063
0.8	0.682	2.35	2.47	1.00	-1.47	-0.055
1.0	0.627	2.16	2.27	1.00	-1.27	-0.047
1.2	0.580	2.00	2.10	1.00	-1.10	-0.041
1.4	0.539	1.86	1.95	1.00	-0.95	-0.035
1.6	0.504	1.74	1.82	1.00	-0.82	-0.031
1.8	0.473	1.63	1.71	1.00	-0.71	-0.027
2.0	0.446	1.54	1.62	1.00	-0.62	-0.023
2.2	0.423	1.46	1.53	1.00	-0.53	-0.020
2.4	0.403	1.39	1.46	1.00	-0.46	-0.017
2.6	0.386	1.33	1.40	1.00	-0.40	-0.015
2.8	0.371	1.28	1.34	1.00	-0.34	-0.013
3.0	0.358	1.23	1.30	1.00		

TABLE 7

Point-by-Point Computation of E_q' and E_q
Condition b: Linear Build-up of Exciter Voltage (Example 6)

t (sec.)	E_q' (p.u.)	I_d (p.u.)	E_q (p.u.)	E_{ex} (p.u.)	$E_{ex} - E_q$ (p.u.)	$\Delta E_q'$ (p.u.)
0+	1.000	3.45	3.62	1.25	-2.37	-0.088
0.2	0.912	3.14	3.30	1.75	-1.55	-0.058
0.4	0.854	2.94	3.09	2.25	-0.84	-0.031
0.6	0.823	2.84	2.98	2.75	-0.23	-0.009
0.8	0.814	2.81	2.95	3.25	$+0.30$	$+0.011$
1.0	0.825	2.84	2.98	3.75	$+0.77$	$+0.029$
1.2	0.854	2.94	3.09	4.25	$+1.16$	$+0.043$
1.4	0.897	3.09	3.25	4.75	$+1.50$	$+0.056$
1.6	0.953	3.28	3.45	5.25	$+1.80$	$+0.067$
1.8	1.020	3.52	3.70	5.75	$+2.05$	$+0.076$
2.0	1.096	3.78	3.97	6.25	$+2.28$	$+0.085$
2.2	1.181	4.07	4.28	6.75	$+2.47$	$+0.092$
2.4	1.273	4.39	4.61	7.25	$+2.64$	$+0.098$
2.6	1.371	4.73	4.96	7.75	$+2.79$	$+0.104$
2.8	1.475	5.08	5.33	8.25	$+2.92$	$+0.109$
3.0	1.584	5.46	5.74			

EXAMPLE 7 97

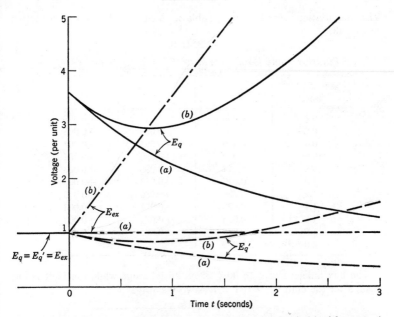

Fig. 42. Variation of E_q and E_q' during three-phase short circuit (a) with constant exciter voltage, $E_{ex} = 1$, (b) with linear build-up of exciter voltage, $E_{ex} = 1 + 2.5t$ (Example 6).

0.5 sec. to 77% of its initial value when the exciter voltage is constant and to 83% when the exciter voltage rises at the assumed rate. It should be remembered, however, that in stability studies the fault is often assumed to be one of less severe type than a three-phase fault and at a less severe location than at the terminals of the generator; furthermore, the fault is not sustained, but is cleared in a few tenths of a second.

Example 7

The generator described in the last example undergoes a three-phase short circuit at its terminals which is cleared 0.2 sec. later. The exciter voltage is constant. Calculate and plot E_q' as a function of time.

Solution. While the short circuit is on the generator, E_q and E_q' vary as calculated in the last example, part a. At the end of 0.2 sec., $E_q = 3.26$ and $E_q' = 0.902$. Just after the clearing of the fault, $E_q = E_q' = 0.902$. Since $E_q/E_q' = 1$, eq. j of the last example becomes:

$$\frac{\Delta E_q'}{\Delta t} = \frac{E_{ex} - E_q'}{T_{d0}' + \Delta t/2} = \frac{1 - E_q'}{5.0 + 0.1} \tag{a}$$

$$\Delta E_q' = \frac{1 - E_q'}{5.1} \Delta t = (1 - E_q') \frac{0.2}{5.1} = \frac{1 - E_q'}{25.5} \tag{b}$$

The computation is carried out in Table 8. A curve of E_q' versus t is plotted in Fig. 43.

TABLE 8

Point-by-Point Computation of E_q' and E_q (Example 7)

t (sec.)	E_q'	$1 - E_q'$	$\Delta E_q'$
0+	1.000		−0.098
0.2	0.902	+0.098	+0.004
0.4	0.906	+0.094	+0.004
0.6	0.910	+0.090	+0.004
0.8	0.914	+0.086	+0.003
1.0	0.917	+0.083	+0.003
1.2	0.920	+0.080	+0.003
1.4	0.923	+0.077	+0.003
1.6	0.926	+0.074	+0.003
1.8	0.929	+0.071	+0.003
2.0	0.932		

The flux linkage drops to 90% of its initial value while the fault is on; then, after the fault is cleared, it rises very slowly.

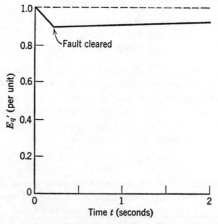

Fig. 43. Variation of E_q' during and after three-phase short circuit cleared in 0.2 sec. (Example 7).

If the fault were cleared in 0.1 sec., the flux linkage would decrease only to about 95% of its initial value.

Example 8

The salient-pole synchronous generator described in Example 4 is delivering power to an infinite bus under the initial conditions specified in that

EXAMPLE 8   99

example. A three-phase short circuit, occurring at the terminals of the generator, is cleared in 0.20 sec. without disconnecting the generator from the bus. Calculate and plot swing curves of the generator for each of the following two conditions: (a) field flux linkage of generator assumed constant; (b) field decrement taken into account, $T_{d0}' = 5.0$ sec.

Solution. *During fault.* During the 0.2-sec. period in which there is a three-phase fault on the terminals of the generator, the output of the generator is zero and the accelerating power P_a is equal to the mechanical power input P_i, which is assumed to be constant. From Example 4, the input is 0.91 per unit, the initial angular displacement is $\delta_0 = 27.5°$, and the inertia constant is $M = 2.32 \times 10^{-4}$. The swing curve can be calculated by eq. w of Example 4:

$$\delta = \delta_0 + \frac{P_a}{2M} t^2 = 27.5° + \frac{0.91}{2 \times 2.32 \times 10^{-4}} t^2$$

$$= 27.5° + 1,964t^2 \qquad (a)$$

This calculation is performed in Table 9.

TABLE 9

COMPUTATION OF SWING CURVE
DURING PERIOD WHEN FAULT IS ON
(EXAMPLE 8)

t (sec.)	t^2	$1,964t^2$ (deg.)	δ (deg.)
0	0	0	27.5
0.05	0.0025	4.9	32.4
0.10	0.0100	19.6	47.1
0.15	0.0225	44.1	71.6
0.20	0.0400	78.5	106.0

The swing curve during this period is the same whether or not field decrement is taken into account. The decrement during this period can be computed as a simple exponential,

$$E_q' = E_q'(0)\epsilon^{-t/T_d'} \qquad (b)$$

The initial value of E_q', from Example 4, is 1.18 per unit. The short-circuit time constant is

$$T_d' = \frac{x_d'}{x_d} T_{d0}' = \frac{0.37}{1.15} \times 5.0 = 1.61 \text{ sec.} \qquad (c)$$

Hence

$$E_q' = 1.18\epsilon^{-t/1.61} \qquad (d)$$

Values of E_q' while the fault is on are calculated in Table 10. E_q' decreases about 12% during this period.

TABLE 10

COMPUTATION OF E_q' DURING PERIOD WHEN FAULT IS ON
(EXAMPLE 8)

t (sec.)	$t/1.61$	$\epsilon^{-t/1.61}$	E_q' (p.u.)
0	0	1.000	1.18
0.05	0.031	0.969	1.14
0.10	0.062	0.940	1.11
0.15	0.096	0.909	1.07
0.20	0.124	0.883	1.04

After clearing of fault — field flux linkage constant. The swing curve will be computed point by point, using a time interval $\Delta t = 0.05$ sec. The second difference of angular position δ is

$$\Delta^2\delta = \frac{(\Delta t)^2}{M} P_a = \frac{(0.05)^2}{2.32 \times 10^{-4}} P_a = 10.8 P_a \qquad (e)$$

where P_a is the accelerating power in per unit and equals $P_i - P_u = 0.91 - P_u$. The power output P_u will be calculated from power-angle equation o of Example 4:

$$P_u = 3.18 \sin \delta - 0.685 \sin 2\delta \qquad (f)$$

which was plotted in Fig. 38, Curve 1. The point-by-point calculation, given in Table 11, starts at $t = 0.20$ sec. with $\delta = 106.0°$ (from the last line

TABLE 11

COMPUTATION OF SWING CURVE AFTER CLEARING OF FAULT
FIELD FLUX LINKAGE ASSUMED CONSTANT (EXAMPLE 8)

t (sec.)	$\sin \delta$	$\sin 2\delta$	$3.18 \sin \delta$	-0.685 $\sin 2\delta$	P_u (p.u.)	P_a (p.u.)	$\Delta^2\delta$ (deg.)	$\Delta\delta$ (deg.)	δ (deg.)
0.20 −	..	..	..	..	0	+0.91			
0.20 +	0.961	−0.530	3.06	+0.36	3.42	−2.51		+34.4	
0.20 avg.	..	..	..	..	1.71	−0.80	−8.6		106.0
								+25.8	
0.25	0.746	−0.994	2.37	+0.68	3.05	−2.14	−23.1		131.8
								+2.7	
0.30	0.713	−1.000	2.27	+0.68	2.95	−2.04	−22.0		134.5
								−19.3	
0.35	0.905	−0.770	2.88	+0.53	3.41	−2.50	−27.0		115.2
								−46.3	
0.40	0.933	+0.672	2.96	+0.46	2.50	−1.59	−17.2		68.9
								−63.5	
0.45	..	..	..	..	..	..	..		5.4

EXAMPLE 8   101

of Table 9). The preceding difference $\Delta\delta$ is taken as the difference of the last two values of δ in Table 9: $106.0° - 71.6° = 34.4°$. Because there is a discontinuity in P_a at $t = 0.20$ sec., the average of the values before and after clearing the fault must be used.

After clearing of fault — field decrement taken into account. The swing curve will be computed point by point as before except that the power output is now given by

$$P_u = 2.70E_q' \sin\delta - 0.685 \sin 2\delta \qquad (g)$$

where E_q' is no longer constant but is computed point by point as follows: By eq. 255 the change of E_q' in time Δt is

$$\Delta E_q' = \frac{E_{ex} - E_q}{T_{d0}' + \left(\dfrac{E_q}{E_q'}\right)\dfrac{\Delta t}{2}} \Delta t = \frac{(1.80 - E_q)0.05}{5.0 + \left(\dfrac{E_q}{E_q'}\right)0.025} \qquad (h)$$

The exciter voltage E_{ex} in this equation is assumed constant and is equal to the value of E_q before occurrence of the fault. From information in Example 4, this value is

$$E_q = E_{qd} + I_d(x_d - x_q) = 1.48 + 0.788(1.15 - 0.75)$$
$$= 1.48 + 0.32 = 1.80 \text{ per unit}$$

The excitation voltage after occurrence of the fault is computed as follows:

$$E_q = E_q' + I_d(x_d - x_d') = E_q' + 0.78I_d \qquad (i)$$

and, by eqs. 224 and 228, with $r = 0$ and E_q and x_d replaced by E_q' and x_d', respectively,

$$I_d = \frac{E_q' - V\cos\delta}{x_d'} = \frac{E_q' - 1.00\cos\delta}{0.37} \qquad (j)$$

For example, just after the fault has been cleared, $E_q' = 1.04$ per unit and $\delta = 106.0°$, the same as just before clearing. Equation j gives:

$$I_d = \frac{1.04 - 1.00\cos 106.0°}{0.37} = \frac{1.04 + 0.28}{0.37} = \frac{1.32}{0.37} = 3.57 \text{ per unit}$$

By eq. i,

$$E_q = 1.04 + 0.78 \times 3.57 = 1.04 + 2.78 = 3.82 \text{ per unit}$$

and by eq. h,

$$\Delta E_q' = \frac{(1.80 - 3.82)0.05}{5.0 + \dfrac{3.82}{1.04} \times 0.025} = \frac{-2.02 \times 0.05}{5.092} = -0.020 \text{ per unit}$$

Therefore, at $t = 0.25$ sec.,

$$E_q' = 1.04 - 0.02 = 1.02 \text{ per unit}$$

The remainder of the point-by-point calculation is carried out in Table 12.

TABLE 12

Computation of Swing Curve After Clearing of Fault (Field Decrement Taken Into Account) (Example 8)

t (sec.)	E_q' (p.u.)	$\cos\delta$	$E_q' - \cos\delta$ (p.u.)	I_d (p.u.)	$0.78 I_d$ (p.u.)	E_q (p.u.)	$1.80 - E_q$ (p.u.)	$\Delta E_q'$ (p.u.)	$\sin\delta$	$\sin 2\delta$	$2.70 E_q' \sin\delta$	$-0.685 \sin 2\delta$	P_u (p.u.)	P_a (p.u.)	$\Delta^2\delta$ (deg.)	$\Delta\delta$ (deg.)	δ (deg.)
0.20−	1.04												0	+0.91			
0.20+	1.04	−0.28	1.32	3.57	2.78	3.82	−2.02		0.961	−0.53	2.70	+0.36	3.06	−2.15			
0.20 avg.	1.04												1.53	−0.62	−7.3	34.4	106.0
0.25	1.02	−0.68	1.70	4.60	3.58	4.60	−2.80	−0.02	0.730	−0.998	2.01	+0.68	2.69	−1.78	−19.2	27.1	133.1
0.30	0.99	−0.78	1.77	4.78	3.73	4.72	−2.92	−0.03	0.629	−0.978	1.68	+0.67	2.35	−1.44	−15.5	7.9	141.0
0.35	0.96	−0.69	1.65	4.46	3.48	4.44	−2.64	−0.03	0.727	−0.998	1.89	+0.68	2.57	−1.66	−17.9	−7.6	133.4
0.40	0.93	−0.31	1.24	3.35	2.62	3.55	−1.75	−0.03	0.951	−0.585	2.39	+0.40	2.79	−1.88	−21.4	−25.5	107.9
0.45	0.91							−0.02	0.875	+0.848	2.15	−0.58	1.57	−0.66	−7.1	−46.9	61.0
0.50																−54.0	7.0

EXAMPLE 8   103

Conclusions. The swing curves for the two conditions are plotted in Fig. 44. The difference between them appears considerable. However, the difference in the maximum angular displacements is only 4° or 5°.

In Example 4, with the same initial value of power as in the present example, the critical time during which the generator could be disconnected from the bus was found to be 0.212 sec. In the present example a three-

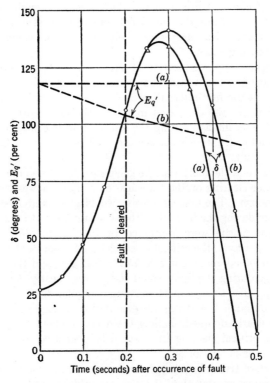

Fig. 44. Effect of field decrement on swing curves (Example 8).

phase short circuit is assumed instead of the disconnection of the generator from the bus. In both cases the power output of the generator is zero during the disturbance. Therefore, for equal switching times the swing curves would be identical for both types of disturbance, if the field flux linkage were assumed constant in both cases. Furthermore, with the assumption of constant flux linkage, the critical switching time is the same for both disturbances; namely, 0.212 sec. Since the three-phase fault actually decreases the flux linkage, the system would be unstable with 0.212-sec. clearing if decrement were taken into account. Nevertheless, decreasing the clearing time to 0.200 (a decrease of only 6%) was found to make the system stable with some margin. The error in determining the critical switching time due to neglecting field decrement in this example is, then, less than 6% — perhaps 4% — in spite of the fact that the flux linkage has decreased about 16% at the instant of maximum swing.

The last example has shown that the error introduced by the assumption of constant flux linkage is hardly great enough, in the case considered, to warrant the additional complication of calculating the field decrement. But are cases likely to arise in which the error would be much greater?

A less severe type or location of short circuit would permit either slower clearing or the transmission of more power without loss of synchronism. If the first alternative is chosen, the increased fault duration is offset by the decreased m.m.f. of the fault current, and the decrease of flux linkage during the fault period is changed but little. If the second alternative is chosen, there is less decrease of flux linkage during the fault.

An increase in the inertia of the generator would also make possible either slower clearing or the transmission of more power without loss of synchronism. The first alternative would give greater reduction of flux linkage during the fault than that encountered with 0.2-sec. clearing. If the inertia were multiplied by four, giving $H = 4 \times 2.5 = 10$ kw-sec. per kva., the critical clearing time for constant flux linkage would be doubled, making it $2 \times 0.21 = 0.42$ sec., and the decrease in flux linkage during the fault would also be very nearly doubled, making it 24%. The time to reach maximum angular displacement would likewise be doubled, and the decrease in flux linkage up to this time would be nearly doubled, making the decrease about 30%. Without doubt, the critical clearing time would be decreased by a significant amount, perhaps by 7 or 8%.

The modern trend, however, is to clear faults as rapidly as possible. Clearing times greater than 0.2 sec. are seldom used on important circuits where system stability is a consideration.

Generator voltage regulators, if used, tend to counteract the decrease of flux linkage resulting from the fault and from the subsequent swinging apart of the machines. Regulator and exciter action is treated in the next chapter. Damping, which has been neglected, somewhat improves stability.

It may be concluded that the assumption of constant flux linkage is a reasonably accurate one unless the time of clearing severe faults is greater than 0.2 sec.

One more example of decrement calculation will be given in order

EXAMPLE 9 105

to illustrate the procedure applicable to a multimachine system and to illustrate the effect of a less severe fault than that in the last example.

EXAMPLE 9

A hydroelectric station is supplying power over a double-circuit transmission line to a metropolitan receiving system which may be regarded as an infinite bus. Initially the hydroelectric station has an output of 1.00 per unit and a high-tension bus voltage of 1.05 per unit. The voltage of

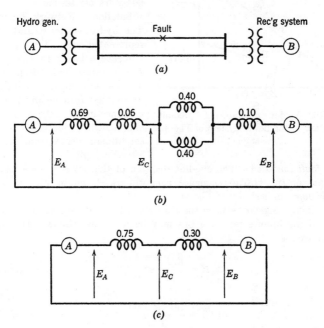

Fig. 45. The power system of Example 9. (a) One-line diagram, (b) positive-sequence network with reactances in per unit, and (c) the same after reduction. E_A represents E_{qd} of the hydroelectric generators; E_B, the voltage of the infinite receiving bus; and E_C, the voltage of the high-tension sending-end bus.

the receiving system is 1.00 per unit. A two-line-to-ground fault occurs at the middle of one transmission circuit and is cleared in 0.15 sec. by the simultaneous opening of the circuit breakers at both ends. Compute the quadrature-axis transient voltage E_q' and the displacement angle δ as functions of time for each of the following assumptions:

1. Constant exciter voltage E_{ex}.
2. Constant direct-axis transient voltage E_q'.

Each transmission circuit has negligible resistance and capacitance and the following reactances: $X_1 = X_2 = 0.40$ per unit; $X_0 = 0.65$ per unit.

The receiving-end transformers have a reactance of 0.10 per unit, and the sending-end transformers, 0.06 per unit. The neutrals of both transformers are solidly grounded. The hydroelectric generators have the following reactances in per unit: $x_d = 1.05$, $x_d' = 0.29$, $x_q = x_q' = 0.69$, and $x_2 = 0.18$. They have a stored kinetic energy at rated speed of 3.00 Mj. per Mva. of rating. Their direct-axis open-circuit transient time constant is 5.0 sec. The system frequency is 60 cycles per second.

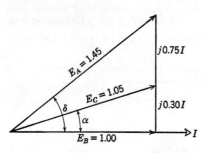

Solution. Network reduction. The hydroelectric generators are represented in the positive-sequence network by the voltage E_{qd} in series with reactance x_q. The network must be reduced to its simplest form — an equivalent π connecting E_{qd}, the infinite bus, and neutral — for each of three conditions: before, during, and after the fault.

FIG. 46. Vector diagram of prefault condition in the power system of Fig. 45 (Example 9).

Prefault condition. The one-line diagram of the power system and the diagram of the positive-sequence network are shown in Fig. 45. The vector diagram is shown in Fig. 46.

The initial angle α between the voltages of the hydrostation high-tension bus and the infinite receiving bus may be found as follows. The power transmitted is

$$P = \frac{E_C E_B}{X} \sin \alpha \qquad (a)$$

$$1.00 = \frac{1.05 \times 1.00}{0.30} \sin \alpha \qquad (b)$$

$$\sin \alpha = \frac{0.30}{1.05} = 0.286 \qquad (c)$$

$$\alpha = 16.6° \qquad (d)$$

The line current **I**, expressed with the voltage **E**$_B$ as reference, is

$$\mathbf{I} = \frac{\mathbf{E}_C - \mathbf{E}_B}{jX} = \frac{1.05\,\underline{/16.6°} - 1.00\,\underline{/0}}{j0.30}$$

$$= \frac{1.006 + j0.30 - 1.00}{j0.30} = \frac{j0.30}{j0.30} = 1.00\,\underline{/0} \qquad (e)$$

EXAMPLE 9   107

and is in phase with $\mathbf{E}_B$. Then

$$\mathbf{E}_A = \mathbf{E}_{qd} = \mathbf{E}_B + j1.05\mathbf{I} = 1.00 + j1.05 = 1.45\,\underline{/46.5^\circ} \qquad (f)$$

$$\delta = 46.5^\circ \qquad (g)$$

$$I_d = I \sin 46.5^\circ = 1.00 \times 0.725 = 0.725 \qquad (h)$$

$$I_q = I \cos 46.5^\circ = 1.00 \times 0.688 = 0.688 \qquad (i)$$

$$E_q' = E_{qd} - I_d(x_q - x_q') = 1.45 - 0.725(0.69 - 0.29)$$
$$= 1.45 - 0.725 \times 0.40 = 1.45 - 0.29 = 1.16 \qquad (j)$$

$$E_q = E_{qd} + I_d(x_d - x_q) = 1.45 + 0.725(1.05 - 0.69)$$
$$= 1.45 + 0.725 \times 0.36 = 1.45 + 0.26 = 1.71 \qquad (k)$$

Fault condition. The three sequence networks, connected in parallel to represent a two-line-to-ground fault at the middle of one circuit, are shown in Fig. 47. The reduction of the network is carried out in Figs. 48 through 54.

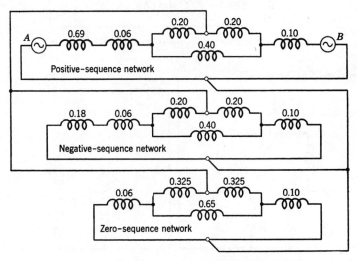

Fig. 47. The sequence networks of the power system of Fig. 45a, interconnected to represent a two-line-to-ground fault (Example 9).

The current of the hydroelectric generators $\mathbf{I}_A$, in terms of their internal voltage $\mathbf{E}_A = \mathbf{E}_{qd}$ and the voltage of the infinite bus $\mathbf{E}_B$, is

$$\mathbf{I}_A = \mathbf{Y}_{AA}\mathbf{E}_A + \mathbf{Y}_{AB}\mathbf{E}_B \qquad (l)$$

where the admittances are

$$\mathbf{Y}_{AA} = \frac{1}{j1.61} + \frac{1}{j2.23} = -j(0.622 + 0.448) = -j1.070$$

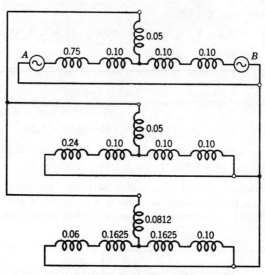

FIG. 48.   Reduction of the network of Fig. 47 — first step.

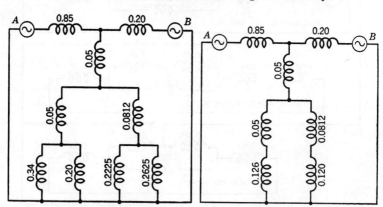

FIG. 49.   Reduction of the network of   FIG. 50.   Reduction of the network of
Fig. 47 — second step.   Fig. 47 — third step.

and

$$\mathbf{Y}_{AB} = \frac{1}{j2.23} = j0.448$$

Hence

$$\mathbf{I}_A = -j1.070\mathbf{E}_A + j0.448\mathbf{E}_B \tag{m}$$

Fault-cleared condition. The positive-sequence network and its reduction
are shown in Fig. 55 with the faulted line disconnected. Under this condition

EXAMPLE 9   109

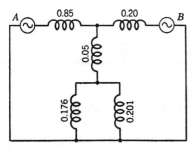

Fig. 51.   Reduction of the network of
Fig. 47 — fourth step.

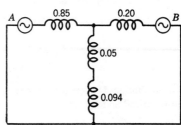

Fig. 52.   Reduction of the network of
Fig. 47 — fifth step.

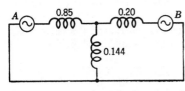

Fig. 53.   Reduction of the network of
Fig. 47 — sixth step.

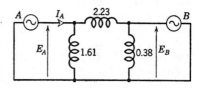

Fig. 54.   Reduction of the network of
Fig. 47 — seventh and last step.

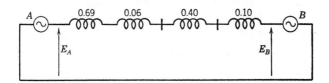

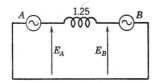

Fig. 55.   Positive-sequence network of the power system of Fig. 45a after the fault
has been cleared.

the admittances are

$$\mathbf{Y}_{AA} = -\mathbf{Y}_{AB} = \frac{1}{j1.25} = -j0.80$$

and the current of the generators is

$$\mathbf{I}_A = j0.80(\mathbf{E}_B - \mathbf{E}_A) \qquad (n)$$

Constants for swing calculations. The inertia constant is

$$M = \frac{GH}{180f} = \frac{1 \times 3.00}{180 \times 60} = \frac{1}{3,600}$$

$$\frac{(\Delta t)^2}{M} = \left(\frac{1}{20}\right)^2 3,600 = 9.00$$

Assumption 1: Constant exciter voltage. The prefault values may be summarized as follows:

$$E_q' = 1.16, \qquad E_d' = E_d = 0, \qquad E_q = E_{ex} = 1.71$$
$$I_d = 0.725, \qquad I_q = 0.688, \qquad \delta = 46.5°$$

Immediately after the instant when the fault occurs, E_q', E_{ex}, and δ retain their prefault values, but E_q, I_d, and I_q undergo sudden changes. To find the new values of these quantities, a value of E_{qd} will be assumed. By use of this, the network will be solved to obtain I_d and I_q; and the value of E_q' will then be calculated. This process will be repeated until E_q' comes out with the correct value, 1.16.

First assume $\mathbf{E}_{qd} = 1.80 \underline{/0}$. By eq. *m*, since $\mathbf{E}_A = \mathbf{E}_{qd}$,

$$\mathbf{I} = -j1.070 \times 1.80 \underline{/0} + j0.448 \times 1.00 \underline{/-46.5°}$$
$$= -j1.925 + 0.448(0.725 + j0.688)$$
$$= -j1.925 + j0.308 + 0.325$$
$$= 0.325 - j1.617$$
$$I_q = 0.325, \qquad I_d = 1.617$$
$$E_q' = E_{qd} - I_d(x_q - x_d')$$
$$= 1.800 - 1.617 \times 0.40$$
$$= 1.800 - 0.647 = 1.153 \text{ (Should be 1.16)}$$

Next try $E_{qd} = 1.810$.

$$\mathbf{I} = -j1.070 \times 1.810 \underline{/0} + j0.448 \times 1.00 \underline{/-46.5°}$$
$$= -j1.933 + 0.325 + j0.308$$
$$= 0.325 - j1.625$$
$$I_q = 0.325, \qquad I_d = 1.625$$
$$E_q' = 1.810 - 1.625 \times 0.40$$
$$= 1.810 - 0.650 = 1.160 \text{ (Correct)}$$
$$E_q = E_{qd} + I_d(x_d - x_q)$$
$$= 1.810 + 1.625 \times 0.36$$
$$= 1.810 + 0.585 = 2.395$$
$$P_u = E_{qd}I_q = 1.810 \times 0.325 = 0.588$$
$$P_i = 1.000$$
$$P_a = P_i - P_u = 0.412 \text{ during fault, 0 before fault, 0.206 average}$$

Take $\Delta t = 0.05$ sec. During the first interval,

$$\Delta E_q' = \frac{(E_{ex} - E_q)\Delta t}{T_{do}' + (E_q/E_q')(\Delta t/2)} = \frac{(1.71 - 2.40)0.05}{5.0 + \dfrac{2.4}{1.2}0.025}$$

$$= \frac{-0.69 \times 0.05}{5.05} = -0.007 \text{ per unit}$$

At the end of the first interval,

$$E_q' = 1.160 - 0.007 = 1.153$$

The angular swing during the first interval is

$$\Delta \delta_1 = \Delta \delta_0 + \frac{(\Delta t)^2}{M} P_{a1} = 0 + 9.00 \times 0.206 = 1.9°$$

Hence, at the end of the first interval,

$$\delta_1 = \delta_0 + \Delta \delta_1 = 46.5° + 1.9° = 48.4°$$

$$\mathbf{E}_q' = 1.153 \,\underline{/0}$$

$$\mathbf{E}_B = 1.00 \,\underline{/-48.4°}$$

Now assume E_{qd} still to be 1.81. Then

$$\mathbf{I} = -j1.070 \times 1.810 \,\underline{/0} + j0.448 \times 1.00 \,\underline{/-48.4°}$$
$$= -j1.933 + j0.448(0.664 - j0.748)$$
$$= -j1.933 + j0.298 + 0.335$$
$$= 0.335 - j1.635$$

$$I_q = 0.335, \qquad I_d = 1.635$$

$$E_q' = 1.810 - 1.635 \times 0.40 = 1.810 - 0.654 = 1.156$$

This is close enough to the correct value, 1.153.

$$P_u = E_{qd}I_q = 1.81 \times 0.335 = 0.606$$

The process is repeated again and again, with results as given in Table 13.

The system is stable. The maximum value of δ is about 89°. The field flux linkage decreases only from 1.160 to 1.116 per unit, a change of 3.8% of the initial value.

Assumption 2: Constant flux linkage. The flux linkage is so nearly constant under assumption 1 that to assume it exactly constant would not change the swing curve significantly. Therefore the swing-curve calculations will not be repeated.

Round-rotor machine with constant flux linkages on both axes of the rotor. Attention will now be turned from the salient-pole machine to the nonsalient-pole, or round-rotor, machine. The alternative assumptions which can be made regarding the round-rotor machine were listed on page 79. Briefly summarized, they are as follows:

1. Constant E_i'.
2. Constant E_d' and E_q'.
3. Varying E_q', but $E_d' = 0$.
4. Varying E_d' and E_q'.

TABLE 13

POINT-BY-POINT CALCULATION OF SWING CURVE (EXAMPLE 9)
Assumption 1: Constant Exciter Voltage

t (sec.)	E_q' (p.u.)	E_{qd} (p.u.)	E_q (p.u.)	$\Delta E_q'$ (p.u.)	I_d (p.u.)	I_q (p.u.)	P_u (p.u.)	P_a (p.u.)	$\Delta^2\delta$ (deg.)	$\Delta\delta$ (deg.)	δ (deg.)
0−	1.160	1.45	1.71		0.725	0.688	1.000	0			46.5
0+	1.160	1.81	2.40	−0.007	1.625	0.325	0.588	+0.412		0	"
0 avg.	1.160							+0.206	+1.9	+1.9	"
0.05	1.153	1.81	2.40	−0.007	1.636	0.335	0.606	+0.394	+3.5	+5.4	48.4
0.10	1.146	1.81	2.41	−0.007	1.668	0.361	0.654	+0.346	+3.1	+8.5	53.8
0.15−	1.139	1.85	2.49		1.769	0.396	0.733	+0.267			62.3
0.15+	1.139	1.45	1.73	0.000	0.789	0.709	1.029	−0.029			"
0.15 avg.	1.139							+0.119	+1.1	+9.6	"
0.20	1.139	1.53	1.88	−0.002	0.975	0.760	1.161	−0.161	−1.4	+8.2	71.9
0.25	1.137	1.59	2.00	−0.003	1.135	0.787	1.250	−0.250	−2.2	+6.0	80.1
0.30	1.134	1.64	2.09	−0.004	1.260	0.799	1.310	−0.310	−2.8	+2.2	86.1
0.35	1.130	1.65	2.12	−0.004	1.296	0.800	1.320	−0.320	−2.9	−0.7	88.3
0.40	1.126	1.635	2.09	−0.004	1.275	0.799	1.308	−0.308	−2.8	−3.5	87.6
0.45	1.122	1.60	2.03	−0.003	1.196	0.796	1.273	−0.273	−2.5	−6.0	84.1
0.50	1.119	1.55	1.94	−0.002	1.176	0.782	1.211	−0.211	−1.9	−7.9	78.1
0.55	1.117	1.48	1.81	−0.001	0.914	0.753	1.115	−0.115	−1.0	−8.9	70.2
0.60	1.116	1.41	1.68	0	0.736	0.702	0.990	+0.010	+0.1	−8.8	61.3
0.65	1.116										52.5

Assumption 1 is the simplest and commonest. It was used in the earlier chapters of this book and is ordinarily used in practice.

Assumption 2 implies constant flux linkages of the main circuits on both axes of the rotor. Observation of the vector diagram, Fig. 33, shows that, if both E_d' and E_q' are constant, $\mathbf{E}'$ is also constant, both as to its magnitude and as to its angle γ with the quadrature axis. Since γ is constant, the angular acceleration of vector $\mathbf{E}'$ is equal to that of the rotor of the machine and, in stability calculations, it is correct to associate the angular inertia of the machine with $\mathbf{E}'$ instead of with the quadrature axis.

In most round-rotor machines the transient reactances in the two axes (x_d' and x_q') are very nearly equal. If $x_d' = x_q'$, then $\mathbf{E}' = \mathbf{E}_i'$ (see Fig. 35), and therefore assumption 2 is identical with assumption 1. The usual association of angular inertia with $\mathbf{E}_i'$ under assumption 1 is then theoretically correct.

If x_d' and x_q' are unequal, a rigorous representation of the round-rotor machine is somewhat more difficult than that of the salient-pole machine, because vector $\mathbf{E}_{qd}$ of a round-rotor machine does not lie on the quadrature axis. The exact representation is described in the second section below. Its use is seldom, if ever, justifiable, however, because it has already been shown that, even for a salient-pole machine, the effect of saliency on transient stability is negligible; that is, x_q' may be assumed equal to x_d' with very little error. It therefore appears perfectly reasonable to make the same assumption for a round-rotor machine, in which the difference between x_d' and x_q' is smaller than it is in a salient-pole machine. The assumption $x_d' = x_q'$ permits the simple method of assumption 1.

Assumption 3 permits the effect of voltage-regulator action on the direct-axis field winding to be taken into account, while the quadrature-axis circuit is assumed to be absent, as it is in a salient-pole machine. The calculating procedure is like that already described and illustrated for a salient-pole machine. Assumption 3 would have good theoretical justification if the quadrature-axis time constant T_q' were very short; however, T_q' is about half of T_d'. Nevertheless, the assumption of saliency in a nonsalient-pole machine should produce no greater error than neglecting saliency in a salient-pole machine does.

Assumption 4 leads to the most exact and least simple method of calculation. The changes of flux linkages of the rotor circuits on both axes due to decrement and voltage-regulator action are taken into account. The procedure is explained in the next two sections of this chapter.

Calculation of change of flux linkages of round-rotor machine. If, for any reason, it is not accurate enough to assume that the flux linkages of the main rotor circuits are constant, then the changes of these linkages can be calculated in a manner similar to that previously described for the salient-pole machine. The only difference is that a separate calculation is made for each axis. By eq. 246, the rate of change of flux linkage of the direct axis is

$$\frac{dE_q'}{dt} = \frac{E_{ex} - E_q}{T_{d0}'}$$

The corresponding equation for the quadrature axis is

$$\frac{dE_d'}{dt} = \frac{-E_d}{T_{q0}'} \qquad [256]$$

where the exciter voltage has been set equal to zero, as there is none on the quadrature axis. For point-by-point calculation, the average rate of change in time interval Δt is, by analogy to eq. 255,

$$\frac{\Delta E_d'}{\Delta t} = - \frac{E_d}{T_{q0}' + \left(\dfrac{E_d}{E_d'}\right)\dfrac{\Delta t}{2}} \qquad [257]$$

Point-by-point calculation of swing curves of multimachine system, taking into account changes of flux linkages of rotor circuits on both axes. Each machine of a multimachine system, whether of salient or nonsalient-pole type, may be represented on the calculating board or on a circuit diagram by a variable e.m.f. $\mathbf{E}_h = E_{hd} + jE_{hq}$ in series with any convenient value of constant reactance x_h. This e.m.f. is related as follows to the voltage $\mathbf{E}' = E_d' + jE_q'$, which depends on the flux linkages of the rotor circuits. Since (by eq. 210)

$$\mathbf{E}' = \mathbf{V} + r\mathbf{I} + jx_d'I_d - x_q'I_q \qquad [258]$$

and, similarly,

$$\mathbf{E}_h = \mathbf{V} + r\mathbf{I} + jx_hI_d - x_hI_q \qquad [259]$$

it follows by subtraction that

$$\mathbf{E}_h = \mathbf{E}' + j(x_h - x_d')I_d - (x_h - x_q')I_q \qquad [260]$$

In the equations given above, the complex quantities are referred to the direct axis of the machine. In terms of components parallel to the quadrature and direct axes, eq. 260 becomes:

$$E_{hd} = E_d' - (x_h - x_q')I_q \qquad [261]$$

$$E_{hq} = E_q' + (x_h - x_d')I_d \qquad [262]$$

These relations are shown in Fig. 56.

The procedure will now be described for calculating the swing curves point by point when this general representation is used. It will be shown later how the procedure can be simplified by appropriate choice of reactance x_h.

1. The network must first be adjusted or solved for normal, or prefault, conditions. When this has been done, the magnitude and phase of the internal voltage $\mathbf{E}_h$ and of the current $\mathbf{I}$ of each generator are known. Terminal voltage $\mathbf{V}$, power P_u, and reactive power Q can also be found if desired. The angular position δ of the quadrature axis of every machine can be found as the phase of $\mathbf{E}_{qd}$, which can be measured or calculated by

$$\mathbf{E}_{qd} = \mathbf{E}_h + j(x_q - x_h)\mathbf{I} \qquad [263]$$

In the steady state, $\mathbf{E}_{qd}$ lies on the quadrature axis. Angle δ and the phase angles of the complex quantities in this paragraph and in the subsequent paragraphs of the procedure are expressed with re-

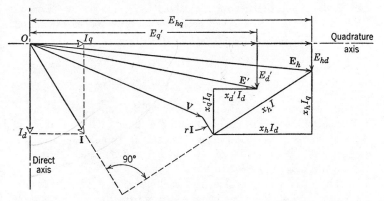

Fig. 56.   Vector diagram of a synchronous machine in the transient state, showing voltage $\mathbf{E}_h$ behind an arbitrary reactance x_h.

spect to an arbitrary reference axis which is common to the entire system. Angle δ being known, the current components I_d and I_q and voltage components E_{hd} and E_{hq} can be measured or calculated, thus making possible the computation of E_d' and E_q' by eqs. 261 and 262. In addition,

$$E_q = E_{hq} + (x_d - x_h)I_d$$
$$= E_{qd} + (x_d - x_q)I_d \qquad [264]$$

$$E_d = 0 \qquad [265]$$

The initial value of exciter voltage E_{ex} is equal to E_d. Thus all quantities can be computed for the prefault condition.

2. Upon the occurrence of the fault, E_d', E_q', E_{ex}, and δ are unchanged at the first instant, but all the other quantities mentioned

in paragraph 1 are changed, and their new values must be found, as follows: New values of I_d and I_q should be assumed and, from them and the old values of E_d' and E_q', E_{hd} and E_{hq} are calculated by eqs. 261 and 262 for every machine. The complex value of applied voltage $\mathbf{E}_h$, referred to the system reference axis, is

$$\mathbf{E}_h = (E_{hd} + jE_{hq})\underline{/\delta - 90°} \qquad [266]$$

The network is now solved for the currents. Since the positions of the quadrature axes are known, the currents can be resolved into components I_d and I_q, which are compared with the assumed values. If they do not agree, the new values of I_d and I_q are used to calculate a new value of $\mathbf{E}_h$. The process is continued until agreement is obtained. Thus the network is solved by a cut-and-try method. The power output P_u of each generator is measured or calculated. New values of E_d and E_q are calculated from

$$E_d = E_{hd} - (x_q - x_h)I_q \qquad [267]$$

$$E_q = E_{hq} + (x_d - x_h)I_d \qquad [268]$$

Conditions immediately after occurrence of the fault are now known.

3. A time interval Δt is chosen and the changes of E_q' and E_d' of each machine in this interval are calculated by eqs. 255 and 257, respectively. New values of E_d' and E_q' are found by adding the increments $\Delta E_d'$ and $\Delta E_q'$ to the old values.

4. The rotor position of every machine at the end of the first interval is computed in the usual way from the inertia constant M and the acceleratng power P_a. (The average of fault and prefault values of P_a is used for the first interval.)

5. The values of E_d' and E_q' are now known from step 3, and the values of δ are known from step 4. This enables us to solve the network again by means of the cut-and-try process described in paragraph 2. Thus new values of I_d and I_q, E_{hd} and E_{hq}, and P_u are obtained.

6. Steps 3, 4, 5, and 2 are repeated as many times as necessary, depending upon how far the swing curves are to be carried out. In step 3 the same value of E_{ex} is used repeatedly if there is no voltage regulator; or, if a regulator is assumed to act, values of E_{ex} are read from the curves of exciter-voltage build-up or build-down.

7. If there is any sudden change in I_d and I_q, due, for example, to the clearing of a fault or the reclosing of a breaker, then the network must be solved for both the old and the new conditions, using in both cases the same values of E_d', E_q', E_{ex}, and δ. The incre-

ments of E_q' and E_d' during the interval after the discontinuity are calculated by using in eqs. 255 and 257 the values of E_q and E_d after the discontinuity. The increment of δ, however, is calculated by using the average accelerating power before and after the discontinuity.

Some special cases will now be considered.

Salient-pole machine. Choose $x_h = x_q$; then $\mathbf{E}_h = \mathbf{E}_{qd}$, $E_{hq} = E_{qd}$, and $E_{hd} = 0$.

In step 1 of the general procedure, eq. 263 is unnecessary, and δ is the angle of $\mathbf{E}_{qd} = \mathbf{E}_h$ not only in the steady state but also in the transient state. Equation 262 becomes

$$E_{qd} = E_q' + (x_q - x_d')I_d \qquad [269]$$

and eq. 261 becomes

$$E_d' = 0 \qquad [270]$$

In step 2 of the procedure, a new value of E_d' does not need to be calculated, because E_d' is always zero. Therefore, only I_d need be assumed, not I_q. Equations 266, 267, and 268 become:

$$\mathbf{E}_{qd} = E_{qd}\underline{/\delta} \qquad [271]$$

$$E_d = 0 \qquad [272]$$

$$E_q = E_{qd} + (x_d - x_q)I_d \qquad [273]$$

Equation 272 holds for both transient and steady states because there is no quadrature-axis rotor circuit.

In step 3 E_d' is still zero.

Round-rotor machine with laminated rotor. The procedure for this unusual type of machine is the same as that for the salient-pole machine except that, since $x_d = x_q = x_h$, eq. 268 becomes simply

$$E_q = E_{qd} \qquad [274]$$

Round-rotor machine with solid rotor and $x_d' \neq x_q'$. This case is perfectly general. Nevertheless, the general procedure described above can be simplified somewhat by choosing x_h equal either to x_d' or x_q'. On the assumption of the former alternative, eqs. 260, 261, and 262 become:

$$\mathbf{E}_h = \mathbf{E}' - (x_d' - x_q')I_q \qquad [275]$$

$$E_{hd} = E_d' - (x_d' - x_q')I_q \qquad [276]$$

$$E_{hq} = E_q' \qquad [277]$$

In step 1 of the procedure, eqs. 263 and 264 become:

$$\mathbf{E}_{qd} = \mathbf{E}_h + j(x_q - x_d')\mathbf{I} \qquad [278]$$

$$E_q = E_q' + (x_d - x_d')I_d \qquad [279]$$

In step 2, E_{hq} need not be calculated since it is equal to E_q'. Therefore, I_d need not be assumed, but only I_q. Equations 267 and 268 become:

$$E_d = E_d' - (x_q - x_q')I_q \qquad [280]$$

$$E_q = E_q' + (x_d - x_d')I_d \qquad [281]$$

The procedure for the assumption of $x_h = x_q'$ will not be described because it offers no particular advantage over the procedure for the assumption of $x_h = x_d'$.

Round-rotor machine with solid rotor and $x_d' = x_q'$. This is the usual type of round-rotor machine. The following simplifications apply in addition to those stated for the preceding case: Equation 260 becomes

$$\mathbf{E}_h = \mathbf{E}' = \mathbf{E}_i' \qquad [282]$$

and eq. 262 becomes

$$E_{hq} = E_q' \qquad [283]$$

In step 2 neither E_{hd} nor E_{hq} need be calculated because they are equal to E_d' and E_q', respectively. Therefore, neither I_d nor I_q need be assumed and the network can be solved without the cut-and-try procedure for finding the values of $\mathbf{E}_h$.

SATURATION

The effects of saliency and of change of field flux linkage have now been treated, but so far the effect of saturation of the iron has been neglected. Saturation will now be considered.

Saturation in a transformer. In a transformer having a closed iron core the fluxes linking the windings can be divided into the mutual flux, the preponderant part of which is wholly in the core, and the several leakage fluxes, which follow paths largely in air and whose reluctance is determined principally by the reluctance of the air paths. Under normal operating conditions the mutual flux constitutes a very large part, and the leakage fluxes a small part, of the flux linking any winding. Consequently, the flux in the core is substantially the same all around the core and is substantially equal to the mutual flux. Saturation of all parts of the core then depends only on the mutual flux. The mutual flux justifiably can be assumed to be a function of the sum of the ampere-turns of all windings on the core, regardless of the positions of the windings. This sum is the exciting m.m.f. The mutual flux is a nonlinear function of the exciting m.m.f. as found from an open-circuit test. The leakage fluxes, on the other hand, are very nearly linear functions of the currents.

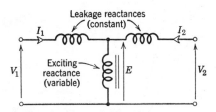

FIG. 57. Equivalent T circuit of an iron-core transformer.

Currents and voltages in a two-winding iron-cored transformer can be calculated from the equivalent T circuit of Fig. 57, which consists of two linear leakage reactances and one nonlinear (iron-cored) exciting reactance. The upshot of this discussion is that saturation in a transformer can be considered as a function of a single variable, the internal e.m.f. E induced in a winding by the mutual flux.*

Saturation in an induction motor can be treated by assuming it to be a function of the air-gap flux (the flux that crosses the air gap from stator iron to rotor iron) and by using an equivalent T circuit similar to that of the transformer.

Saturation in a synchronous machine. In a synchronous machine the air gap ordinarily is longer than in an induction motor, and the leakage fluxes constitute a greater portion of the total flux. There is less justification in the case of a synchronous machine than in the case of a transformer, or even of an induction machine, for assuming that the saturation of all parts of the core varies as a function of a single variable when the load and the power factor change. Nevertheless, the assumption is usually made in texts on a-c. machinery that the saturation is a function of the air-gap flux. Let us see to what conclusions this assumption leads and whether those conclusions are in accord with experimental facts.

Saturated nonsalient-pole machine in the steady state. Based upon the assumption that saturation is a function of the air-gap flux only, the vector diagram of a nonsalient-pole synchronous generator in the

*This treatment is not applicable to some types of current transformers.

steady state is as shown in Fig. 58. The air-gap flux ϕ_a induces in the armature winding a positive-sequence e.m.f. $\mathbf{E}_a$, which is proportional in magnitude to ϕ_a and lags 90° behind it. It is assumed that the generator is delivering a lagging current $\mathbf{I}$, which, flowing through the

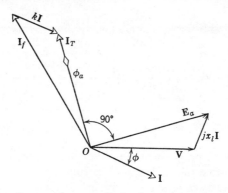

Fig. 58. Vector diagram of a nonsalient-pole synchronous generator operating in the steady state with lagging current.

armature leakage reactance x_l, produces a voltage drop $jx_l\mathbf{I}$ 90° ahead of $\mathbf{I}$. The armature terminal voltage is $\mathbf{V} = \mathbf{E}_a - jx_l\mathbf{I}$. To produce air-gap flux ϕ_a, an m.m.f. $n_f\mathbf{I}_T$ is required, where n_f is the number of turns in the field winding and I_T is the current read from the no-load saturation curve (Fig. 59) corresponding to armature voltage E_a. Thus saturation is assumed to depend upon E_a. The required m.m.f. $n_f\mathbf{I}_T$ is the vector sum of two components: field m.m.f. $n_f\mathbf{I}_f$ and armature m.m.f. $n_a\mathbf{I}$. The latter m.m.f. is also called armature reaction. Upon dividing by n_f, we find that the fictitious field current $\mathbf{I}_T$ is the vector sum of the actual field current $\mathbf{I}_f$ and the field equivalent of armature reaction $(n_a/n_f)\mathbf{I} = k\mathbf{I}$, as shown in Fig. 58. Given the armature terminal voltage V, armature current I, and terminal power-factor angle ϕ, one can find the required field current I_f as follows: Find air-gap voltage $\mathbf{E}_a$ by vector addition of $\mathbf{V} + jx_l\mathbf{I}$. From the no-load saturation curve read I_T corresponding to E_a. Then find I_f by vector subtraction $\mathbf{I}_T - k\mathbf{I}$, where $\mathbf{I}_T$ leads $\mathbf{E}_a$ by 90° and $k\mathbf{I}$ is in phase with $\mathbf{I}$.

At zero power factor, lagging current, vector triangles V, x_lI, E_a and I_T, kI, I_f collapse to collinearity and the following relations are true arithmetically:

$$V = E_a - x_lI \tag{284}$$

$$I_f = I_T + kI \tag{285}$$

The **zero-power-factor rated-current saturation curve** (Fig. 59) is a graph of armature terminal voltage V against field current I_f with armature current I held constant at its full-load value and power-factor angle ϕ constant at 90° lag. According to eqs. 284 and 285, any point $B'(I_f, V)$ on the zero-power-factor curve lies to the right by a constant distance kI and downward by a constant distance $x_l I$

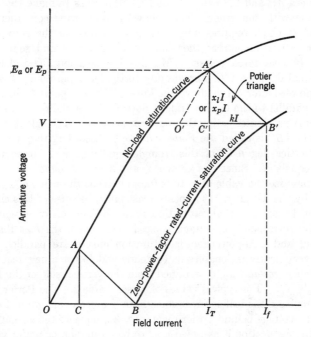

Fig. 59. No-load and zero-power-factor rated-current saturation curves and the Potier triangle.

from the corresponding point $A'(I_T, E_a)$ on the no-load saturation curve. The latter curve portrays V against I_f for $I = 0$, but eqs. 284 and 285 show that at no load $V = E_a$ and $I_f = I_T$. Hence the no-load saturation curve shows E_a versus I_T for any load, in accordance with our previous assumptions. Given the no-load saturation curve and constants x_l and k, one can construct a zero-power-factor saturation curve for any constant armature current I by displacing the given curve downward by distance $x_l I$ volts and to the right by kI amperes. Saturation curves for other power factors can be constructed through use of the vector diagram (Fig. 58). From these curves the field current required for any load current and terminal voltage can be found.

By experiment it is found that the zero-power-factor saturation curve is indeed parallel to the no-load saturation curve. That is, one curve can be made to coincide with the other by shifting every point of it through the same vectorial distance $AB = A'B'$, Fig. 59. This fact furnishes a way of determining armature leakage reactance x_l and effective turns-ratio k. One curve can be drawn on tracing paper, and distances AC and CB can be found by trial so as to make this curve coincide with the other. The following alternative construction is available which requires only two given points on the zero-power-factor saturation curve: the short-circuit point B and some other point B' near rated voltage. Measure line segment BO and lay off the equal distance $B'O'$ horizontally to the left from point B' on the zero-power-factor curve above the knee. Through point O' draw line $O'A'$ parallel to the lower, straight portion OA of the no-load saturation curve and intersecting that curve at point A'. Triangle $A'B'C' =$ triangle ABC is called the *Potier triangle*.[1] According to our hypothesis, vertical leg $A'C'$ of this triangle equals x_lI and horizontal leg $B'C'$ equals kI. Since I is known, x_l and k can be found.

In practice the value of x_l thus found exceeds the value of x_l calculated by the designer. It appears reasonable, because of this circumstance, to suppose that saturation is not a function of air-gap flux (or the corresponding voltage E_a). Nevertheless, the fact that the no-load and zero-power-factor saturation curves are parallel, or at least very nearly so, enables us to define and to use a new reactance, the *Potier reactance x_p*, determined from the vertical side of the Potier triangle, x_pI. For typical values of x_p see Table 2. The Potier reactance replaces the leakage reactance x_l in the vector diagram, Fig. 58, and the voltage behind Potier reactance, E_p, replaces the air-gap voltage E_a. Saturation is assumed now to be a function of Potier voltage E_p instead of E_a. The use of Potier reactance and voltage is justified by the fact that through their use one can construct not only the zero-power-factor saturation curve but also saturation curves for other power factors which agree well with curves determined by load tests.

If there were no saturation, the no-load and zero-power-factor constant-current "saturation curves" would be straight parallel lines (Fig. 60), and there would be no unique way of resolving the constant separation between those parallel lines into vertical and horizontal components representing Potier reactance drop and armature reaction, respectively. Indeed, instead of assuming some of each (QR and RP), one could go to either extreme: (1) assume that the horizontal distance MP between the curves was due to armature reaction and that the Potier reactance was zero, or (2) assume that the vertical distance

NP between the curves was due to reactance drop and that the armature reaction was zero. In the first case I_v is the field current required to generate terminal voltage V on open circuit, and MP is the field current required to overcome armature reaction. The actual field current required to generate terminal voltage V at rated-current zero-power-factor load is I_f, which is the sum of I_v and MP. In the second

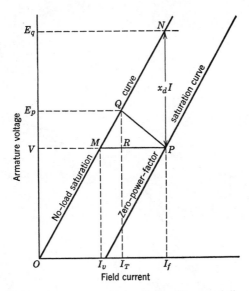

Fig. 60. No-load and zero-power-factor "saturation curves" of unsaturated synchronous generator.

case, V is the terminal voltage, NP is the synchronous reactance drop x_dI, and $E_q = V + x_dI$ is the internal voltage behind synchronous reactance, or the excitation voltage. Note the proportionalities between armature voltages and field currents represented by the same points on the no-load line:

$$\frac{V}{I_v} = \frac{NP}{MP} = \frac{E_q}{I_f} = \frac{E_p}{I_T} = \omega M_f \qquad [286]$$

Indeed, in the usual per-unit system, $\omega M_f = 1$, so that each component of armature voltage is numerically equal to the corresponding component of field current. Vector diagrams showing conditions at any power factor can be drawn either entirely with current vectors or entirely with voltage vectors. The second alternative is generally used in practice, with the result that the fictitious internal voltage E_q, which, in an unsaturated machine, is proportional to the field current, is the vector sum of terminal voltage V and reactive drop $x_d I$.

Voltage vector diagram of saturated nonsalient-pole machine. It is desirable to extend the voltage vector diagram to cover the case of a saturated synchronous machine. For this purpose, the field current

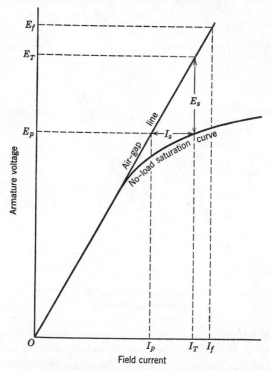

FIG. 61. Graphical construction for finding the components of field current and armature voltage due to saturation corresponding to Potier voltage E_p. The components are I_s and E_s, respectively.

and its components in the previous vector diagram (Fig. 58) are converted into corresponding armature voltages by means of the "air-gap line," which is an extension of the lower, straight portion of the no-load saturation curve (Fig. 61). The vector current triangle I_T, kI, I_f in Fig. 58 is replaced by the corresponding vector voltage triangle $\mathbf{E}_T$, $jx_a\mathbf{I}$, $\mathbf{E}_f$. This voltage triangle is then swung clockwise 90° so that $\mathbf{E}_T$ lies along $\mathbf{E}_a$. Furthermore, $\mathbf{E}_a$ and x_l in Fig. 58 are replaced by

$\mathbf{E}_p$ and x_p, respectively.   The resulting vector diagram is shown in Fig. 62.

In Fig. 61 it will be noted that the field current I_T corresponding to any particular Potier voltage E_p consists of two components: I_p, the field current required to drive the flux across the air gap, and I_s, the additional field current required to drive the flux through the saturated iron.   The corresponding armature voltages, read on the air-gap line, are E_p and E_s, the sum of which is E_T.   In the absence of saturation,

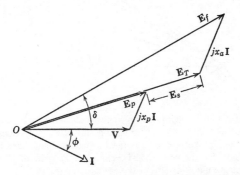

FIG. 62.   Vector voltage diagram of a nonsalient-pole synchronous generator. This diagram is derived from that of Fig. 58 by replacing $\mathbf{E}_a$ and x_l by $\mathbf{E}_p$ and x_p, respectively, and by replacing the field-current vectors by corresponding voltage vectors, rotated 90° clockwise.

$E_s = 0$ and $E_p = E_T$.   In this case vector $\mathbf{E}_T$ would not jut beyond vector $\mathbf{E}_p$, as in Fig. 62, but would coincide with $\mathbf{E}_p$, and vector $jx_a\mathbf{I}$ would lie on the same line with $jx_p\mathbf{I}$, as shown in Fig. 63.   The sum of x_p and x_a is x_d, the unsaturated synchronous reactance.   The vector sum of $\mathbf{V}$ and $jx_d\mathbf{I}$, or of $\mathbf{E}_p$ and $jx_a\mathbf{I}$, is $\mathbf{E}_q$, corresponding to the field current that would be required if there were no saturation.   Even if there is saturation, vectors $jx_a\mathbf{I}$ and $\mathbf{E}_s$ may be added to $\mathbf{E}_p$ in the opposite order from that shown in Fig. 62.   This is done in Fig. 63. The vector sum of $\mathbf{E}_q$ and $\mathbf{E}_s$ is $\mathbf{E}_f$, the voltage corresponding to the field current of the saturated machine.

The procedure for finding the field current of a saturated nonsalient-pole machine may be summarized as follows: *Find* $\mathbf{E}_q = \mathbf{V} + jx_d\mathbf{I}$ *just as it would be found for an unsaturated machine.   Then, as a correction for saturation, add to it* $\mathbf{E}_s$, *in phase with* $\mathbf{E}_p = \mathbf{V} + jx_p\mathbf{I}$. The magnitude E_s is found from the no-load saturation curve at ordinate E_p as shown in Fig. 61.   The magnitude of the sum, $\mathbf{E}_f = \mathbf{E}_q + \mathbf{E}_s$, equals the field current in per unit.   The phase of $\mathbf{E}_f$, and not of $\mathbf{E}_q$, indicates the position of the quadrature axis.

Ordinarily very little error in E_f is produced by adding $\mathbf{E}_s$ in phase with $\mathbf{E}_q$ instead of in phase with $\mathbf{E}_p$. Then both $\mathbf{E}_q$ and $\mathbf{E}_f$ represent the position of the quadrature axis. However, this procedure causes some error in δ.

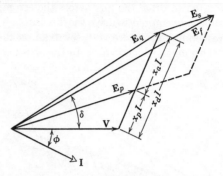

FIG. 63. Vector voltage diagram of a nonsalient-pole synchronous generator, derived from that of Fig. 62 by adding $\mathbf{E}_s$ and $jx_a\mathbf{I}$ to $\mathbf{E}_p$ in reverse order. E_q is proportional to the field current of an unsaturated machine; E_f, to that of a saturated machine. $\mathbf{E}_s$, the correction for saturation, is parallel to $\mathbf{E}_p$ and has a magnitude found from the construction of Fig. 61.

Vector diagram of saturated salient-pole machine. If the same assumptions and reasoning regarding saturation that were applied to the nonsalient-pole machine are applied to the salient-pole machine,

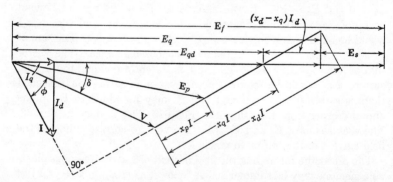

FIG. 64. Vector voltage diagram of a saturated salient-pole synchronous generator in the steady state.

the vector diagram of Fig. 64 is obtained. Here voltage $\mathbf{E}_q$ is calculated in the same way as for an unsaturated salient-pole machine, and then $\mathbf{E}_s$ is added to it as a correction for saturation. E_s is a function of E_p as shown in Fig. 61. For convenience, $\mathbf{E}_s$ is taken parallel to $\mathbf{E}_q$ rather than to $\mathbf{E}_p$. The theoretical justification for doing so is possibly greater with the salient-pole machine than with the non-salient-pole machine. The sum of $\mathbf{E}_q$ and $\mathbf{E}_s$ is $\mathbf{E}_f$, a fictitious armature voltage proportional to the field current.

Saturated synchronous machine in the transient state. In the transient state, as well as in the steady state, saturation is assumed to depend upon E_p, the voltage behind Potier reactance. (The relation between E_p and E_s, the correction to E_q for saturation, was given in Fig. 61.)

The correction for saturation affects the calculation of change of field-flux linkage; that is, of $E_q{}'$. Equation 241 is still valid, but, upon changing it into a voltage equation, we must use

$$\omega M_f i_f = E_f \qquad [287]$$

instead of E_q (eq. 242). As a result, the voltage equation replacing eq. 246 is

$$\frac{dE_q{}'}{dt} = \frac{E_{ex} - E_f}{T_{d0}{}'} = \frac{E_{ex} - E_q - E_s}{T_{d0}{}'} \qquad [288]$$

For point-by-point calculation, eq. 255 is replaced by

$$\frac{\Delta E_q{}'}{\Delta t} = \frac{E_{ex}(t + \Delta t/2) - E_q - E_s}{T_{d0}{}' + \left(\dfrac{E_q + E_s}{E_q{}'}\right)\dfrac{\Delta t}{2}} \qquad [289]$$

To find E_s, it is necessary to know E_p. The latter can be measured easily on a calculating board if the machine is represented in the network as shown in Fig. 65. If the machine is represented, as previously discussed, by any reactance x_h and the voltage E_h behind this reactance, x_h may be divided into two parts, x_p and $x_h - x_p$, as shown in Fig. 65a. Then E_p is the voltage of the common terminal of the two reactors. If the machine is represented by x_q and E_{qd}, the reactances are x_p and $x_q - x_p$, as shown in Fig. 65b. If E_p cannot be measured, it can be calculated thus:

$$\mathbf{E}_p = \mathbf{E}_h - j(x_h - x_p)\mathbf{I} \qquad [290]$$

Except for the addition of the correction for saturation, the point-by-point calculation of $E_q{}'$ and the swing curves is carried out as previously described. During a sudden change of current, E_q' is constant, but E_p and E_h change.

Saturation has little effect upon transient stability and it is usually neglected, especially when E_q' or E_i' is assumed constant. Actually x_d' varies somewhat with saturation,[41] though not nearly to the extent that x_d changes. Any change in x_d' affects the relation between terminal voltage and E_d', but such changes are usually neglected.

In steady-state stability studies (treated in Chapter XV), saturation is an important factor. It will be discussed further in that chapter.

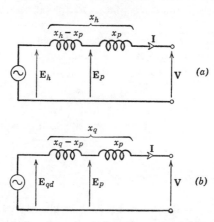

FIG. 65. Representation of a saturated synchronous machine as part of a network. The use of two reactors in series makes possible the measurement of $\mathbf{E}_p$, the voltage behind Potier reactance.

Short-circuit ratio. The short-circuit ratio of a synchronous machine is defined as the ratio of the field current required to produce rated voltage at rated speed and no load to the field current required to produce rated armature current under a sustained three-phase short circuit. This definition is illustrated by Fig. 66, where OA/OB is the short-circuit ratio.

If there were no saturation, the short-circuit ratio would be equal to the reciprocal of the synchronous reactance. Saturation has the effect of increasing the short-circuit ratio.

The short-circuit ratio has significance with respect to both the performance of the machine and its cost.[69] The lower the short-circuit ratio, the greater is the change in field current required to maintain constant terminal voltage for a given change in load (armature current) and the lower is the steady-state stability limit. Thus, a machine of low short-circuit ratio requires an excitation system that is able to provide large changes of field current quickly and reliably. It is more dependent upon its excitation system than is a machine of high short-circuit ratio, but, given a suitable excitation system, can give as satisfactory performance under load as does the machine of high short-circuit ratio. An appropriate excitation system can also increase the steady-state stability limit.

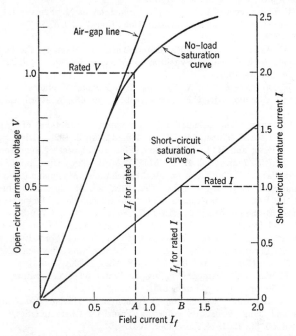

Fig. 66. Typical saturation curves of a steam-turbine-driven generator. The short-circuit ratio is OA/OB.

The lower the short-circuit ratio, the lower are the size, weight, and cost of the machine. Hence, as a result of improvements which have been made in excitation systems, there has been a trend toward the use of generators of lower short-circuit ratio and, consequently, of lower cost.

It is practical to build steam-turbine-driven generators with short-circuit ratios anywhere in the range from 0.5 to 1.1. Most modern generators of this type have ratios in the range from 0.8 to 1.0, but it appears likely that 0.7 will become more generally used. Water-wheel-driven generators usually have higher short-circuit ratios, up to 2.0, whereas synchronous condensers may have ratios as low as 0.4.

REFERENCES

1. A. Potier, "Sur la réaction d'induit des alternateurs" (Armature Reaction of Alternators), *L'Éclairage Électrique* (Paris), vol. 24, pp. 133–41, 1900.

2. R. E. Doherty, "A Simplified Method of Analyzing Short Circuit Problems," *A.I.E.E. Trans.*, vol. 42, pp. 841–9, 1923.

3. R. E. Doherty and C. A. Nickle, "Synchronous Machines — I and II," *A.I.E.E. Trans.*, vol. 45, pp. 912–47, 1926.

4. R. E. Doherty and C. A. Nickle, "Synchronous Machines — III, Torque-Angle Characteristics Under Transient Conditions," *A.I.E.E. Trans.*, vol. 46, pp. 1–18, 1927.

5. R. W. Wieseman, "Graphical Determination of Magnetic Fields, Practical Applications to Salient-Pole Synchronous Machine Design," *A.I.E.E. Trans.*, vol. 46, pp. 141–54, 1927.

6. R. E. Doherty and C. A. Nickle, "Synchronous Machines — IV, Single-Phase Short Circuits," *A.I.E.E. Trans.*, vol. 47, pp. 457–87, April, 1928. Disc., pp. 487–92.

7. P. L. Alger, "The Calculation of the Armature Reactance of Synchronous Machines," *A.I.E.E. Trans.*, vol. 47, pp. 493–512, April, 1928. Disc., pp. 512–3.

8. R. H. Park and B. L. Robertson, "The Reactances of Synchronous Machines," *A.I.E.E. Trans.*, vol. 47, pp. 514–35, April, 1928. Disc., pp. 535–6.

9. R. H. Park, "Definition of an Ideal Synchronous Machine and Formula for the Armature Flux Linkages," *Gen. Elec. Rev.*, vol. 31, pp. 332–4, June, 1928.

10. R. H. Park, "Two-Reaction Theory of Synchronous Machines — Part I, Generalized Method of Analysis," *A.I.E.E. Trans.*, vol. 48, pp. 716–30, July, 1929.

11. R. E. Doherty and C. A. Nickle, "Synchronous Machines — V, Three-Phase Short Circuit," *A.I.E.E. Trans.*, vol. 49, pp. 700–14, April, 1930.

12. F. C. Lindvall, "The Educational Value of the Theorem of Constant Linkages," *Gen. Elec. Rev.*, vol. 33, pp. 273–8, May, 1930.

13. C. F. Wagner, "Damper Windings for Water Wheel Generators," *A.I.E.E. Trans.*, vol. 50, pp. 140–51, March, 1931.

14. L. A. Kilgore, "Calculation of Synchronous Machine Constants — Reactances and Time Constants Affecting Transient Characteristics," *A.I.E.E. Trans.*, vol. 50, pp. 1201–14, December, 1931.

15. S. H. Wright, "Determination of Synchronous Machine Constants by Test — Reactances, Resistances, and Time Constants," *A.I.E.E. Trans.*, vol. 50, pp. 1331–51, December, 1931.

16. L. P. Shildneck, "Synchronous Machine Reactances — A Fundamental and Physical Viewpoint," *Gen. Elec. Rev.*, vol. 35, pp. 560–5, November, 1932.

17. R. H. Park, "Two-Reaction Theory of Synchronous Machines — II," *A.I.E.E. Trans.*, vol. 52, pp. 352–5, June, 1933.

18. S. B. Crary, L. P. Shildneck, and L. A. March, "Equivalent Reactances of Synchronous Machines," *A.I.E.E. Trans.*, vol. 53, pp. 124–32, 1934.

19. L. A. March and S. B. Crary, "Armature Leakage Reactance of Synchronous Machines," *A.I.E.E. Trans.*, vol. 54, pp. 378–81, April, 1935. Disc., pp. 1116–8.

20. Charles Kingsley, Jr., "Saturated Synchronous Reactance," *A.I.E.E. Trans.*, vol. 54, pp. 300–5, March, 1935. Disc., pp. 1111–3, October, 1935.

21. T. A. Rogers, "Test Values of Armature Leakage Reactance," *Elec. Eng.*, vol. 54, pp. 700–5, July, 1935.

22. B. L. ROBERTSON, "Tests on Armature Resistance of Synchronous Machines," *Elec. Eng.*, vol. 54, pp. 705–9, July, 1935.

23. L. A. KILGORE, "Effects of Saturation on Machine Reactances," *A.I.E.E. Trans.*, vol. 54, pp. 545–50, May, 1935. Disc., pp. 1113–6, October, 1935.

24. W. A. THOMAS, "Negative-Sequence Reactance of Synchronous Machines," *A.I.E.E. Trans.*, vol. 55, pp. 1378–85, December, 1936. Disc., vol. 56, pp. 903–4, July, 1937.

25. A. S. LANGSDORF, "Contributions to Synchronous-Machine Theory," *A.I.E.E. Trans.*, vol. 56, pp. 41–8, January, 1937. Disc., pp. 907–9, July, 1937.

26. C. CONCORDIA and H. PORITSKY, "Synchronous Machine with Solid Cylindrical Rotor," *A.I.E.E. Trans.*, vol. 56, pp. 49–58 and 179, January, 1937. Disc., pp. 906–7, July, 1937.

27. S. B. CRARY, "Two-Reaction Theory of Synchronous Machines," *A.I.E.E. Trans.*, vol. 56, pp. 27–31 and 36, January, 1937. Extension to machines having capacitance in the armature circuit. Disc., pp. 905–6, July, 1937.

28. STERLING BECKWITH, "Approximating Potier Reactance," *A.I.E.E. Trans.*, vol. 56, pp. 813–8, July, 1937. Disc., pp. 1318–9.

29. B. L. ROBERTSON, T. A. ROGERS, and C. F. DALZIEL, "The Saturated Synchronous Machine," *A.I.E.E. Trans.*, vol. 56, pp. 858–63, July, 1937. Disc., pp. 1502–3, December, 1937.

30. C. CONCORDIA, "Two-Reaction Theory of Synchronous Machines With Any Balanced Terminal Impedance," *A.I.E.E. Trans.*, vol. 56, pp. 1124–7, September, 1937.

31. JAMES B. SMITH and CORNELIUS N. WEYGANDT, "Double-Line-to-Neutral Short Circuit of an Alternator," *A.I.E.E. Trans.*, vol. 56, pp. 1149–55, September, 1937.

32. A. R. MILLER and W. S. WEIL, JR., "Alternator Short-Circuit Currents Under Unsymmetrical Terminal Conditions," *A.I.E.E. Trans.*, vol. 56, pp. 1268–78, October, 1937.

33. C. F. WAGNER, "Unsymmetrical Short Circuits on Water-Wheel Generators Under Capacitive Loading," *A.I.E.E. Trans.*, vol. 56, pp. 1385–95, November, 1937. Disc., vol. 57, pp. 406–7, July, 1938.

34. B. R. PRENTICE, "Fundamental Concepts of Synchronous Machine Reactances," *A.I.E.E. Trans.*, vol. 56, supplement, pp. 1–21, 1937.

35. EDITH CLARKE, C. N. WEYGANDT, and C. CONCORDIA, "Overvoltages Caused by Unbalanced Short Circuits — Effect of Amortisseur Windings," *A.I.E.E. Trans.*, vol. 57, pp. 453–66, August, 1938. Disc., pp. 466–8.

36. C. CONCORDIA, S. B. CRARY, and J. M. LYONS, "Stability Characteristics of Turbine Generators," *A.I.E.E. Trans.*, vol. 57, pp. 732–41, 1938. Disc., pp. 741–4.

37. R. B. GEORGE and B. B. BESSESEN, "Generator Damper Windings at Wilson Dam," *A.I.E.E. Trans.*, vol. 58, pp. 166–71, April, 1939. Disc., pp. 171–2.

38. W. W. KUYPER, "Analysis of Short-Circuit Oscillograms," *A.I.E.E. Trans.*, vol. 60, pp. 151–3, April, 1941. Disc., pp. 752–3.

39. THOMAS C. MCFARLAND, "Correction for Saturation," *A.I.E.E. Trans.*, vol. 61, pp. 233–5, May, 1942.

40. REINHOLD RÜDENBERG, "Saturated Synchronous Machines Under Transient Conditions in the Pole Axis," *A.I.E.E. Trans.*, vol. 61, pp. 297–306, June, 1942. Disc., pp. 444–5.

41. CHAS. A. WAGNER, "Machine Characteristics," Chapter 7 of *Electrical*

Transmission and Distribution Reference Book by Central Station Engineers of the Westinghouse Elec. & Mfg. Co., East Pittsburgh, Pa., 1st edition, 1942.

42. R. V. SHEPHERD and C. E. KILBOURNE, "The Quadrature Synchronous Reactance of Salient-Pole Synchronous Machines," *A.I.E.E. Trans.*, vol. 62, pp. 684–9, November, 1943. Disc., p. 926.

43. E. L. HARDER and R. C. CHEEK, "Regulation of A-C Generators With Suddenly Applied Loads," *A.I.E.E. Trans.*, vol. 63, pp. 310–8, June, 1944.

44. A. W. RANKIN, "The Equations of the Idealized Synchronous Machine," *Gen. Elec. Rev.*, vol. 47, pp. 31–6, June, 1944.

45. GORDON F. TRACY and WILLIAM F. TICE, "Measurement of the Subtransient Impedances of Synchronous Machines," *A.I.E.E. Trans.*, vol. 64, pp. 70–6, February, 1945. Disc., pp. 429–31.

46. C. CONCORDIA and F. J. MAGINNISS, "Inherent Errors in the Determination of Synchronous-Machine Reactances by Test," *A.I.E.E. Trans.*, vol. 64, pp. 288–94, June, 1945. Disc., pp. 491–2.

47. A. W. RANKIN, "Per-Unit Impedances of Synchronous Machines," *A.I.E.E. Trans.*, vol. 64, pp. 569–73, August, 1945.

48. C. CONCORDIA, S. B. CRARY, C. E. KILBOURNE, and C. N. WEYGANDT, JR., "Synchronous Starting of Generator and Motor," *A.I.E.E. Trans.*, vol. 64, pp. 629–34, September, 1945. Disc., p. 956.

49. A. W. RANKIN, "Per-Unit Impedances of Synchronous Machines — II," *A.I.E.E. Trans.*, vol. 64, pp. 839–41, December, 1945.

50. A. W. RANKIN, "The Direct- and Quadrature-Axis Equivalent Circuits of the Synchronous Machine," *A.I.E.E. Trans.*, vol. 64, pp. 861–8, December, 1945.

51. A. W. RANKIN, "Asynchronous and Single-Phase Operation of Synchronous Machines," *A.I.E.E. Trans.*, vol. 65, pp. 1092–102, 1946.

52. C. CONCORDIA and M. TEMOSHOK, "Resynchronizing of Generators," *A.I.E.E. Trans.*, vol. 66, pp. 1512–8, 1947.

53. A. M. ANGELINI, "General Topogram for Synchronous Machines," *C.I.G.R.E.*, 1948, Report 114.

54. G. D. FLOYD and H. R. SILLS, "Generator Design to Meet Long Distance Transmission Requirements in Canada," *C.I.G.R.E.*, 1948, Report 131.

55. GABRIEL KRON, "Steady-State Equivalent Circuits of Synchronous and Induction Machines," *A.I.E.E. Trans.*, vol. 67, part I, pp. 175–81, 1948.

56. L. T. ROSENBERG, "A Semiempirical Approach to Voltage Dip — with Suddenly Applied Loads on A-C Generators," *A.I.E.E. Trans.*, vol. 68, part I, pp. 160–6, 1949. Disc., pp. 166–7.

57. WILLIAM C. DUESTERHOEFT, "The Negative-Sequence Reactances of an Ideal Synchronous Machine," *A.I.E.E. Trans.*, vol. 68, part I, pp. 510–3, 1949. Disc., pp. 513–4.

58. N. E. WILSON, "Transients in 2-Phase Synchronous Machines," *A.I.E.E. Trans.*, vol. 68, part II, pp. 1360–7, 1949.

59. C. CONCORDIA, "The Differential Analyser as an Aid in Power System Analysis," *C.I.G.R.E.*, 1950, Report 311.

60. H. S. KIRSCHBAUM, "Per-Unit Inductances of Synchronous Machines," *A.I.E.E. Trans.*, vol. 69, part I, pp. 231–4, 1950.

61. SAAD L. MIKHAIL, "Potier Reactance for Salient-Pole Synchronous Machines," *A.I.E.E. Trans.*, vol. 69, part I, pp. 235–8, 1950.

62. ROBERT D. CAMBURN and ERIC T. B. GROSS, "Analysis of Synchronous Machine Short Circuits," *A.I.E.E. Trans.*, vol. 69, part II, pp. 671–8, 1950. Disc., pp. 678–9.

63. GABRIEL KRON, "Classification of the Reference Frames of a Synchronous Machine," *A.I.E.E. Trans.*, vol. 69, part II, pp. 720–7, 1950.

64. SAAD L. MIKHAIL, "Symmetrical Short Circuits on Saturated Alternators," *A.I.E.E. Trans.*, vol. 69, part II, pp. 1554–62, 1950.

65. CHARLES CONCORDIA, "Synchronous Machine Damping and Synchronizing Torques," *A.I.E.E. Trans.*, vol. 70, part I, pp. 731–7, 1951.

66. CHARLES CONCORDIA, *Synchronous Machines — Theory and Performance*, John Wiley & Sons, Inc., New York, 1951.

67. JOH. GRABSCHEID, "The Transient E.m.f. Induced in the Armature Winding and the Transient Active Power of a Synchronous Alternator Connected to an Infinite Bus through External Impedances," *C.I.G.R.E.*, 1952, Report 335.

68. F. K. DALTON and A. W. W. CAMERON, "Simplified Measurement of Subtransient and Negative-Sequence Reactances in Salient-Pole Synchronous Machines," *A.I.E.E. Trans.*, vol. 71, part III, pp. 752–6, October, 1952. Disc., pp. 756–7.

69. C. M. LAFFOON, "The Significance of Generator Short-Circuit Ratio," *Westinghouse Engineer*, vol. 12, pp. 207–8, November, 1952.

PROBLEMS ON CHAPTER XII

1. Discuss the energy relations in the following two cases considered in the text as examples of applications of the law of constant flux linkages: (a) copper ring suddenly removed from a permanent magnet, (b) relay armature suddenly released.

2. Show whether and how the theorem of constant flux linkages applies to closed circuits having series capacitance, initially charged. Does it hold if the capacitance is suddenly changed by switching or by mechanical motion of the plates?

3. A transformer having self-inductances L_1 and L_2 and mutual inductance M is operating in the steady state with voltage $e = E_m \sin \omega t$ applied to the primary terminals and with the secondary terminals open. At time t_1 the secondary terminals are suddenly short-circuited. Derive expressions for the primary and secondary currents, neglecting resistance. Assume the primary voltage to be unaffected by the short circuit.

4. Plot the currents of the preceding problem for a transformer having $k = 0.9$ (a) if the short circuit is applied at $t_1 = 0$, (b) if it is applied at $t_1 = \pi/2\omega$.

5. A single-phase generator, having armature self-inductance L_a, field inductance L_b, and mutual inductance $M = M_m \cos \omega t$, is initially operating at no load and at field current I_0. At time $t = t_1$ the armature is suddenly short-circuited. Derive expressions for the armature and field currents, neglecting resistance.

6. Plot the currents of the preceding problem for a generator for which $M_m/\sqrt{L_a L_b} = 0.8$, short-circuited at the instant when the armature flux linkage is a maximum.

7. Prove that the magnetic energy stored in two coupled circuits is $W = \frac{1}{2}(\psi_a i_a + \psi_b i_b)$.

8. By use of the expression for stored magnetic energy just given and the

relation that torque is the derivative of energy with respect to angle, plot
the torque of the single-phase generator for which $M_m/\sqrt{L_aL_b} = 0.8$, short-
circuited at the instant when the armature flux linkage is zero.

9. Prove, by the method suggested in the footnote on p. 6, that mutual
inductance is the same in both directions.

10. A circuit of inductance L_1 is carrying current I_1 when suddenly
additional inductance L_2 is switched into the circuit in series with L_1.
What is the current in the circuit right after the switching? Discuss energy
relations in the circuit.

11. A circuit of inductance L_1 carrying current I_1 and another circuit of
inductance L_2 carrying current I_2 are initially so located with respect to
one another that their mutual inductance is zero. How much mechanical
work must be done on the system to move one coil with respect to the
other so that the mutual inductance becomes M, (a) if the motion is very
sudden? (b) if the motion is very gradual and the two currents remain constant at their original values?

12. An e.m.f. $e = 1 + 3t$ volts is applied at $t = 0$ to a circuit having
a resistance of 1 ohm and an inductance of 1 henry. The initial current is
1 amp. Find the current in the circuit (a) analytically and (b) by point-
by-point computation from $t = 0$ to 3 sec.

13. Repeat the last problem with an initial current of 4 amp.

14. What initial current in Prob. 12 would lead to a linear increase
of current?

15. Show both analytically and by the graphical "follow-up" method
what wave form of voltage must be applied to an R-L circuit to obtain a
linearly increasing current, which begins at zero at zero time.

16. It is known that the differential equation

$$\frac{dx}{dt} + \frac{x}{T} = 0 \qquad (a)$$

has the solution

$$x = A\epsilon^{-t/T} \qquad (b)$$

Show that the corresponding difference equations

$$\frac{x_{n+1} - x_n}{\Delta t} + \frac{x_n}{T} = 0 \qquad (c)$$

and

$$\frac{x_{n+1} - x_n}{\Delta t} + \frac{x_n}{T + (\Delta t/2)} = 0 \qquad (d)$$

have the solutions

$$x_n = A\epsilon^{-n\Delta t/T_1} \qquad (e)$$

and

$$x_n = A\epsilon^{-n\Delta t/T_2} \qquad (f)$$

respectively. Find T_1 and T_2 as functions of T and Δt. Find the percentage
errors in T_1 and T_2 in terms of the number of points per time constant
$(T/\Delta t)$.

17. Find the negative-sequence inductance L_2 of a salient-pole synchronous machine without amortisseur windings in terms of the actual self- and mutual inductances of the windings. Neglect field resistance.

18. Prove that if sinusoidal negative-sequence voltages are impressed on the armature windings of a synchronous machine the negative-sequence reactance is the "harmonic mean" of x_d'' and x_q''.

19. A turbogenerator having the reactances and time constants listed below is initially operating with no load and with an armature voltage of 1.2 per unit. Then a three-phase short circuit is applied. Calculate and plot d-c. and a-c. components of armature current and resultant armature current versus time, assuming a fully offset wave.

$$x_d = 1.15 \text{ per unit} \qquad T_a = 0.15 \text{ sec.}$$

$$x_d' = 0.25 \text{ per unit} \qquad T_d' = 1.50 \text{ sec.}$$

$$x_d'' = 0.10 \text{ per unit} \qquad T_d'' = 0.03 \text{ sec.}$$

20. The measurements given in Table 14 were made on the ordinates of the envelopes of the oscillogram of one armature current taken when a three-phase short circuit was suddenly applied to an unloaded turbogenerator

TABLE 14

MEASUREMENTS OF SHORT-CIRCUIT OSCILLOGRAM (PROBLEM 20)

Time (cycles)	Ordinates of Envelopes (inches)		Time (cycles)	Ordinates of Envelopes (inches)	
	Upper	Lower		Upper	Lower
0	2.63	−0.63	15	0.86	−0.62
1	2.24	−0.50	20	0.75	−0.63
2	1.96	−0.44	25	0.67	−0.61
3	1.73	−0.41	30	0.63	−0.59
4	1.56	−0.42	40	0.54	−0.54
5	1.44	−0.44	50	0.48	−0.48
6	1.33	−0.45	60	0.43	−0.43
7	1.24	−0.48	90	0.32	−0.32
8	1.16	−0.50	120	0.25	−0.25
10	1.05	−0.55	∞	0.15	−0.15

rated at 10,000 kva., 11.8 kv., three-phase, 60 cycles, 1,800 r.p.m. The open-circuit voltage was 5.9 kv. The scale factor of the oscillogram is 1,930 amp. per inch (instantaneous value). Find the direct-axis reactances (in per unit) and time constants (in seconds).

21. Draw to scale a vector diagram (similar to Fig. 34) of a salient-pole synchronous generator having the following reactances (in per unit):

$$x_d = 1.15 \qquad x_d' = 0.37$$

$$x_q = 0.75 \qquad x_q' = 0.75$$

Neglect resistance. Take the load current as 1.00 per unit at a power factor of 0.91 lag with respect to the terminal voltage, which is 1.00 per unit.

22. Draw to scale a vector diagram (similar to Fig. 35) for a turbogenerator having the following per-unit reactances:

$$x_d = 1.15 \qquad x_d' = 0.20$$

$$x_q = 1.00 \qquad x_q' = 0.20$$

Neglect resistance. The machine is operating in the steady state with load current and terminal voltage as specified in the preceding problem.

23. Work Example 4 with 50% external reactance between the generator and the infinite bus. The terminal conditions stated in that example still apply to the generator terminals, so the voltage of the infinite bus is different.

24. Would it be correct to represent a salient-pole machine on a calculating board by a source of voltage E_q' in series with an adjustable reactance, ranging from x_d' to x_q'? If so, what would be the proper value of reactance as a function of angle $\delta + \phi$ between E_q' and I?

CHAPTER XIII

EXCITATION SYSTEMS

In the last chapter, methods were given for calculating the field current and field flux linkage of a synchronous machine when the voltage applied to its field circuit was either constant or varying as a known function of time. In this chapter, the methods of supplying field voltage, the methods of making it vary, the methods of calculating its variation as a function of time, and the effect of such variation on power-system stability are presented.

Description of excitation systems. The field windings of synchronous machines are nearly always supplied with direct current from d-c. generators called *exciters*. Former practice, now almost obsolete, was for a station to have an excitation bus fed by a number of exciters operating in parallel and supplying power to the fields of all the a-c. generators in the station. The present practice is for each a-c. generator to have its own exciter, which is usually direct-connected to the main generator but sometimes is driven by a motor or a small prime mover or both. The advantages of the *unit-exciter scheme* over the common-excitation-bus scheme are:

1. *Greater reliability.* Trouble on one exciter affects only one a-c. generator. Reliability of the excitation system is of utmost importance. It is better to disconnect a generator from the bus than to let it run for any length of time without excitation because in the latter case the remaining generators have to supply not only the load but also the reactive power for magnetizing the generator that has lost its own excitation.*

2. *Saving in rheostat losses.* No rheostats are needed in the field circuits of the main generators for controlling the voltage or reactive power because the exciter-field rheostats can be used instead, and these operate at a much lower power level than do the main-generator field rheostats.

3. *Simpler layout of the station.* The excitation bus, much of the

---

*Loss-of-field relay protection is described in Chapter X, Vol. II.

switchgear associated with that bus, and main-field rheostats are eliminated. All exciters need not have the same rated voltage.

4. *Better suitability to the use of automatic voltage regulators.* The division of reactive power between generators can be controlled automatically by the voltage regulators. (See section on "Parallel operation.")

In what follows the unit-exciter scheme is assumed. Though with this scheme the excitation of the main a-c. generator could be regulated by means of either a main-field rheostat or an exciter-field rheostat, the latter is generally used, both because rheostat losses are less and because the control equipment is less cumbersome.

Exciters are shunt- or compound-wound* and are rated at either 125 or 250 volts. They normally deliver 0.5% to 3% of the rated power of the main machine.

Some exciters operate self-excited, others are separately excited, and still others use a combination of self- and separate excitation. The excitation of a separately excited exciter is sometimes furnished by a rectifier or storage battery, but is supplied ordinarily from a smaller d-c. generator called a *pilot exciter*. The conventional pilot exciter is operated at approximately constant voltage, the excitation of the a-c. generator being controlled, as before, by the field rheostat of the main exciter. The pilot exciter is flat-compounded, and is rated at 1.5% to 5% of the kilowatt rating of the main exciter. In some of the newer methods of excitation, the pilot exciter is a rotating amplifier, operated at varying voltage.

The *advantages of separately excited exciters* are:

1. *Quicker response* of the exciter voltage to a change in the resistance of the regulating rheostat. The reason for, and the advantage of, quicker response are explained later in this chapter.

2. *Stable operation at low voltage.* Some synchronous machines are required occasionally to operate with low excitation. This is true of a synchronous condenser when taking lagging volt-amperes from a bus in order to hold down the bus voltage. It is also true of a generator required to charge a long, lightly loaded, high-voltage line having much capacitance. If the excitation of the a-c. machine is reduced to a low value by decreasing the voltage of a self-excited exciter, the exciter may become unstable; that is, its voltage is likely to drift away from the desired value. By special design (having a reduced section of the main poles which begins to saturate

*Shunt-wound exciters respond more uniformly to the control of voltage regulators than compound-wound exciters do.

at 15 to 20% of rated voltage), a self-excited exciter can be made to operate stably at voltages down to 25% of its rated value. A separately excited exciter, however, can be operated stably at as low a voltage as required.

The disadvantages of separate excitation from a constant-voltage pilot exciter are:

1. The complication of an additional rotating machine with its maintenance of brushes, commutator, etc.

2. A larger field rheostat for the main exciter.

The first disadvantage holds for the rotating-amplifier type of pilot exciter also, but the second does not.

Unless one of the advantages listed above is required, a self-excited exciter is used. Self-excitation is commoner than separate excitation on small a-c. generators (about 15 Mva. and below), whereas the contrary holds for large a-c. generators.

The combination of self- and separate excitation of the main exciter is found in some of the newer excitation schemes using rotating regulators. These schemes will be described later.

The excitation of the synchronous machine is usually controlled, as already stated, by means of a regulating rheostat in the field circuit of the main exciter. This rheostat may be varied either manually or automatically. In the latter case, a generator-voltage regulator is employed.

Manual control of the generator voltage is usually satisfactory for generators at attended stations the load of which changes slowly, as on turbogenerators of large metropolitan systems. In some such systems, the use of voltage regulators was formerly considered to be more of a hazard than a benefit, for instances occurred in which a sticking contact or an accidental ground in the regulator reduced the field current to such a low value that the generator pulled out of step.[58] Recently, voltage regulators have come into use on metropolitan systems because of the availability of more reliable and more effective regulators, because of the need for operation of generators at high power factor at times of light load — a condition under which a good voltage regulator significantly raises the margin of steady-state stability, and because of the use of generators of lower short-circuit ratio. Voltage regulators are necessary on synchronous condensers (the purpose of which is to control the voltage), on water-wheel-driven generators (to hold down the voltage in case of loss of load and consequent overspeed), and on steam-turbine-driven generators subject to sudden changes in load. They aid stability of all synchronous machines.

Types of excitation system. The principal types of excitation system now in use (having automatic voltage regulation) are the following:

1. *Self-excited exciter and direct-acting rheostatic type of voltage regulator* (Fig. 1). The voltage regulator changes the resistance in the field circuit of the exciter. The voltage-sensitive element of the regulator (for example, a solenoid) acts directly on the rheostat to vary its resistance. This system is commonly used on the smaller a-c. generators. The voltage regulators are described in more detail later in this chapter.

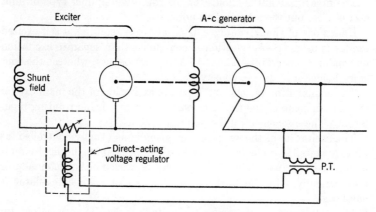

FIG. 1. Excitation of a-c. generator with self-excited exciter and direct-acting rheostatic voltage regulator.

2. *Main and pilot exciters and indirect-acting rheostatic type of voltage regulator* (Fig. 2). When a small deviation of voltage occurs, the voltage-sensitive element of the regulator closes contacts which control a motor-driven switch which raises or lowers the resistance of the field rheostat of the main exciter. If the voltage deviation is greater, additional contacts are closed which short-circuit the field rheostat to produce a rapid build-up of the alternating voltage or contacts are opened which introduce the entire resistance of the rheostat to produce rapid build-down. This regulator has the disadvantage of a "dead band," that is, a small range of voltage in which no corrective action is produced. This dead zone reduces the accuracy of voltage regulation and prevents the regulator from increasing steady-state stability. Until recently this has been the standard scheme of excitation for large machines. The voltage regulators are described in a later section of this chapter.

3. *Rotating main exciter with electronic pilot exciter and electronic regulator.*[24] The electronic pilot exciter is a polyphase rectifier using thyratron tubes or the like.

The a-c. supply for the rectifier may be either the main power system or a permanent-magnet generator direct-connected to the main machine. The electronic regulator controls the firing angle of the tubes

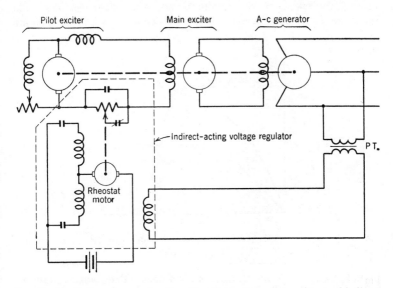

FIG. 2. Excitation of a-c. generator with main exciter, pilot exciter, and indirect-acting rheostatic voltage regulator.

and thus varies the output voltage of the rectifier which is impressed on the field winding of the main exciter. No field rheostat is used. This system has been applied principally to synchronous condensers but also to some generators.

4. *Electronic main exciter and electronic regulator.*[20,24,40,41] A six-phase rectifier of larger capacity, using ignitron tubes, supplies direct current to the field of the main generator. Again, the regulator controls the firing angle of the rectifier tubes. The anodes of each pair of tubes are connected to their load through a two-pole circuit breaker. When this breaker is opened, the load can be carried by the remaining four tubes. Thus, tubes can be replaced without shutting down the unit. The power supply for the rectifier is either the main a-c. generator or an auxiliary polyphase generator, usually direct-driven. If the supply is from the main a-c. generator, series compensation[20] may

be employed to boost the voltage in proportion to the reactive current fed from the generator.

Electronic main and pilot exciters have operated very satisfactorily but are not widely used because both their first cost and their maintenance cost have been found to be greater than for other types of excitation systems.

5. *Main exciter, rotating amplifier, and static voltage regulator.* The main exciter is either an ordinary shunt-wound machine or a shunt-

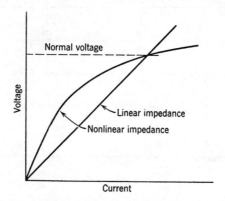

Fɪɢ. 3. Voltage-current characteristics of elements used in impedance-type voltage regulator.

wound machine with additional field windings. The rotating amplifier is a d-c. machine especially designed as a power amplifier. Such machines, known by the trade names of Amplidyne (General Electric Company), Rototrol (Westinghouse Electric Corporation), or Regulex (Allis-Chalmers Manufacturing Company), are described in a later section of this chapter. The important feature of such machines is that a large output may be controlled by a few watts' input, which can be supplied by a static type of regulator having no dead band and no moving parts. Such regulators are accurate and reliable. They are of either of two types, electronic or impedance. The electronic regulator compares the constant voltage drop across a glow tube or across a resistor in the plate circuit of a pentode with the rectified alternating voltage being controlled, the difference being applied to a control-field winding of the amplifier, or each voltage being applied to one of a pair of such windings, the m.m.f.'s of which are opposed. The impedance type of regulator[19] compares the current through a nonlinear impedance (usually an iron-cored inductor) with that through a linear impedance (usually a capacitor). See Fig. 3. When the alternating voltage is correct, the currents through the two impedances are equal. When the voltage is high or low, one current or the other predominates and, after rectification, excites the control-field winding (or windings) of the rotating amplifier. In some cases, where more power gain is required, a magnetic amplifier has been placed between the voltage regulator and the rotating amplifier.[51]

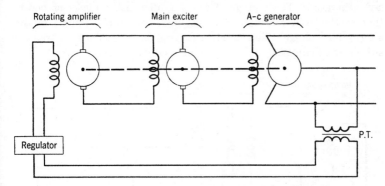

FIG. 4. Excitation of a-c. generator by main exciter which is separately excited from a rotating amplifier controlled by the voltage regulator.

Several different methods of exciting the main exciter are used. One (Fig. 4) is to excite the main exciter separately from the output of the rotating amplifier.[31] However, it is generally better to use some combination of self- and separate excitation of the main exciter

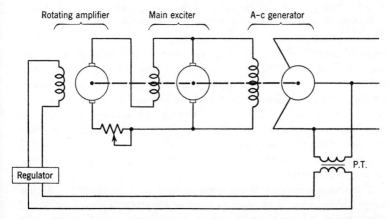

FIG. 5. Excitation of a-c. generator by main exciter which is both self-excited and separately excited by a rotating amplifier connected in series with the shunt-field circuit of the main exciter.

so that the rotating amplifier can be removed from service for maintenance without shutting down the generating unit.

One such method is to connect the rotating amplifier in series with the self-excited shunt field (Fig. 5).[24,51,53] The field rheostat is so adjusted that when the amplifier voltage is zero the exciter operates self-excited to supply the proper field current for average load on the a-c. generator. The voltage of the amplifier either bucks or boosts that of the exciter armature, as required for proper control of the alternating voltage. The amplifier may be disconnected by a transfer switch, the main exciter then being manually controlled.

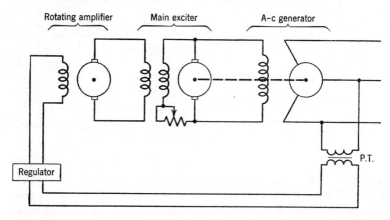

Rotating amplifier   Main exciter   A-c generator

Regulator

P.T.

Fig. 6. Excitation of a-c. generator by main exciter with two field windings one of which is self-excited, the other separately excited by a rotating amplifier.

Another method (Fig. 6) is for the main exciter to have one shunt-connected field winding with rheostat adjusted to provide excitation for average conditions and another field winding separately excited by the rotating amplifier, which either bucks or boosts the self-excitation as required.[31] This method has the advantage of having no switching in the main field winding of the exciter, but has the disadvantage of requiring a special type of exciter.

These schemes using rotating amplifiers have been extensively employed in recent years.

6. *Rotating amplifier as main exciter and static regulator.*[32] A two-stage Rototrol has been used as the main exciter. One advantage of this scheme is its rapid response because of the use of a series field winding on the Rototrol. (See the next section of this chapter for further explanation.)

7. *Main exciter, magnetic amplifier, and static regulator.*[55,57] This
scheme, which is one of the newest, is similar in general to scheme 5
with an exciter with two field windings, except that the rotating amplifier is replaced by a magnetic amplifier.

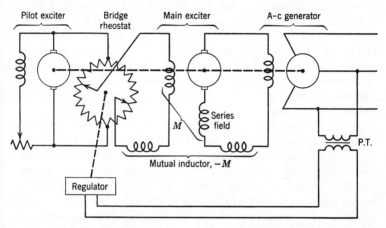

Fig. 7. Excitation of a-c. generator by main exciter with series and separate
excitation.

Exciter with series winding.[25,59] The increase of field current of the
a-c. generator which is induced by an increase of lagging reactive
armature current, due to a short circuit or to swinging of the machine,
can be utilized in a series-field winding on the exciter to raise the
exciter armature e.m.f.   This e.m.f. can be raised much more quickly
by means of the series field than it can be by suddenly reducing the
resistance in the shunt or separately excited field winding of the
exciter or even by suddenly raising the voltage applied to such winding by a rotating amplifier.   The increased e.m.f. tends to maintain
the increased field current of the a-c. generator and so diminishes the
rate of decay of this current.

Figure 7 shows an exciter with a series-field winding and a separately
excited field winding.   The latter is supplied with current from a pilot
exciter through a rheostat controlled by the voltage regulator.   There
appears also in the figure a mutual inductor (transformer) the purpose
of which is as follows.   A sudden increase of current in the series-field
winding tends to induce a decrease of current in the separately excited
field circuit, thus decreasing the effectiveness of the series field in
raising the armature flux and e.m.f.   To prevent this, the two circuits
are decoupled by the addition of an external mutual inductance equal

and opposite to the mutual inductance between the two field windings in the exciter itself.

The provision of series excitation on the exciter increases the time constant of the alternator field circuit by decreasing the equivalent resistance of that circuit. The RI drop, which is proportional to the current in that circuit, is compensated, wholly or partly, by a component of exciter armature e.m.f. which is also proportional to the current (saturation being avoided). The increased time constant means a slower decay of alternator field current and field flux linkage. Overcompensation can provide an increasing flux linkage.

Series excitation is beneficial both to transient stability and to steady-state stability.

On the other hand, the inclusion of the inductance of the series-field winding of the exciter in the field circuit of the a-c. generator raises the transient reactance of the generator slightly and thus diminishes proportionally the increase of field current required to maintain constant flux linkage of the field circuit. There also occurs a redistribution of this flux linkage, the linkage of the exciter series field being increased while the linkage of the field winding of the a-c. generator is correspondingly decreased. These disadvantageous effects are believed to be small.

Rotating amplifiers.[37,44,56] Since special d-c. generators of several types play such an important part in modern schemes of excitation, it seems worth while to give a short description of these machines.

The *Rototrol* is similar in construction to an ordinary d-c. generator except that the magnetic circuit is designed so that it does not saturate in the working range. The machine has a self-exciting series-field winding (connected in series with the armature, the load, and a "tuning" resistor) and also has one or more control-field windings for separate excitation. The tuning resistor is adjusted so that the "resistance line" coincides as nearly as possible with the straight part of the saturation curve. Thus the series field can supply all or very nearly all the m.m.f. required at any voltage. The control-field winding or windings supply the small difference needed in the steady state because of noncoincidence of the resistance line with the saturation curve, as well as the m.m.f. needed under transient conditions to force the voltage up or down.

The *Regulex* differs from the Rototrol in that the self-excitation is supplied by a shunt-connected field winding instead of a series-connected one. Therefore, the transient performance is characterized by an additional time constant.

Both the Rototrol and the Regulex are single-stage amplifiers with positive feedback. They have power gains of the order of 25,000 to 50,000.

The *Amplidyne* is a d-c. machine of special construction having two sets of brushes 90 elec. deg. apart, one set of brushes being short-circuited. The control-field winding or windings are located on what we may call the direct axis and produce a speed voltage on the quadrature axis. The brushes on the quadrature axis are short-circuited; hence a small m.m.f. in the control-field winding produces a large current through the short circuit and a large m.m.f. (cross-magnetizing armature reaction) in the quadrature axis. Rotation of the armature with respect to the quadrature-axis flux induces a speed voltage between the direct-axis brushes, which are the output terminals. When load is connected to these terminals, the armature reaction resulting from the load current would oppose the m.m.f. of the control-field winding, thus constituting a negative feedback which would reduce the gain were not this armature reaction counteracted by a compensating winding, distributed in slots in the pole faces and carrying the load current. The Amplidyne is inherently a two-stage amplifier, and gives a power gain of from 10,000 to 250,000. It has a short time constant, of the order of 0.05 to 0.25 sec.

A Rototrol having two stages of amplification in one 4-pole machine has been built.[28,29] The armature is lap-wound without equalizers. Two diametrically opposite poles, which in a conventional machine would have the same polarity, are magnetized as the north and south poles of a two-pole machine by the control windings of the first stage. The output of this stage is taken from two diametrically opposite brushes and is used to energize the control-field winding of the second stage, wound on all four poles in the normal manner for a four-pole machine. The output of the second stage is taken from all four brush arms. Self-excited series or shunt windings, as already described for the single-stage Rototrol or Regulex, may be connected to this stage. Additional windings to compensate for armature reaction and to aid in commutation are connected as described in Ref. 28.

Drives for exciters. The excitation system of a large synchronous machine, and especially that of a generator, must have the utmost reliability. The exciters should require but little maintenance and they should be driven by a means which is reliable even during low voltage or short circuits on the main power system and which will permit the generator to be started up even when the main power system is dead. If the main exciter is separately excited, the pilot exciter also requires an equally reliable drive. If the main exciter is both self- and separately excited, with separate excitation controlled by a rotating amplifier, the requirements for reliable drive of the latter are not so stringent, for the main exciter can be operated, if necessary, on hand control with self-excitation.

Direct-connected exciters are the most widely used and may be considered as the standard type. Direct connection gives the most reliable drive, not being affected by troubles on the a-c. system. The record of reliability is very good.[52] Some maintenance, such as changing brushes, must be done while the exciter is under load, or at least while it is rotating, and this involves some hazard. The speed of the exciter must be equal to that of the main generator rather than that which gives the best design for the exciter. The limitations of the direct-connected exciter have been felt in two different directions, on slow-speed water-wheel-driven generators and on very large high-speed turbine-driven generators. On slow-speed generators, direct-connected exciters are larger and more expensive and have a slower response than higher speed separately driven exciters. Turbine-generator units are being manufactured in larger capacities than before, thus requiring exciters of larger rating. The new units are usually built for 3,600 r.p.m., whereas, in the past, lower speeds were common. The turbines, generators, boilers, and auxiliaries have become more reliable, thus permitting longer times of operation between shutdowns for maintenance. Thus there is a desire for greater reliability of the exciter, while, at the same time, the larger ratings and speeds increase the difficulties of commutation. A lower speed facilitates the design of a reliable exciter of large rating.

Gear-driven exciters permit the exciter speed to be different from the speed of the main generator, while retaining the reliability of the direct drive.

Motor-driven exciters[21,39,49] present advantages in addition to freedom in the choice of speed. The exciter may be placed in a less expensive and more convenient location than at the end of the generator shaft. There commutation is better because of the absence of vibration transmitted from the turbine foundation. Moreover, if a spare source of excitation is available, maintenance work on the exciter can be done with the exciter shut down but without shutting down the main generator.

The motor-driven exciter requires a reliable source of electric power. In some stations the motor may be fed from a house generator, which also supplies power to other station auxiliaries. In other stations the motor is fed through a transformer from the main a-c. generator or the main a-c. bus, in which case the alternating voltage is subject to reduction or interruption during system disturbances. In order for the excitation system to be reliable, it should be able to provide suitable ceiling voltage and rate of response when the motor is operated on sustained low voltage equal to 70% of normal voltage or during total absence of voltage (due to severe faults) of 12 to 15 cycles' duration. This may be accomplished by providing the following features:

1. Inertia of the motor-generator set increased by addition of a flywheel to a value $H = 5$ (based on exciter name-plate kilowatt rating).

2. Use of an induction motor having maximum torque of about five times its full-load torque.

3. An exciter ceiling voltage of at least 120% of its rated voltage when the driving motor is operating at 70% of its rated voltage.

Hydrogen cooling.[24,52] Hydrogen-cooled synchronous condensers operating at speeds up to 900 r.p.m. have been furnished with direct-connected main exciters located in a hydrogen-filled compartment which can be isolated from the main condenser compartment when maintenance is to be done on the exciter. It has been found that hydrogen cooling of the exciter not only reduces the temperature rise of the exciter but also decreases the wear of the commutator and brushes. Hydrogen cooling has been proposed for the exciters of turbogenerators.

Tirrill voltage regulators. In the past, the commonest type of generator-voltage regulator was the *vibrating type*, or *Tirrill regulator*. This regulator has contacts which open and close continually several times per second. When closed, they short-circuit the regulating rheostat, and the exciter-field current and armature voltage build up. When the contacts are open, the rheostat is reinserted in the field circuit, causing the field current and armature voltage to decrease. Because the period of vibration of the contacts is much shorter than the time constant of the exciter-field circuit, the percentage fluctuation in the field current and armature voltage is not great. The average values of these quantities depend upon the time of engagement of the contacts, which may be defined as the ratio of the time that the contacts are closed to the period of vibration. A change in the time of engagement has the same average effect as changing the setting of an exciter-field rheostat.

One type of vibrating regulator, having a d-c. vibrating magnet, is shown in Fig. 8. The main contacts are mounted on two pivoted arms, each of which is actuated by an electromagnet. The winding of one electromagnet is supplied with direct voltage from the exciter armature; the other, with alternating voltage from the main generator (through a potential transformer). A decrease of either the alternating or the direct voltage tends to close the main contacts, and an increase of either voltage tends to open them.

When the alternating voltage is correct, the upward force of the a-c. magnet is in equilibrium with the unbalanced weight of the magnet core and counterweight. Furthermore, the force of this magnet is

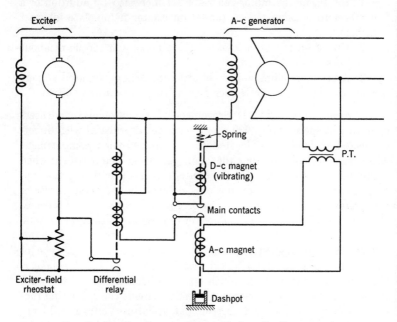

FIG. 8. Tirrill voltage regulator with d-c. vibrating magnet.

independent of position throughout a certain range; therefore the magnet core is in equilibrium in any position in this range if the alternating voltage is at its normal value. This magnet is heavily damped by means of a dashpot. Therefore, if the alternating voltage is wrong, the magnet slowly moves the main contacts which it controls.

The d-c. magnet is not damped. Its force is opposed by the tension of a spring. This magnet and the contact actuated by it are in continual vibration, caused by the following chain of events. If the exciter voltage is high, the upward pull of the d-c. magnet on its core overcomes the force of the spring and opens the main contacts. Opening of the main contacts causes a differentially wound relay to open its contacts (which can handle more current than the main contacts) and thereby to insert resistance in the exciter-field circuit. Thereupon the exciter armature voltage decreases, weakening the d-c. magnet sufficiently to allow the spring to close the main contacts again. Closing of the main contacts closes the relay contacts, which short-circuit the exciter-field rheostat and make the exciter voltage build up. The process is repeated over and over again, with the result that the exciter armature voltage constantly increases and decreases through a small range, as shown in Fig. 9.

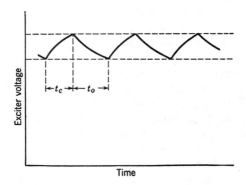

FIG. 9.   Effect of vibrating regulator on exciter voltage during steady conditions of main generator. The ratio t_c/t_o is constant.

The time of engagement of the vibrating main contacts is such that the average force exerted by the magnet during a cycle of vibration equals the average force of the spring. This relation follows from the fact that the average momentum of the magnet core is zero and the fact that the force transmitted through the contacts is negligible. As a consequence of this relation, the average exciter voltage depends upon the position of the main contact that is actuated by the a-c. magnet, because the position of this contact controls the average position of the vibrating contact and hence the average spring tension.

If the alternating voltage is too low, the a-c. magnet slowly raises the main contact which it controls. The higher this contact is raised, the greater is the average exciter voltage, and when the exciter voltage has been increased enough to raise the alternating voltage to the correct value, the a-c. magnet comes to rest. Similarly, if the alternating voltage is too high, the a-c. magnet lowers its main contact, lowers the exciter voltage, and lowers the alternating voltage to the correct value. Because of the design of the a-c. magnet, the alternating volt-

age is restored to the same value regardless of the amount of load on
the main generator.

It may be asked why the motion of an a-c. magnet alone could not
be used to operate the main contacts and thus to cut resistance in and
out of the exciter-field circuit. The reason for adding the d-c. magnet
is to prevent overshooting of the alternating voltage. The inductance
of the field circuit of the a-c. generator causes changes of the alternating voltage to lag behind changes of the exciter voltage. If the exciter
voltage should continue to build up until the alternating voltage had
risen to the desired value, the exciter voltage would then be too high
for the steady state and the alternating voltage would continue to
rise even if the exciter voltage should begin to decrease because of
regulator action. The exciter voltage would continue to decrease
until the alternating voltage had gone through a maximum and decreased to normal. At that time the exciter voltage would be too low
for the steady state and the alternating voltage would continue to
decrease. Thus large oscillations of the alternating voltage would
occur, which might or might not die out. Such oscillations are prevented by the d-c. magnet operating the main contacts in anticipation
of the action of the a-c. magnet.

Although the Tirrill regulator gives good voltage regulation, it requires more maintenance than the more modern types, it is noisy,
and there is a possibility that a sticking contact may cause the voltage to go too high.

Rheostatic voltage regulators. The Tirrill regulator was superseded
by regulators of the rheostatic type in which the regulating resistance
is varied continuously or in small steps instead of being first completely
cut in, then completely cut out. Under steady conditions, all parts of
the regulator are at rest; therefore the wear is small.

Rheostatic regulators can be classified into direct-acting and indirect-
acting types. In the direct-acting type, the voltage-sensitive element
of the regulator (for example, a magnet or a torque motor) controls
the rheostat through a direct mechanical connection. Special types of
rheostats must be used, so that only a small motion and small amount
of energy are required to vary the resistance from one extreme to the
other. In the indirect-acting type of rheostatic regulator, the voltage-
sensitive element operates contacts which, in turn, control a motor to
drive the rheostat. This action suffices to correct small or gradual
changes of voltage, but the motion of the rheostat is too slow for
rapid correction of sudden, large changes. When such changes occur,
additional contacts on the voltage-sensitive element actuate relays

which cut in or out the entire regulating resistance in order to correct the abnormal voltage as rapidly as the response of the exciter and of the main generator will permit.

Direct-acting voltage regulators. Typical of these are the General Electric "Diactor," the Westinghouse "Silverstat," and the Allis-Chalmers (Brown-Boveri) rocking-contact regulator. The first two

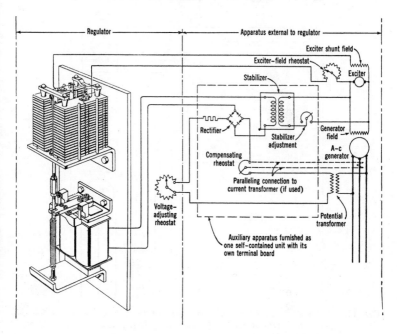

Fig. 10. "Diactor" direct-acting exciter-rheostatic voltage regulator for a-c. generator. (*By courtesy of General Electric Company.*)

are shown in Figs. 10 and 11, respectively. In both these regulators the voltage-sensitive element is an electromagnet, the winding of which is energized from one phase of the a-c. circuit whose voltage is to be controlled, through a potential transformer, a voltage-adjusting rheostat (manually operated), and a dry rectifier. A small motion of the armature of the electromagnet acts to cut the required amount of resistance in or out of the regulating rheostat in the exciter-field circuit.

The two regulators differ principally in the form of the regulating rheostat.

The rheostat of the "*Diactor*" consists of two or four stacks of non-metallic resistance plates. Each resistance plate has a silver-button insert, slightly thicker than the plate, passing through the plate at the front end. Insulating spacers separate the plates at the rear of the stack. At the center of the stack there are metal contact plates between the resistance plates. As the contact plates are thicker than

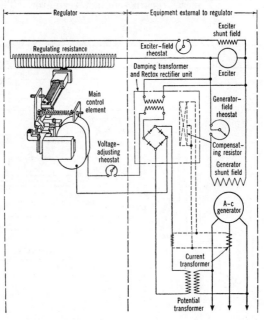

FIG. 11. "Silverstat" direct-acting exciter-rheostatic voltage regulator for a-c. generator. (*By courtesy of Westinghouse Electric Corporation.*)

either the protruding portion of the silver buttons or the insulating spacers, they act as fulcrums on which the resistance plates may rock. They also form electric contacts between the resistance plates. The stack is operated by a rod, which, under the tension of a spring, pulls down the front end of the top plate. The pull of the spring is counteracted by the force of the electromagnet.

When the resistance plates are tilted back so that the silver buttons are separated, the rheostat is in the position of maximum resistance, as shown in Fig. 12a. The current path is then through the alternate resistance plates and metal contact plates. If the stack is gradually tilted forward, its resistance is gradually reduced, both because of a decrease in contact resistance between the resistance plates and metal

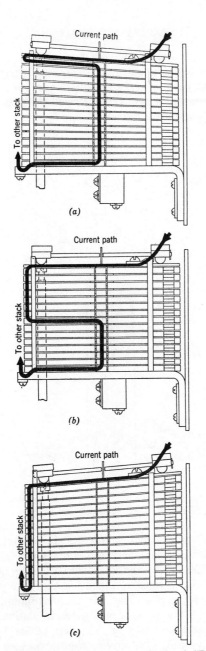

FIG. 12. Paths of current through rheostatic stack of "Diactor" generator-voltage regulator. (a) High-resistance position, (b) medium-resistance position, (c) low-resistance position. (*By courtesy of General Electric Company.*)

155

contact plates and because the resistance plates are progressively short-circuited by the silver buttons as they come together. Figure 12b shows the current path for an intermediate position. In the position of minimum resistance, shown in Fig. 12c, all the resistance plates are short-circuited by the silver buttons.

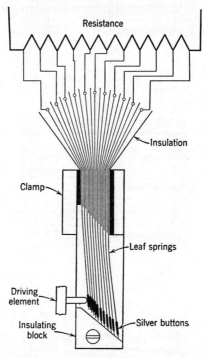

Fig. 13. The "Silverstat" rheostat. (*By courtesy of Westinghouse Electric Corporation.*)

The "*Silverstat*" differs from the rheostat just described in that the resistors are stationary and only the contact assembly is movable (see Fig. 13). Taps from the stationary rheostat are brought by wires to a set of leaf springs, clamped together at one end, with insulation between adjacent springs. In the maximum-resistance position the free ends of the springs rest upon an insulating block, and the springs do not touch one another. A silver button is set into each spring near the free end. The driving element presses on the springs and causes the silver buttons to come together and successively short-circuit sections of resistance.

Both the "Diactor" and the "Silverstat" employ as a damping device a transformer, the primary winding of which is connected across the exciter armature, the secondary winding in series with the rectifier output terminals and the coil of the control magnet. A voltage appears across the secondary terminals of this transformer only when the d-c. primary voltage is rising or falling. When the voltage of the exciter is rising as a result of regulator action, the voltage of the a-c. generator rises with considerable lag. However, the secondary

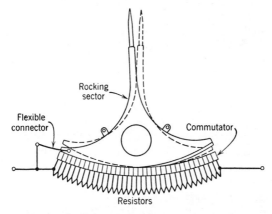

Fig. 14. Rocking-contact rheostat, used in Allis-Chalmers (Brown-Boveri) generator-voltage regulators.

voltage of the damping transformer under these circumstances is of such polarity that it appears to the regulator coil that the alternating voltage is rising faster than it actually is. In this manner overshooting of the exciter and generator voltages is prevented, or is limited to a small amount, depending upon the amount of damping feedback introduced.

It should be remarked that excitation systems containing voltage regulators are *closed-cycle control systems*. Concerning such systems, various investigators have worked out a mathematical theory for explaining and predicting such characteristics as accuracy, speed, hunting, and damping. References 15 and 16 discuss the "Silverstat" and "Diactor" regulators, respectively, from this viewpoint.

The *Allis-Chalmers (Brown-Boveri) voltage regulator* has a rocking-contact rheostat, shown in Fig. 14. This rheostat has a stationary commutator consisting of a large number of segments insulated from one another and arranged in a circular arc. These stationary segments are connected to resistors. The moving contact is sector-shaped.

Its contact surface, which rides in a V-shaped groove on the inner surface of the commutator, is a curved strip of carbon of somewhat smaller radius than that of the commutator. A rocking motion of the sector causes it to make contact with various segments of the commutator, thus cutting resistance in or out. One or more of these sectors is actuated either by a solenoid or by a split-phase torque motor, opposed by a spring. A damping device, consisting of either a dashpot or an eddy-current brake, is coupled to the main moving parts through a "recall spring." When a change of voltage occurs, the initial motion of the sectors is greater than required, but, as the deviation of voltage from normal decreases, the recall spring pulls the sector back fast enough to prevent the voltage from overshooting.

Indirect-acting voltage regulators. The use of the direct-acting regulators described above is confined to small- and medium-sized a-c. generators (up to about 25 Mva. at 1,200 r.p.m. or higher) having self-excited exciters. For larger generators, and for those with separately excited exciters, the exciter-field rheostats become too large to be directly actuated by the voltage-sensitive element. Therefore motor-driven face-plate rheostats are resorted to, and the rheostat motor is controlled by the normal contacts of the voltage regulator for correcting gradual changes of voltage. Quick-response contacts also are provided for raising or lowering the voltage as rapidly as possible. These contacts actuate high-speed contactors which cut the regulating resistance all in or all out, as required. As already stated, the quick-response contacts are actuated by voltage deviations larger than those actuating the normal contacts. Great voltage deviations are caused by large, sudden changes of load, by short circuits, and by generator swings.

Use of polyphase voltage. In the past it was customary to furnish the voltage-sensitive element of the regulator with one line-to-line voltage. This practice is still followed on the regulators for small generators. If, however, it is important that the regulator always raise the excitation when a fault occurs, it is preferable to use all three line-to-line voltages. The reason is that, if a single line-to-line voltage is used, it may increase, rather than decrease, during a fault on another phase, thereby causing the generator excitation to be lowered instead of raised. The voltages of the three-phase circuit, usually obtained through two potential transformers connected V–V, can be utilized in any of the following ways:

1. The output of a positive-sequence filter network is applied to the regulator coil.

2. The d-c. output of a three-phase rectifier is applied to the coil.

3. The voltage-sensitive element is a three-phase induction torque motor.

Westinghouse Type BJ indirect-acting exciter-rheostatic generator-voltage regulator. The circuits of this regulator are shown in Fig. 15. The voltage-sensitive element is an electromagnet supplied with direct current from a three-phase rectifier. This magnet actuates two sets of contacts, the normal-response contacts L and R and the quick-response contacts AL and AR.

Voltage deviations of $\pm 0.5\%$ cause one of the normal-response contacts to close. If the voltage is low, contact R closes, energizing the coil of contactor NR, which runs the main-exciter rheostat motor in the direction to cut resistance out of the rheostat. Similarly, if the voltage is high, contact L closes, energizing contactor NL, which runs the motor in the opposite direction. The rheostat motor has two series-field windings, one for each direction of rotation.

Voltage deviations of ± 1.5 to 5% (depending upon the setting) cause one of the quick-response contacts to close in addition to one of the normal-response contacts. If the voltage is low, contact AR closes, energizing contactor QR, which short-circuits the main-exciter field rheostat and an additional field-forcing-up resistor. This action gives maximum speed of build-up of the exciter voltage. At the same time the rheostat motor is cutting resistance out of the rheostat. If the voltage is high, contact AL closes, energizing contactor QL which inserts the field-forcing-down resistor into the exciter-field circuit. This causes the exciter voltage to build down rapidly. At the same time the rheostat motor is cutting resistance into the field rheostat.

Each set of regulator contacts is equipped with an *antihunt device* in the form of a coil (NH and QH) which, when energized, increases the gap distance between contacts R and L (or AR and AL) so as temporarily to decrease the sensitivity of the regulator.

Suppose that a small deviation from normal voltage occurs. Either contact L or contact R closes and energizes NR or NL. These contactors not only operate the rheostat motor, as already described, but also through additional contacts operate antihunt device NH, and through a third set of contacts shunt the coil of the contactor with a capacitor-resistor timing circuit. The antihunt device opens contact R or L and would de-energize the corresponding contactor were its coil not shunted with the timing circuit. The contactor is de-energized after a short time delay, which permits the rheostat arm to be driven a definite distance — for example, from one button to the next on the rheostat face-plate. After the rheostat motor stops, it is desirable to provide a time delay to allow the a-c. machine voltage to reach a steady value. Such delay is obtained by means of a dashpot on the antihunt device, which prevents the regulator contacts from immediately returning to their normal position. After expiration of this

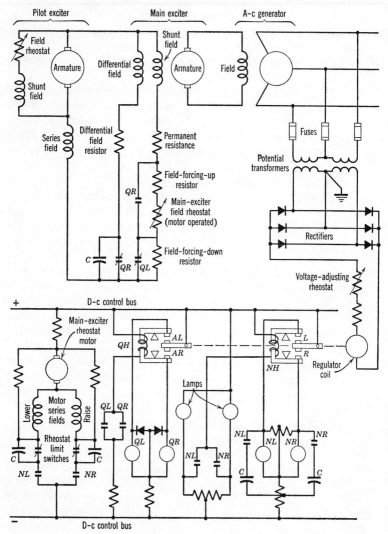

FIG. 15. Simplified circuits of Westinghouse Type BJ indirect-acting exciter-rheostatic generator-voltage regulator. (*By courtesy of Westinghouse Electric Corporation.*)

delay, the normal-response contacts will again close if the alternating voltage has not returned to normal. This will start another cycle of operation such as just described, and these cycles will continue until normal alternating voltage has been restored.

When the original deviation is large enough, the regulator contacts will remain closed even though the antihunt device changes the contact setting. The rheostat motor will then run continuously until the alternating voltage gets within the zone for which the antihunt device is set, whereupon intermittent action, as previously described, restores the voltage to normal.

The antihunt device on the quick-response contacts works in a manner similar to that just described for the device on the normal-response contacts.

General Electric Type GFA-4 indirect-acting generator-voltage regulator. See Fig. 16 for the circuit diagram. The voltage-sensitive element is a three-phase torque motor (an induction motor with solid cylindrical steel rotor) whose motion is opposed by a spring. Mounted on the shaft of the torque motor is a contact assembly comprising four contact arms, arranged in two pairs: the accelerating contacts ($R2$ and $L2$) in the rear and the notching contacts ($R1$ and $L1$) in the front. Each pair consists of a raising contact ($R1$ or $R2$) on the left and a lowering contact ($L1$ or $L2$) on the right. Between the two notching contacts is a metal star wheel, and between the two accelerating contacts is a smooth wheel. Both wheels are driven at 4 r.p.m. by the contact motor. When the voltage is normal, none of the four contacts touches a wheel. When the voltage deviates from normal, the torque motor tilts the contact assembly, causing one or two of the contacts to touch the rotating wheels and complete the circuit to a contactor. If the voltage is slightly too low, the raising notching contact $R1$ intermittently touches the star wheel, causing the rheostat pilot motor to run intermittently in the direction to cut out resistance. Likewise, if the voltage is slightly too high, the lowering notching contact $L1$ touches the star wheel, causing the pilot motor to cut resistance in. Time is allowed between points on the star wheel for the alternating voltage to approach a steady value. In addition, as each point on the star wheel engages the contact $R1$ or $L1$, it gives the latter a mechanical impulse which tends to restore the contact assembly to the neutral position. This action, in conjunction with the intermittent operation of the rheostat, prevents overtravel of the latter and consequent hunting. There is also a magnetic damping device to prevent excessive oscillation of the contact assembly.

The greater the voltage deviation from normal, the greater is the time of engagement of the notching contacts, causing the rheostat motor to run faster.

If the voltage deviation is great enough, one of the accelerating contacts touches the smooth wheel and operates a high-speed relay which cuts in or out all the regulating resistance. At the same time the rheostat motor runs at full speed.

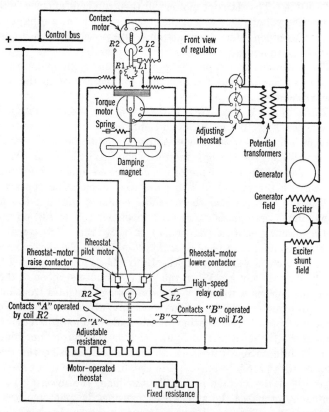

FIG. 16. Elementary connection diagram of General Electric Type GFA-4 indirect-acting exciter-rheostatic voltage regulator with face-plate-type series rheostat and self-excited exciter. (*By courtesy of General Electric Company.*)

Allis-Chalmers Type J indirect-acting generator-voltage regulator. This regulator has a rocking-contact rheostat similar to those used on the direct-acting regulators made by the same company. In the indirect-acting regulator, however, the rheostat is motor-driven. The rheostat motor is controlled through relays by "rheostat-inching" contacts driven by the voltage-sensitive element, a torque motor with a hollow cylindrical rotor. The engagement of the rheostat-inching contacts is not continuous, since the relays which control the motor also introduce antihunting rheostats into the circuit of the torque motor, thereby changing its voltage setting. This causes the torque motor to open the contacts again, de-energizing the rheostat relays and motor. As a result the rheostat is moved in short steps and over-travel is prevented.

When larger voltage deviations occur, the control element closes another set of contacts, which cause field-forcing contactors to cut in or out large blocks of regulating resistance.

Parallel operation. When a-c. generators are operated in parallel on the same bus, the division of reactive power between generators is controlled by their excitation. If voltage regulators are used, they must be modified so that they will not only hold the bus voltage constant but also give the proper division of reactive power. Modern voltage regulators are intended for use with individual nonparalleled exciters. When so used, the regulator is adapted most simply for parallel operation by the provision of *cross-current compensation*. In this method the voltage furnished to the voltage-sensitive element of each regulator is increased in proportion to the lagging reactive current supplied by its own machine. Then, if a machine is supplying more than its share of reactive current, its regulator will act as though the bus voltage were too high: that is, it will decrease the excitation and thereby decrease the reactive current supplied by its machine. The result of cross-current compensation is to give a slightly drooping curve of voltage versus load. The amount of droop is usually negligible, however. If each machine is given the same droop at rated current, zero power factor, then the machines will divide the reactive current in proportion to their kilovolt-ampere ratings.

Figures 10 and 11 show, in dashed lines, how cross-current compensation is added to the circuits of direct-acting regulators. A biasing voltage proportional to the current in one phase wire is added vectorially to the voltage between the other two wires. At zero power factor lagging, the biasing voltage augments the main voltage; at zero power factor leading, it subtracts from the main voltage; and at unity power factor, it adds in quadrature and thus has little effect.

If the drooping voltage characteristic is objectionable, a flat characteristic can be obtained by *differential cross-current compensation*. In this method each regulator is biased with the difference of the reactive current in its own machine and the average of such currents in the other machines instead of with the reactive current of its own machine alone.

If there is reactance between regulated generators or stations, not less than 6% based on the rating of the smaller machine or station, the regulators can be operated successfully without cross-current compensation. Because of the prevalent practices of operating generators as units with their step-up transformers (paralleled on the high-voltage side) and of using bus-sectionalizing reactors in metropolitan systems where step-up transformers are not used, the required amount of reactance is usually present between machines in the same station, and therefore cross-current compensation is seldom required. However, compensation is still recommended unless the reactance is somewhat greater than 6%.

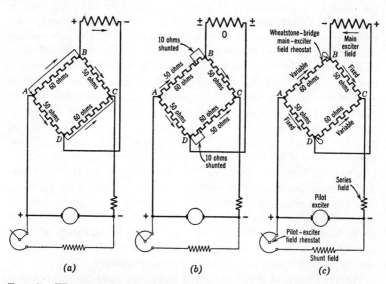

FIG. 17. Wheatstone-bridge rheostat for wide-range control of excitation. (a) Full positive excitation applied to main-exciter field, (b) approximately zero excitation applied to main-exciter field, (c) slightly negative excitation applied to main-exciter field. (*By courtesy of General Electric Company.*)

Wide-range excitation. As previously mentioned, synchronous condensers or generators with line-charging functions must sometimes operate at very low excitation. Because a self-excited exciter becomes unstable if operated at too low a voltage, it is necessary either to use a main-generator field rheostat or to separately excite the exciter. The latter alternative is preferable from the standpoint of ease of control.

Sometimes synchronous condensers are required to operate with reversed excitation in order to increase the lagging reactive power drawn by the condenser. Three methods of accomplishing this wide-range control are:

1. A Wheatstone-bridge field rheostat (Fig. 17).
2. A differential-field winding on the main exciter, operated at constant current (Fig. 15).
3. Use of a rotating amplifier.

Excitation limits.[22,31,58] In some installations it may be desirable to provide upper or lower limits to the excitation. An upper limit may be provided to prevent overheating of the field winding or to limit the armature current of synchronous condensers even though such limitation allows the voltage to drop below the desired value. A lower limit is sometimes used on generators to insure against loss of synchronism due to insufficient excitation. The lower limit may be fixed or it may be a function of the load on the machine. The variable lower limit is preferable to the fixed limit, for it allows better control of the voltage at light load while insuring adequate excitation for stability at heavy load. In the earliest installations of a variable lower excitation limit, the limit was a function of the position of the throttle or gate of the prime mover. More recently it has been a function of active power output of the generator.

Excitation limits are most easily provided in the excitation systems using static regulators.

Relation of excitation system to the stability problem. Increased speed of exciter response was one of the first means suggested and applied for improving power-system stability. The excitation system affects stability under both transient and steady conditions. One can understand this by recalling that the power transmitted in a two-machine system is, according to the approximate equation, proportional to the product of the internal voltages of the two machines, divided by the reactance. Even when calculated more rigorously, the power is increased if either internal voltage is increased. These statements hold regarding the power at any particular value of angular separation, and hence also for the maximum power. It is also true on a multimachine system that raising the internal voltages increases the power that can be transmitted between any two machines or groups of machines. Therefore, it is apparent that raising the internal voltages increases the stability limits.

Under transient conditions power is calculated with the use of the transient reactances of the synchronous machines and the voltages behind transient reactance (which, it will be recalled, are proportional to field flux linkage). Upon the occurrence of a fault, the flux linkages are initially the same as they were just before the fault occurred. During the fault, however, the flux linkages decay at a rate described by the short-circuit time constant $T_d{}'$, which is least in the event of a three-phase short circuit at the terminals of the machine and is somewhat greater for less severe types and locations of fault.

If the fault is sustained for a long time, a machine may survive the first swing of its rotor, but, because of the continued decrease of its field flux linkage, it may pull out of step on the second swing or on subsequent swings. An excitation system controlled by an automatic voltage regulator causes the flux linkage first to decrease more slowly and then to increase (see curves of $E_q{}'$ in Fig. 42 of Chapter XII). As a result, a machine which does not go out of step on the first few swings will not go out of step on subsequent swings of the same disturbance. On a more severe disturbance, however, it may pull out of step on one of the first few swings. Park and Bancker[11] state that a moderate exciter response (150 to 250 volts per second for 250-volt fields) is usually sufficient to prevent loss of synchronism on other than the first swing. They further state that the gain in stability limit due to a higher response than this is small in comparison with the gain obtainable with this value of response. In substantiation of these statements they report the results of calculations made on a water-wheel generator feeding a load center over transmission lines of three different lengths, namely, 60, 120, and 250 miles. The power which could be carried without loss of synchronism on the first swing, after the occurrence of a line-to-ground fault on the generator bus, with fast enough exciter response (about 600 volts per second) to maintain constant field linkages was found to be only from 4% to 6% greater than the power that could be carried with exciter response (150 to 200 volts per second) sufficient to prevent pullout on the second swing. Nevertheless, it is still true that the higher the speed of exciter response, the greater is the power limit.

Floyd and Sills[34] express similar conclusions regarding the necessary speed of response of excitation systems for water-wheel-driven generators, saying that, if a rate of response of 1.5 or 2.0 per unit is specified, there is a very little gain in stability over that obtained with a rate of 1.0. (See page 170 for the definition of nominal exciter response expressed in per unit.)

Back in 1928, clearing times of 30 to 60 cycles were not uncommon.

Under those conditions the action of the excitation system during a fault was an important factor in power-system stability. However, high-speed clearing of faults has become the standard practice wherever stability is critical. With short fault duration, the decrease of flux linkages during the fault is small and the effect of the excitation system on the linkages during this period is likewise small.

After the fault has been cleared and the synchronous machines are swinging apart, the armature current still has a demagnetizing effect, though a smaller effect than that during the fault. (Recall that, when the machines have swung 180° apart, the currents are the same as those caused by a three-phase fault about half-way between machines.) Therefore, even when high-speed clearing is used, the excitation system can lessen the decrease of flux linkages or — better still — cause an increase of linkages. This it can do more effectively after the fault has been cleared than before because the demagnetizing effect of the armature current is smaller. Thus the excitation system can aid transient stability appreciably even though high-speed clearing of faults is employed. The faster the excitation system responds to correct low voltage, the more effective it is in improving stability.

Concordia[47] has shown that the exciter response required to give the same stability limit as that obtained with constant flux linkage is not constant but increases with increasing switching time. In other words, the required exciter time constant decreases with the increase of switching time, as shown by the following results calculated for a 200-mile transmission system:

Switching Time (sec.)	Exciter Time Constant (sec.)
0.02	2.7
0.06	0.7
0.10	0.3

These results indicate that the effect of fault-clearing time is even more important than is indicated by the usual transient stability studies in which constant flux linkages are assumed.

In the steady state, power is calculated with the use of saturated synchronous reactances and the voltages behind these reactances (which are proportional to the respective field currents). If the voltages are constant, the power limit is reached when the phase angle between the voltages becomes 90°. An automatic voltage regulator tends to hold the terminal voltages constant. If it were entirely successful in doing so under all conditions, the power limit would be reached when the angle between terminal voltages reached 90°. In other words, the power limit would depend upon the reactance of the circuits between machines, instead of upon this (external) reactance plus the internal (synchronous) reactances. The power limit would be greatly raised by such ideal voltage regulation, particularly if the internal reactance were the major part of the total reactance.

Unfortunately, voltage regulators cannot raise the power limit to anything near the theoretical value just discussed. Even though the regulator itself acts without delay, the field circuits of the exciter and of the main generator are sluggish. Consequently, the desired restoration of voltage cannot always be obtained rapidly enough to increase the electric power in a way to match the mechanical power and thus to prevent power differentials that pull the machines out of synchronism.

It has been found by tests, however, that the use of quick-response excitation systems does raise the steady-state stability limit a substantial amount. The limit is approximately equal to that calculated on the assumption of constant voltage behind a reactance intermediate between saturated synchronous reactance and transient reactance. In other words, quick-response excitation counteracts approximately half of the armature reaction.

Stable operation with automatic voltage regulators at values of power beyond the stability limit obtainable with hand control of the excitation is termed *dynamic stability*. The excitation system, by increasing the internal voltage, must increase the synchronizing power more rapidly than the increase of angle decreases the synchronizing power. The gain in stability limit obtainable by this means is relatively great in the case of machines connected without external reactance, but is relatively small when the external reactance is large.

Although the use of quick-response excitation and voltage regulators for increasing steady-state stability was proposed as long ago as 1928,[8,9,10] they have been little used for this purpose. The reasons probably are:

1. In most cases the prudent loading of lines is determined by the transient stability limit, which is lower than the steady-state power limit.

2. The gain in steady-state stability limit ascribable to the excitation system is small if the external impedance is large, as it usually is where stability is an important factor in limiting the power transmitted.

3. Operators have been hesitant to depend upon automatic voltage regulators for stable operation at rated load.

An application of quick-response excitation for increasing the steady-state stability limit has been made to ship-propulsion systems having a synchronous generator and a synchronous motor connected through negligible external reactance.[18] By this means it was possible to use much smaller synchronous machines than could have been used otherwise.

The recent trend toward the use of turbogenerators of lower short-circuit ratio, and hence of lower inherent steady-state stability, has aroused interest in the use of quick-response excitation. Even though the generators are normally stable when operated with hand control of excitation, the use of suitable voltage regulators increases the margin of stability.

To be effective in increasing the steady-state stability limit, the excitation system should have a voltage regulator with no dead band.

Quick-response excitation, in addition to raising stability limits, diminishes the disturbance to voltage caused by such events as a short circuit, the opening of a transmission line, swinging of machines, or the disconnection of a generator; and thus it improves the quality of electric power service.

Dynamic stability is discussed further in Chapter XV.

Definitions of exciter response. In the foregoing discussion of how system stability is affected by excitation systems, the term "exciter response" was used without definition. Definitions of this term adopted by the A.I.E.E.[17] will now be quoted and commented upon.

"Exciter response is the rate of increase or decrease of the main-exciter voltage when resistance is suddenly removed from or inserted in the main-exciter field circuit," as by the action of the voltage regulator. The response may be expressed either in volts per second or in per-unit voltage per second.   In the latter case, the base voltage is not usually the rated voltage of the exciter, as might be expected, but rather the nominal collector-ring voltage of the main generator, a quantity which is defined below.   (Note that this base voltage differs from that used in the last chapter, where it was the voltage required to send through the field winding of the main generator the current required to give rated voltage on the air-gap line.)

The actual rate of response of a particular exciter varies with such circumstances as (1) speed of rotation, (2) whether the exciter is self-excited or separately excited, (3) if separately excited, its initial field-circuit voltage and resistance, (4) the initial armature voltage and current, (5) the amount of resistance cut in or out of the field circuit, and (6) the load on the exciter during build-up or build-down, a load determined not only by the characteristics of the field circuit of the main generator but also by transient field current induced by changes of the armature current of the main generator. Moreover, the rate of response during build-up is usually different from that during build-down. Even with all the foregoing conditions fixed, the response varies from instant to instant during the process of build-up or build-down.

Since the exciter response depends upon so many different factors it is necessary to define a "nominal exciter response" which is a definite quantity for a particular excitation system and thus is suitable as a basis for specifications, guarantees, and tests, as well as for approximate comparison of the effectiveness of different excitation systems.

The *nominal exciter response* is defined as the numerical value obtained when the nominal collector-ring voltage is divided into the slope, expressed in volts per second, of that straight-line voltage-time curve which begins at nominal collector-ring voltage and continues for one-half second, under which the area is the same as the area under the no-load voltage-increase-time curve of the exciter starting at the same initial voltage and continuing for the same length of time.

Nominal collector-ring voltage is the voltage required across the collector rings to generate rated kilovolt-amperes in the main machine at rated voltage, speed, frequency, and power factor, with the field winding at a temperature of 75 degrees Centigrade.[17]

When nominal exciter response is determined by test, the exciter shall be operating at normal speed and with normal rheostat and field connections. In applying the short circuit to the rheostat, only the regulating resistance, and not any permanent resistance supplied to limit the field current, shall be short-circuited.* If the exciter is separately excited, the voltage of the pilot exciter or other source of excitation shall be the same as will be used in actual operation.

The definition of nominal exciter response may be understood better by perusal of Fig. 18. The actual build-up of voltage, starting at nominal collector-ring voltage Oa, will follow a curve somewhat like aed. This curve may be determined either by test or by calculation, as explained later in this chapter. Straight line ac is drawn so that the area under it is equal to that under the actual build-up curve during the first half-second. The nominal exciter response is then the slope of line ac in volts per second, divided by Oa in volts.

The justification for this particular way of defining nominal exciter response is somewhat as follows: The time of 0.5 sec. is chosen because

---

*In the excitation system of Fig. 15, for example, both the "main-exciter field rheostat" and the "field-forcing-up resistor" would be short-circuited when testing for exciter response, but the "permanent resistance" would not be.

the time during which quick-response excitation is applied in practice is of this order of magnitude. The area under the curve during this time is used instead of the increase of voltage during the same time, because, when the exciter voltage is applied to an inductive load of negligible resistance, the change in flux produced thereby is equal to this area. In symbols,

$$\Delta\phi = \int_0^{\Delta t} e \, dt$$

The nominal response is defined for build-up, rather than build-down, because the former action is required during and immediately after

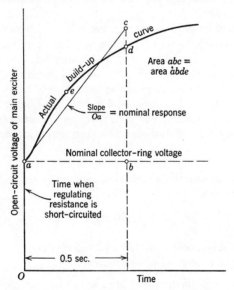

FIG. 18. Illustrating the definition of "nominal exciter response."

the presence of a fault in order to improve system stability. The definition specifies that the exciter be unloaded, because change of voltage caused by load is not great and because both test and calculation are simplified immensely by the assumption of no load.

   Ceiling voltage is the value that the open-circuit voltage of the exciter will attain ultimately if the regulating rheostat remains short-circuited.

Typical values of exciter response and of other exciter quantities. The *nominal collector-ring voltage* of the a-c. generator is usually between

72% and 95% of the rated voltage of the exciter (between 90 and 120 volts for a 125-volt exciter, or twice those values for a 250-volt exciter). As an average value, 80% (100 volts) may be taken.

The *ceiling voltage* varies considerably, but typical values are from 120% to 135% of rated voltage (150 to 165 volts for a 125-volt exciter). A considerable difference between ceiling voltage and nominal collector-ring voltage is necessary to obtain rapid build-up of the exciter voltage.

The *exciter voltage required to drive enough current in the field winding of the a-c. generator to generate rated voltage of the latter on the air-gap line* is about 37% of the rated voltage of the exciter (45 volts for a 125-volt exciter). This quantity was used as the unit of exciter voltage in the preceding chapter.

The standard value of *exciter response* is about 1.0 unit (100 volts per second for a 125-volt exciter). More rapid rates up to 2.0 units (200 volts per second) are obtainable at a small additional cost. Still faster rates up to about 5.0 units (500 volts per second) can be provided. "Superexcitation," with response as high as 6,000 to 7,000 volts per second on a 250-volt field (30 to 35 units), has been attained by employing an exciter rated at 600 volts with a ceiling of about 1,000 volts. This very high rate of response has been employed on synchronous condensers.

Quick-response excitation systems are usually characterized by the following features:

    1. An exciter having a high value of nominal response and a high ceiling voltage.

    2. A reliable mechanical drive for the exciter.

    3. A quick-acting voltage regulator.

These features will be discussed in turn.

1. Fast response of the exciter can be achieved (*a*) by subdividing the field winding into several parallel paths with external series resistance in each path in order to obtain a short time constant, and (*b*) by using separate excitation (pilot exciter). High rotational speed is helpful in achieving a short time constant. A high ceiling voltage requires an exciter of larger size than usual.

2. The importance of reliable mechanical drive for the exciter can be appreciated by considering the conditions that prevail during a fault on the main a-c. circuit. The field current of the generator undergoes an increase, induced by the sudden increase of lagging armature current. At the same time, the exciter is called upon to increase its voltage as rapidly as possible. Thus the exciter must deliver current

higher than normal at a voltage higher than normal, which means that both electrical output and mechanical input are much higher than normal. If the exciter is motor-driven, it should be noted that the motor voltage may be subnormal during the fault, thereby reducing the pullout torque of the motor. Direct drive of the exciter from the main prime mover, of course, is very reliable.*

3. If an indirect-acting exciter-rheostatic voltage regulator with high-speed field-forcing contacts is used, the time lag of the regulator in the event of a fault on the a-c. system consists of the time required for the voltage-sensitive element to close its contacts plus the time for the high-speed relay or contactor to close its contacts. This lag should be as small as possible. In present regulators it is about 3 cycles (0.05 sec.). After the regulator has short-circuited the regulating resistance in the field circuit of the exciter, there is nothing more that the regulator can do to increase the exciter response.

To insure that the regulator will act correctly for all types of short circuit, the voltage-sensitive element of the regulator should be controlled by the voltage of all phases of the three-phase circuit. Methods of accomplishing this have already been described.

If the exciter has a differential-field winding, the regulator should open it when rapid build-up is required, for otherwise it decreases the exciter response.

Calculation of exciter response — general remarks. The definition of exciter response, the importance of quick response, and some of the means of attaining it have been discussed. There remain to be treated the quantitative calculation of exciter response and whatever conclusions can be drawn from such calculations.

Exciter response is shown most completely by curves of exciter armature voltage as a function of time. Such curves for an existing exciter can be determined most easily and accurately by test. A two-element oscillograph is used, one element to record the armature voltage, the other to trace a timing wave. For an exciter not yet built, or one which it is proposed to alter, the voltage-time curve must be calculated. Thus it may be determined whether a proposed design will meet requirements or whether an existing machine can be modified to meet them. Such calculations will now be considered.

The voltage-time curves may be for either increasing or decreasing

---

*If a fault persists, the speed of a motor-driven exciter will drop. Therefore, in order to obtain equal actual response, a higher nominal exciter response is needed for a motor-driven exciter than for a direct-driven exciter, the speed of which is maintained.

voltage ("build-up" or "build-down"), but the former is more important than the latter for power-system stability. If an exciter-rheostatic voltage regulator is used, build-up is initiated by the sudden removal of resistance from the field circuit of the exciter; build-down, by the sudden insertion of resistance. The voltage-time curves may be calculated for a loaded or an unloaded exciter. Though the result for the loaded exciter is what is actually wanted, both calculation and test are much simpler for the unloaded than for the loaded exciter. Furthermore, the voltage-time curves of separately excited machines for the two conditions differ by only a few per cent. For these reasons, the build-up of voltage of unloaded exciters will be analyzed first, and that of loaded exciters will be considered later.

Response of unloaded exciter. The circuit diagrams for separate excitation and self-excitation of the main exciter are shown in Figs. 19 and 20, respectively. These diagrams also show some of the notation

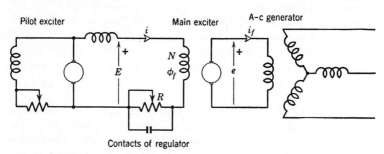

FIG. 19. Circuit diagram of separately excited exciter.

that will be used. The characteristics of the two excitation systems are considerably different from one another, particularly in their speed of response, as will appear from the analysis.

The equation of voltage around the field circuit of the main exciter, whether separately or self-excited, is:

$$N \frac{d\phi_f}{dt} + Ri = E \text{ or } e \qquad [1]$$

where N = number of field turns in series.
  ϕ_f = flux in each field core, in webers.
  R = field-circuit resistance, in ohms.
  i = field current, in amperes.
  E = pilot-exciter armature voltage.
  e = main-exciter armature e.m.f., in volts.

The equation applies to separate excitation if E is used, and to self-excitation if e is used.

If the pilot exciter is flat-compounded, its voltage E may be taken as constant. If the pilot exciter is undercompounded or shunt-wound and is conservatively applied, its armature voltage may be assumed to decrease linearly with load. This assumption is handled conveniently by taking E as a constant equal to the no-load voltage of the pilot exciter and increasing R by the proper amount to account for the linear decrease of voltage.

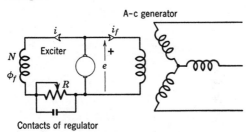

FIG. 20. Circuit diagram of self-excited exciter.

If the field winding is arranged in several parallel paths, R and i may be taken either per path or for all paths in parallel, the product Ri being the same in either case.

Equation 1 takes no cognizance of the effect of eddy currents induced in solid parts of the magnetic circuit. Eddy currents oppose, and hence retard, any change of flux. Their effect will be discussed again in the section on "Calculation of nominal exciter response."

For our present purpose it is advisable to replace ϕ_f by e, the armature voltage, because the magnetization curve of the exciter gives e versus i, rather than ϕ_f versus i. If the exciter is running at constant speed, which may be safely assumed, then the armature voltage e is proportional to the flux ϕ_a which crosses the air gap and links the armature conductors; that is,

$$e = k\phi_a \qquad [2]$$

where

$$k = \frac{Znp}{60a} \qquad [3]$$

where Z = total number of conductors on armature.

$\quad\quad n$ = speed of rotation of exciter (r.p.m.).

$\quad\quad p$ = number of poles.

$\quad\quad a$ = number of parallel paths through the armature.

a is equal to 2 for a simplex wave winding, and is equal to p for a simplex lap winding; for a multiplex winding the foregoing values are multiplied by the degree of multiplicity, that is, by 2 for a duplex winding, by 3 for a triplex winding, and so on.

Now ϕ_f, the flux linking the field winding, exceeds ϕ_a, the flux linking the armature winding, by ϕ_l, the leakage flux. The leakage flux passes from pole to pole without entering the armature iron, a large part of it passing between pole tips as shown in Fig. 21. It is feasible to treat the leakage flux according to either of two different assumptions: first, that it is proportional to the armature flux; or, second, that it is

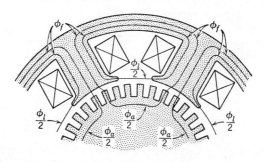

FIG. 21. Armature or air-gap flux ϕ_a, leakage flux ϕ_l, and field flux $\phi_f = \phi_a + \phi_l$.

proportional to the field current. These two assumptions would be equivalent to one another if the armature flux were proportional to the field current, that is, if there were no saturation. Saturation is present, however, as shown by the curvature of the magnetization curve; and the two different assumptions stated above differ as to the assumed effect of saturation on the leakage flux. The first assumption, namely, that the leakage flux is proportional to the armature flux, assumes that the leakage flux is affected by saturation to the same degree as is the armature flux. This probably overemphasizes the effect of saturation on the leakage flux. The leakage flux is less affected by saturation than is the armature flux because the former passes over a longer air gap than the latter does and because the highest saturation is usually found in the teeth. The second assumption, namely, that the leakage flux is proportional to the field current, assumes that the leakage flux is not affected by saturation at all. It is equivalent to assuming a constant leakage inductance. This assumption probably underestimates the effect of saturation on the leakage flux. No doubt the truth lies somewhere between the solutions obtained from these two assumptions. Because both assumptions lead to results which differ by a negligible amount, it does not matter greatly which assumption is used.

The two assumptions may be formulated algebraically as follows: According to the first assumption,

$$\phi_l = c_1\phi_a \qquad [4]$$

and since

$$\phi_f = \phi_a + \phi_l \qquad [5]$$

it follows that

$$\phi_f = (1 + c_1)\phi_a = \sigma\phi_a \qquad [6]$$

where σ is a constant known as the *coefficient of dispersion*. The value of σ must be greater than 1, and usually is in the range from 1.1 to 1.2. In other words, the leakage flux is from 10% to 20% of the useful or armature flux. According to the second assumption,

$$\phi_l = c_2 i \qquad [7]$$

and

$$\phi_f = \phi_a + c_2 i = \phi_a + \frac{L_l}{N} i \qquad [8]$$

where L_l is the leakage inductance.

If the ratio $(\sigma - 1)$ of leakage flux ϕ_l to useful flux ϕ_a is known for some point on the air-gap line of the magnetization curve having coordinates e_{ag} and i_{ag}, the leakage inductance can be computed from the relation:

$$L_l = \left(\frac{\phi_l}{\phi_a}\right)\frac{e_{ag}}{i_{ag}}\frac{N}{k} \qquad [8a]$$

Using eqs. 2 and 6, the differential equation (1) becomes

$$\frac{N\sigma}{k}\frac{de}{dt} + Ri = E \text{ or } e \qquad [9]$$

for the assumption of constant coefficient of dispersion. Using eqs. 2 and 8, it becomes

$$\frac{N}{k}\frac{de}{dt} + L_l\frac{di}{dt} + Ri = E \text{ or } e \qquad [10]$$

for the assumption of constant leakage inductance.

In eqs. 9 and 10, e is a nonlinear function of i, as given by the magnetization curve; hence eqs. 9 and 10 are differential equations with variable coefficients. For solving such equations at least four different methods are available, namely:

1. Formal integration.

2. Graphical integration.

3. Point-by-point calculation.

4. Use of differential analyzer or of other numerical computers.

These methods will now be discussed briefly.

A *solution by formal integration*[1] requires that the variable coefficients can be expressed in terms of one of the variables and that the resulting expression can be integrated by formal methods. In the case of exciter transients, this means that the magnetization curve must be represented by an empirical equation, such as the Fröhlich equation,

$$e = \frac{ai}{b+i} \qquad [11]$$

or the modified Fröhlich equation,

$$e = \frac{ai}{b+i} + ci \qquad [12]$$

in which a, b, and c are constants chosen to make the equation best fit the test data. If eq. 11 or 12 is substituted into eq. 9 or 10, the equations may be integrated by separation of variables i and t, and an explicit solution for t may be obtained.

In the *method of graphical integration*, the equation is rearranged so as to express time t as an integral. The integrand is determined by a graphical construction involving the use of the magnetization curve. It is then plotted against the independent variable, and the integral is evaluated by measuring the area under the curve. The particular methods presented in this chapter are those of R. Rüdenberg.[1,3]

In the *point-by-point calculations*, one or more of the time derivatives are usually assumed to remain constant throughout a short interval of time, their values during the interval being determined from conditions at the beginning, or preferably at the middle, of the interval. The value of a dependent variable at the end of an interval is taken as its value at the beginning of the interval plus its time derivative during the interval multiplied by the length of the interval. A variation of the point-by-point method consists in assuming an increment in one of the dependent variables and computing the corresponding increment of time. The point-by-point method is widely applicable to the solution of all kinds of transient problems — in fact, to the solution of all kinds of differential equations. The reader has already encountered applications of it to the solution of the swing equation of a machine and to the calculation of field transients in the main generator.

A *differential analyzer* is a machine for integrating and for solving differential equations.[12] Other types of numerical computers which have been developed recently, such as the relay and electronic types, can be used for the same purpose. Obviously the application of the machine-integration method is limited by the fact that in most cases no suitable computing machine is available.

Of the four methods listed for solving the differential equations of the exciter, the most useful and convenient are the solution by graphical integration and the point-by-point solution. These methods will now be described in detail, as applied to the solution of eqs. 9 and 10.

Voltage-time curves of unloaded separately excited exciter by the method of graphical integration. First, a *constant coefficient of dispersion* will be assumed, making eq. 9 applicable:

$$\frac{\sigma N}{k} \frac{de}{dt} + Ri = E \qquad [13]$$

$$\frac{\sigma N}{k} \frac{de}{dt} = E - Ri \qquad [14]$$

Build-up. Let subscripts 1 and 2 be used to denote the initial and final conditions, respectively. Thus, the armature voltage and field current build up from a point on the magnetization curve having coordinates i_1 and e_1 to a point having coordinates i_2 and e_2. Now multiply eq. 14 by e_2/E.

$$\frac{\sigma N e_2}{kE} \frac{de}{dt} = e_2 - \frac{Re_2}{E} i \qquad [15]$$

or

$$T \frac{de}{dt} = \Delta e \qquad [16]$$

where

$$T = \frac{\sigma N e_2}{kE} \qquad [17]$$

and

$$\Delta e = e_2 - \frac{Re_2}{E} i = e_2 - \frac{e_2}{i_2} i \qquad [18]$$

T is a constant having the dimensions of time and, therefore, plausibly may be called a "time constant." It should be remembered, however, that, as the build-up of neither e nor i is exponential, T cannot be given the same interpretation as the time constant of a linear circuit. T is equal to the field flux linkage divided by the field Ri drop, both being taken for the final condition. For this condition the flux linkage is

$$N\phi_{f2} = N\sigma\phi_{a2} = N\sigma\frac{e_2}{k} \qquad [19]$$

and the Ri drop is $Ri_2 = E$. The final field flux linkage may be written also as Li_2, where L is the nominal exciter field inductance, equal to the field flux linkage per unit field current at the final condition. The time constant then takes the familiar-appearing form

$$T = \frac{Li_2}{Ri_2} = \frac{L}{R} \qquad [20]$$

Δe (eq. 18) may be given the following geometric interpretation (see Fig. 22a): On the same coordinates with the magnetization curve

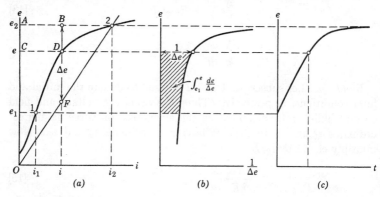

Fig. 22. Build-up of voltage of separately excited exciter, obtained by the method of graphical integration. Constant coefficient of dispersion is assumed.

draw a straight line through the origin and the final operating point i_2, e_2. The slope of this line is $e_2/i_2 = Re_2/E$, and for any given abscissa i the ordinate of the line is

$$\frac{e_2}{i_2}i = \frac{e_2}{E}Ri \qquad [21]$$

Δe is then the vertical distance from this line up to the horizontal line drawn through the intersection of this line and the magnetization curve. By eq. 16, the rate of change of armature voltage e is proportional to Δe.

Solving eq. 16 for t, we obtain

$$t = T\int_{e_1}^{e}\frac{de}{\Delta e} \qquad [22]$$

which gives the time required for the voltage to build up from its initial value e_1 to any value e. The integral may be evaluated graphically by plotting $1/\Delta e$ as a function of e and measuring the area between the curve and the e axis between the lower limit e_1 and a running upper limit e.

The whole process of graphical solution is illustrated in Fig. 22. In Fig. 22a the magnetization curve is drawn, and on the same axes there is drawn a sloping straight line $O2$ through the origin and the final operating point 2 on the magnetization curve, and also a horizontal

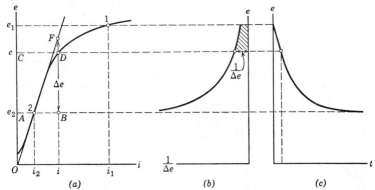

FIG. 23. Build-down of voltage of separately excited exciter, obtained by the method of graphical integration. Constant coefficient of dispersion is assumed.

straight line $A2$ through the final operating point. The value of Δe corresponding to any given value of e is then found as the distance FDB from the sloping line $O2$ to the horizontal line $A2$ along a vertical line through point D which lies on the magnetization curve at ordinate $e = OC$. Corresponding values of e and Δe are tabulated. The reciprocal of Δe is calculated and plotted versus e, as shown in Fig. 22b. The shaded area is measured for various values of e. This area, multiplied by T, gives the value of t corresponding to e, and e is plotted against t in Fig. 22c.

In order to allow for the retarding effect of eddy currents in the iron upon build-up, T may be increased by an empirical amount.

Build-down. Build-down is handled in exactly the same manner as build-up. The process is illustrated in Fig. 23. The sloping line $O2$ is again drawn through the final operating point, but is steeper than before. Δe is now a negative quantity. The time constant T is smaller than it was for build-up, because e_2 is smaller (see eq. 17).

Constant leakage inductance. If constant leakage inductance is assumed instead of constant coefficient of dispersion, the analysis is slightly different. Equation 10, which holds for this case, may be written thus:

$$\frac{N}{k}\frac{d}{dt}\left(e + \frac{L_l k}{N}i\right) = E - Ri \qquad [23]$$

$$\frac{N}{k}\frac{d}{dt}(e + e') = E - Ri \qquad [24]$$

where

$$e' = \frac{L_l k}{N}i \qquad [25]$$

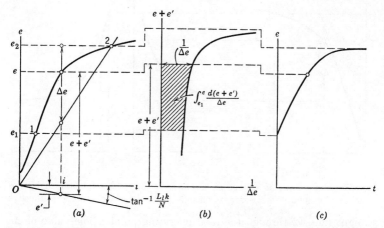

FIG. 24. Build-up of voltage of separately excited exciter, obtained by the method of graphical integration with the assumption of constant leakage inductance.

Multiply eq. 24 by e_2/E, obtaining

$$\frac{Ne_2}{kE}\frac{d}{dt}(e + e') = e_2 - \frac{Re_2}{E}i \qquad [26]$$

$$T\frac{d}{dt}(e + e') = \Delta e \qquad [27]$$

$$t = T\int_{e_1}^{e}\frac{d(e + e')}{\Delta e} \qquad [28]$$

where

$$T = \frac{Ne_2}{kE} \qquad [29]$$

$$\Delta e = e_2 - \frac{Re_2}{E}i \qquad [30]$$

EXAMPLE 1   183

T is now defined differently than it was for the analysis based on constant coefficient of dispersion, but Δe is the same.

Equation 28 is solved graphically by the process shown in Fig. 24. As shown in Fig. 24a, e' is represented by the distance between the i axis and the straight line having a slope $-L_l k/N$. In Fig. 24b, $1/\Delta e$ is plotted against $e + e'$. In all other respects the process is the same as that used for constant coefficient of dispersion.

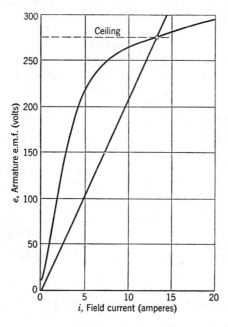

FIG. 25. Magnetization curve of exciter (Examples 1 and 2).

EXAMPLE 1

The following data pertain to an exciter:

Rated voltage	250 volts
Rated output	100 kw.
Rated speed (n)	1,800 r.p.m.
Number of poles (p)	6
Type of armature winding	simplex lap
Number of armature slots	108
Number of conductors per slot	4
Coefficient of dispersion (σ)	1.15

Shunt wound

Number of field turns per pole	1,500
Number of field circuits	1
Field resistance	14.6 ohms

The magnetization curve is given in Fig. 25.

The exciter is operating without load and is separately excited from a 250-volt source. Initially the field circuit is open. It is then closed through such resistance as to give an ultimate voltage of 275. Plot armature voltage and field current as functions of time. Increase the time constant by 5% to allow for the effect of eddy currents in the yoke.

TABLE 1

CALCULATION OF BUILD-UP OF VOLTAGE OF
SEPARATELY EXCITED EXCITER (EXAMPLE 1)

e (volts)	$\dfrac{e_2}{i_2} i$ (volts)	Δe (volts)	$\dfrac{1}{\Delta e}$ (kv.$^{-1}$)
7	0	275	3.64
50	20	255	3.92
100	38	237	4.22
150	59	216	4.63
200	87	188	5.31
230	119	156	6.41
250	159	116	8.62
260	187	88	11.35
270	240	35	28.6
273	260	15	67
275	275	0	∞

Solution. The time constant is given by eq. 17, in which k is given by eq. 3. Here

Z = total number of conductors on armature = 108 slots × 4 conductors per slot = 432.

a = number of parallel paths in armature, which for simplex lap winding is equal to the number of poles. Hence $a = 6$.

$$k = \frac{Znp}{60a} = \frac{432 \times 1,800 \times 6}{60 \times 6} = 12,960$$

The time constant, without correction for eddy currents, is (by eq. 17)

$$T' = \frac{\sigma Ne_2}{kE} = \frac{1.15 \times (1,500 \times 6) \times 275}{12,960 \times 250} = 0.879 \text{ sec.}$$

Increase this value by 5% to allow for the effect of eddy currents.

$$T = 1.05 \times 0.879 = 0.922 \text{ sec.}$$

EXAMPLE 1   185

TABLE 2

CALCULATION OF BUILD-UP OF VOLTAGE OF
SEPARATELY EXCITED EXCITER (EXAMPLE 1), CONT'D.

e (volts)	Area $\int \dfrac{de}{\Delta e}$	t (sec.)	i (amp.)
7	0	0	0
20	0.05	0.05	0.4
50	0.16	0.15	1.0
80	0.28	0.26	1.5
100	0.36	0.34	1.9
130	0.49	0.45	2.5
150	0.58	0.54	3.0
180	0.73	0.67	3.6
200	0.83	0.77	4.3
220	0.94	0.87	5.2
230	1.00	0.92	5.8
240	1.07	0.99	6.5
250	1.15	1.06	7.7
260	1.24	1.15	9.0
270	1.41	1.30	11.7
273	1.52	1.41	12.5
275	∞	∞	13.2

In Fig. 25 the final operating point is indicated by a small circle on the magnetization curve at the specified ceiling voltage of 275. The corresponding field current is 13.2 amp. A straight line is drawn through this point and the origin. The field-circuit resistance is $250/13.2 = 18.9$ ohms, of which $18.9 - 14.6 = 4.3$ ohms is added externally.

Corresponding to arbitrarily chosen values of e ranging from 0 to 275 volts, the values of Δe are read from Fig. 25 by the construction indicated in Fig. 22a. These values of Δe are entered in Table 1, and the values of $1/\Delta e$ are computed and tabulated there. In Fig. 26, $1/\Delta e$ is plotted versus e and the graphical determination of

$$\int_{e_1}^{e} \frac{de}{\Delta e}$$

is carried out by counting squares. The areas so determined are entered in Table 2. These values, multiplied by $T = 0.922$ sec., give the value of t corresponding to e. The corresponding value of i is read from the magnetization curve (Fig. 25) and entered in Table 2. In Fig. 27, e and i are plotted as functions of t. Note that the curve of e versus t is *almost straight* until the ceiling voltage is nearly reached.

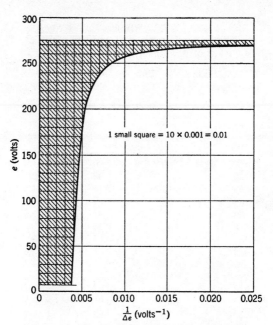

Fig. 26. Graphical integration (Example 1).

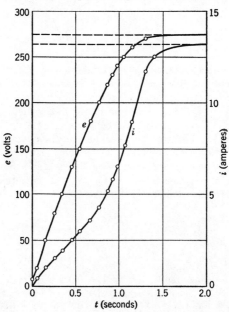

Fig. 27. Build-up of armature voltage and field current of separately excited exciter (Example 1).

Voltage-time curves of unloaded self-excited exciter by the method of graphical integration. Assuming a *constant coefficient of dispersion*, eq. 9 holds:

$$\frac{\sigma N}{k}\frac{de}{dt} + Ri = e \tag{31}$$

$$\frac{\sigma N}{k}\frac{de}{dt} = e - Ri \tag{32}$$

$$T\frac{de}{dt} = \Delta e \tag{33}$$

$$t = T\int_{e_1}^{e}\frac{de}{\Delta e} \tag{34}$$

where

$$T = \frac{\sigma N}{k} \tag{35}$$

$$\Delta e = e - Ri \tag{36}$$

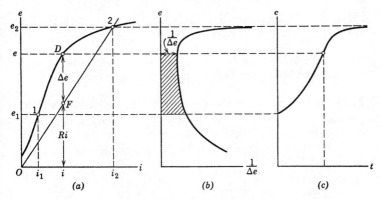

FIG. 28. Build-up of voltage of self-excited exciter, obtained by the method of graphical integration. Constant coefficient of dispersion is assumed.

Time constant T for the self-excited machine is different from those previously used for the separately excited machine (eqs. 17 and 29) in that it is independent of the final value of armature voltage. Hence the same value of T applies both to build-up and to build-down.

The graphical interpretation of Δe is shown in Fig. 28a. It is the vertical distance from point F on the "field-resistance line" $O2$ (drawn from the origin to the final operating point) to point D on the magnetization curve. The abscissa of both points represents the field current i, while the ordinate of point D represents the armature voltage e for the particular operating condition.

Figure 28 shows the whole process of finding the build-up of voltage graphically. Except for the values of T and Δe, this process is like that used for the separately excited machine. Note that Δe is small at first, increases to a maximum, and then decreases to zero. This is reflected in the slope of the voltage-time curve (Fig. 28c), which has a different shape from that for separate excitation (Fig. 22c).

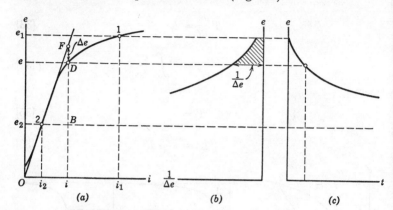

FIG. 29. Build-down of voltage of self-excited exciter, obtained by the method of graphical integration. Constant coefficient of dispersion is assumed.

Figure 29 illustrates the procedure for finding the build-down curve. Δe is again represented by the distance FD from the field-resistance line to the magnetization curve, but is now negative.

Constant leakage inductance. With this assumption, eq. 24 holds if E is replaced by e.

$$\frac{N}{k} \frac{d}{dt} (e + e') = e - Ri \qquad [37]$$

$$T \frac{d}{dt} (e + e') = \Delta e \qquad [38]$$

$$t = T \int_{e_1}^{e} \frac{d(e + e')}{\Delta e} \qquad [39]$$

where

$$T = \frac{N}{k} \qquad [40]$$

$$\Delta e = e - Ri \qquad [41]$$

EXAMPLE 2   189

The graphical solution is performed with e' represented as in Fig. 24, but Δe determined as in Figs. 28 and 29.

EXAMPLE 2

The exciter described in Example 1 is operated at no load with self-excitation. Plot curves showing armature voltage and field current versus time. The initial and final values are to be the same as in Example 1.

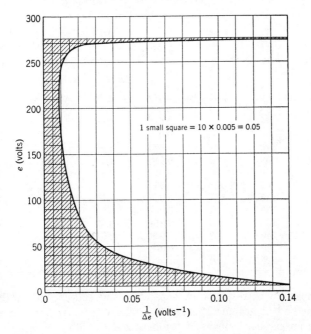

1 small square = 10 × 0.005 = 0.05

FIG. 30. Graphical integration (Example 2).

Solution. For self-excitation the time constant is given by eq. 35. As in Example 1, this value will be increased by 5% to allow for the retarding effect of eddy currents,

$$T = 1.05\frac{\sigma N}{k} = \frac{1.05 \times 1.15 \times 9{,}000}{12{,}960} = 0.840 \text{ sec.} \qquad (a)$$

Values of Δe are read from Fig. 25 according to the construction shown in Fig. 28a and are listed in Table 3. In Fig. 30 $1/\Delta e$ is plotted against e and the areas are measured by counting squares and are entered in Table 3. These areas, multiplied by $T = 0.840$ sec., give the value of t corresponding to e. Values of i corresponding to e are read from the magnetization curve

(Fig. 25). In Fig. 31 e and i are plotted against t. The values of e and i for separate excitation are plotted in the same figure for comparison. It is evident that separate excitation gives much faster build-up of e and i than self-excitation does, particularly at the low values of e.

TABLE 3

CALCULATION OF BUILD-UP OF ARMATURE VOLTAGE AND FIELD CURRENT
OF SELF-EXCITED EXCITER (EXAMPLE 2)

e (volts)	Ri (volts)	Δe (volts)	$\dfrac{1}{\Delta e}$ (volt^{-1})	Area	t (sec.)	i (amp.)
7	0	7	0.143	0	0	0
10	2	8	0.125	0.36	0.30	
20	9	11	0.091	1.39	1.17	0.4
30	13	17	0.059	2.12	1.78	
40	18	22	0.045	2.62	2.20	
50	20	30	0.033	3.00	2.52	1.0
70	26	44	0.023	3.56	2.99	
100	38	62	0.016	4.12	3.46	1.9
150	59	91	0.011	4.78	4.01	3.0
200	87	113	0.009	5.25	4.40	4.3
230	119	111	0.009	5.52	4.64	5.8
250	159	91	0.011	5.72	4.80	7.7
260	187	73	0.014	5.85	4.91	9.0
270	240	30	0.033	6.05	5.08	11.7
273	260	13	0.077			
275	275	0	∞			13.2

Comparison of response of separately and self-excited machines. The method of graphical integration which has just been described affords an excellent means of comparing the exciter response for the two different kinds of excitation. If, in making the comparison, we assume constant coefficient of dispersion, the response is given, for either kind of excitation, according to eqs. 16 and 33, by

$$\frac{de}{dt} = \frac{\Delta e}{T} \qquad [42]$$

In this expression both Δe and T are defined differently for separate excitation than for self-excitation.

The time constant is defined as

$$T = \frac{\sigma N}{k} \qquad \text{for self-excitation (eq. 35)}$$

and as

$$T = \frac{\sigma N}{k} \cdot \frac{e_2}{E} \qquad \text{for separate excitation (eq. 17)}$$

The former is fixed by the design of the exciter, whereas the latter can be controlled by the external circuit. It is possible to raise the pilot-exciter voltage E without changing the ceiling voltage (which, for build-up, is e_2), provided the field-circuit resistance R is increased

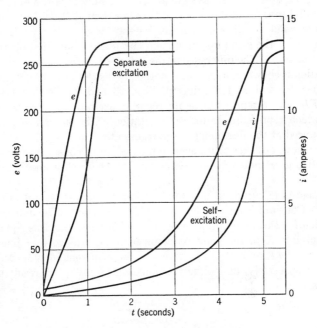

FIG. 31. Build-up of armature voltage e and field current i of separately and self-excited exciters (Examples 1 and 2).

in proportion to E. This can be done by the addition of external series resistance. By this means the resistance of the field circuit is increased without changing its inductance; hence the time constant L/R is decreased. During build-down the difference between the two time constants is still more pronounced, as then, for separate excitation, e_2/E is very small.

It is apparent that separate excitation has an advantage over self-excitation in the possibility of decreasing the time constant by external means. The chief difference between the two kinds of excitation, however, is not in the factor T, but in Δe of eq. 42. The latter quantity is defined as

$$\Delta e = e_2 - \frac{e_2}{i_2} i \qquad \text{for separate excitation (eq. 18)}$$

and as

$$\Delta e = e - \frac{e_2}{i_2} i \qquad \text{for self-excitation (eq. 36)}$$

During build-up e_2 is always greater than e, since it is the final value of e; and during build-down e_2 is always less than e. In either case the absolute value of Δe is greater for separate excitation than for self-excitation, if the same magnetization curve and same final operating point are used. The difference in the values of Δe for the two kinds of excitation is shown more vividly by the graphs than by the equations; see Figs. 22 and 28 for build-up, Figs. 23 and 29 for build-down. Line FB, which represents Δe for separate excitation, is greater than FD, which represents Δe for self-excitation. The difference is most pronounced at the beginning of the transient.

It is now obvious that, even for equal time constants, separate excitation gives much faster exciter response than self-excitation does.

Voltage-time curves of unloaded exciter by point-by-point calculation.[13] Constant leakage inductance will be assumed. The differential equation for this assumption is eq. 10. In order to put this equation into suitable form for point-by-point solution, replace the time derivatives, de/dt and di/dt, by ratios of finite increments, $\Delta e/\Delta t$ and $\Delta i/\Delta t$, respectively, and solve the equation for Δt. The result is as follows:

$$\Delta t = \frac{(N/K)\Delta e + L_l \Delta i}{E \text{ (or } e) - Ri} \qquad [43]$$

It is used in the following way. The ordinates of the magnetization curve are divided into increments Δe, which may be taken as 10 volts each for a 250-volt exciter.* For each value of e, the corresponding value of i is read from the magnetization curve and tabulated. The difference between successive values gives Δi. For i in the denominator, and also for e in the case of self-excitation, the average values for the interval (half the sum of the two end values) are used. With all quantities in the right-hand member of eq. 43 known, Δt is calculated. It denotes the time required for the armature voltage to change by an

---

*Δe now signifies the increment of e during a time interval Δt. It should not be confused with the Δe used in the method of graphical integration.

amount Δe. The curve of voltage versus time can be plotted from the increments of voltage and time, starting at zero time with the known initial value of voltage. The first and last intervals may have different values of Δe from the others; there is no necessity for using equal values throughout.

The advantage of assuming Δe and calculating Δt, instead of the reverse, is that by so doing the average values of e and i for the interval are easily determined. The use of average values, instead of values at the beginning of an interval, greatly reduces the cumulative error.

If constant coefficient of dispersion is assumed instead of constant leakage inductance, eq. 9 yields

$$\Delta t = \frac{(\sigma N/K)\Delta e}{E \text{ (or } e) - Ri} \qquad [44]$$

which is solved in the manner just described except that Δi need not be found.

Calculation of nominal exciter response. The methods of obtaining a voltage-time curve of an unloaded exciter by test and by two kinds of calculation have been described. After such a curve has been obtained for voltage build-up starting at the nominal collector-ring voltage of the main machine, the nominal exciter response is easily calculated by reference to the definition. First it is necessary to obtain the area under the curve during the first half-second. This area may be measured by a planimeter or found by counting squares on the graph paper. If the curve has been calculated by the point-by-point method, the area under it is readily calculated by summing the products of each Δt by the average value of voltage e for the interval.

It is necessary next to find the slope of that straight line under which the area during 0.5 sec. is equal to the area under the voltage-time curve during the same time. In Fig. 18 this line is ac. Let its slope be called m.

$$m = \frac{bc}{ab} = \frac{bc}{0.5} = 2bc \qquad [45]$$

since $ab = 0.5$ sec. If the areas under the line and under the curve are equal, they will still be equal if the area of the rectangle below nominal collector-ring voltage is subtracted from each. Let the remaining area $abdea$ under the curve and above this voltage be denoted by A. Line ac must be determined so that the area of triangle abc is equal to A. The area of the triangle is half the product of base and altitude.

Hence

$$A = \tfrac{1}{2}(ab)(bc) \qquad [46]$$

Since $ab = 0.5$ sec.,

$$A = \tfrac{1}{2}(0.5)(bc) = \frac{bc}{4} \qquad [47]$$

$$bc = 4A \qquad [48]$$

When this value of bc is substituted into eq. 45, the slope is given in terms of the area as

$$m = 8A \qquad [49]$$

It is not necessary actually to draw line ac, because its slope can be found by measuring area $abdea$ under the exciter build-up curve, and multiplying it by 8.

Finally, the nominal exciter response is the slope thus found divided by nominal collector-ring voltage.   In Fig. 18,

$$\text{Nominal exciter response} = \frac{8 \times \text{area } abdea \text{ in volt-seconds}}{\text{length } Oa \text{ in volts}} \qquad [50]$$

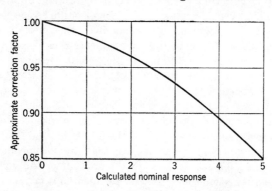

FIG. 32.   Correction factors for the effect of eddy currents on nominal exciter response.   (W. A. Lewis, *Elec. Jour.*[13])

Correction for the screening effect of eddy currents.[13]   If the voltage-time curve was found by calculation in which the effect of eddy currents was neglected, the calculated nominal response will be too high. It should be corrected for the effect of eddy currents by multiplying the uncorrected value of nominal response by a correction factor read from Fig. 32.   The correction factors plotted there were found by

EXAMPLE 3   195

comparison of calculated values with values found by test on exciters with rolled steel frames and laminated pole pieces. The effect of eddy currents on the response of such exciters is seen to be small except at high values of response. If the no-load saturation curve is obtained by test, the accuracy of the calculated nominal response after application of the correction factor can be expected to be within ±5% of the value found by test. Note that the correction factors apply only to the over-all effect of eddy currents on nominal response, not to individual ordinates of the voltage-time curve. The shape of this curve as found by test may differ greatly from the corresponding calculated curve.

EXAMPLE 3

Calculate the nominal response of the exciter described as follows:

Rated output	167 kw.
Rated voltage	250
Rated speed	1,200 r.p.m.
Number of poles	6
Number of field turns per pole	1,450
Number of parallel paths of field	3
Field resistance per path at 75 C.	27 ohms
$k = e/\phi_a$	10,080
Leakage flux/useful flux on the air-gap line $= \sigma - 1$	0.15
No-load saturation curve	see Fig. 33

when used with an a-c. generator having a

Nominal collector-ring voltage	190

The following data pertain to external apparatus in the field circuit of the exciter:

External resistance (for all paths)	11.6 ohms
Separate excitation	
Voltage of pilot exciter	250

NOTE: This example is taken from an article by W. A. Lewis in the *Electric Journal*[13] by permission.

Solution. In contrast with Examples 1 and 2, this example will be computed by the point-by-point method and under the assumption of constant leakage inductance.

To find the leakage inductance L_l use eq. 8a and the fact that the leakage flux is 15% of the useful flux at any point on the air-gap line (straight part of the saturation curve). Take the point (marked in Fig. 33) $e_{ag} = 100$ volts,

$i_{ag} = 0.82$ amp. per path.   The number of turns in series is

$$N = \frac{1,450 \text{ turns per pole} \times 6 \text{ poles}}{3 \text{ parallel paths}} = 2,900 \text{ turns per path} \quad (a)$$

$$\frac{N}{k} = \frac{2,900}{10,800} = 0.288 \text{ sec.} \quad (b)$$

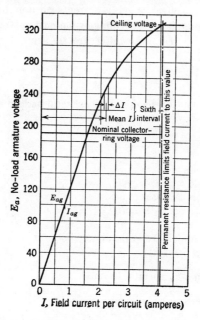

FIG. 33.   No-load saturation curve of exciter (Example 3).   (*Reprinted from Ref. 13 by permission.*)

The leakage inductance is

$$L_l = \left(\frac{\phi_l}{\phi_a}\right)\frac{e_{ag}}{i_{ag}}\frac{N}{k} = 0.15\,\frac{100}{0.82} \times 0.288 = 5.27 \text{ henrys per path} \quad (c)$$

The field-circuit resistance per path is

$$R = 27 + (3 \times 11.6) = 27 + 34.8 = 61.8 \text{ ohms} \quad (d)$$

Point-by-point computation is performed as indicated by eq. 43, which becomes:

$$\Delta t = \frac{(N/k)\Delta e + L_l \Delta i}{E - Ri} = \frac{0.288\,\Delta e + 5.27\,\Delta i}{250 - 61.8i} \quad (e)$$

EXAMPLE 3   197

The response curve is computed in Table 4, columns 1 through 11. Figure 33 shows how Δi and the mean i are found for the sixth interval (e, 240 to 250 volts). The computed response curve is drawn in Fig. 34.

The area under the response curve and above 190 volts for 0.5 sec. is computed in columns 12 and 13 of Table 4. Since the last interval (310 to

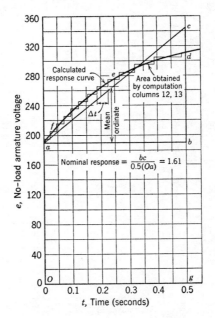

FIG. 34. Computed response curve of exciter (Example 3). (*Reprinted from Ref. 13 by permission.*)

320 volts) runs from $t = 0.488$ to 0.666 sec., it is necessary to divide it into two parts at $t = 0.500$ sec. From the response curve (Fig. 34), the corresponding value of e is 311 volts. The area is $A = 38.3$ volt-sec.

The slope of straight line ac (Fig. 34) under which the area is equal to that under the response curve is, by eq. 49,

$$m = 8A = 8 \times 38.3 = 306 \text{ volts per second} \qquad (f)$$

The nominal exciter response is

$$\frac{306}{190} = 1.61 \text{ units} \qquad (g)$$

Application of the correction factor 0.97 read from Fig. 32 gives:

$$\text{Nominal response} = 1.61 \times 0.97 = 1.57 \text{ units} \qquad (h)$$

TABLE 4

COMPUTATION OF EXCITER RESPONSE. EXCITER: 167 Kw., 250 Volts, 1,200 R.P.M., Six Poles (Example 3)

1	2	3	4	5	6	7	8	9	10	11	12	13
					Calculation of Response Curve						Calculation of Area	
e	i	Δi	$L_d \Delta i$ $5.27 \times$ Col. 3	$(N/k)\Delta e$ 0.288×10	Numerator Col. 4 + Col. 5	Mean i	$R \times$ (Mean i) $61.8 \times$ Col. 7	$E - Ri$ $250-$ Col. 8	Δt Col. 6 $\div$ Col. 9	t Σ Col. 10	Mean Ordinate	ΔA Col. 10 $\times$ Col. 12
190	1.57											
200	1.66	0.09	0.47	2.88	3.35	1.62	100	150	0.022	0.022	5	0.1
210	1.76	0.10	0.53	2.88	3.41	1.71	106	144	0.024	0.046	15	0.4
220	1.87	0.11	0.58	2.88	3.46	1.82	113	137	0.025	0.071	25	0.6
230	1.97	0.10	0.53	2.88	3.41	1.92	119	131	0.026	0.097	35	0.9
240	2.08	0.11	0.58	2.88	3.46	2.03	125	125	0.028	0.125	45	1.3
250	2.21	0.13	0.69	2.88	3.57	2.15	133	117	0.031	0.156	55	1.7
260	2.36	0.15	0.79	2.88	3.67	2.29	142	108	0.034	0.190	65	2.2
270	2.52	0.16	0.84	2.88	3.72	2.44	151	99	0.038	0.228	75	2.9
280	2.70	0.18	0.95	2.88	3.83	2.61	161	89	0.043	0.271	85	3.7
290	2.91	0.21	1.11	2.88	3.99	2.81	174	76	0.053	0.324	95	5.0
300	3.16	0.25	1.32	2.88	4.20	3.04	188	62	0.068	0.392	105	7.1
310	3.45	0.29	1.53	2.88	4.41	3.31	204	46	0.096	0.488	115	11.0
320	3.78	0.33	1.74	2.88	4.62	3.62	224	26	0.178	0.666	125	
311 320		Final interval (310 to 320 volts) divided into two parts							0.012 0.166	0.500	120	1.4 $\overline{38.3}$ Total area

Voltage-time curve of unloaded exciter having rotating-amplifier e.m.f. in series with its shunt-field circuit. The circuit diagram for this type of excitation is shown in Fig. 35. The equation of voltages around the closed path is

$$N \frac{d\phi_f}{dt} + Ri = e + E \qquad [51]$$

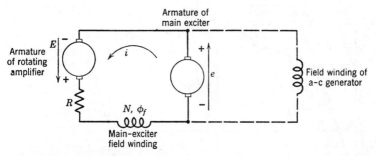

Fig. 35. Circuit diagram of rotating-amplifier pilot exciter in series with shunt-field circuit of main exciter.

E, the armature e.m.f. of the rotating amplifier, is positive when boosting e, the armature e.m.f. of the main exciter. If constant coefficient of dispersion is assumed, this equation becomes:

$$\frac{\sigma N}{k} \cdot \frac{de}{dt} = e - (Ri - E) \qquad [52]$$

or, abbreviating as in eq. 33,

$$T \frac{de}{dt} = \Delta e \qquad [53]$$

where

$$T = \frac{\sigma N}{k} \qquad [54]$$

as before (eq. 35), but

$$\Delta e = e - (Ri - E) \qquad [55]$$

which differs from the previous expressions for Δe. The graphical representation of the new Δe is given in Fig. 36a. Here the curve of e versus i is the magnetization curve of the main exciter, as before. The curves of $Ri - E$ versus i are straight lines parallel to the field resistance line Ri but displaced vertically a distance E representing the e.m.f. of the rotating-amplifier pilot exciter. This displacement is downward if the pilot exciter is boosting; upward, if bucking.

Δe is the vertical distance between the magnetization curve and the straight line $Ri - E$.

Assume that the field rheostat is adjusted so that, with no e.m.f. in the pilot exciter, the e.m.f. of the main exciter is e_0. Then the straight line through the origin and intersecting the magnetization

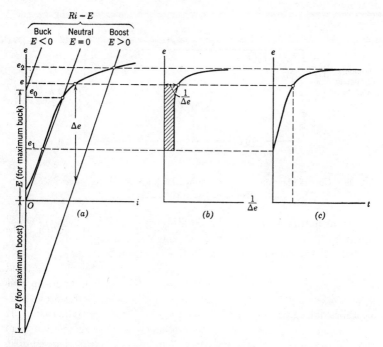

Fig. 36. Build-up of voltage of exciter having armature of pilot exciter in series with the shunt-field circuit of the main exciter (Fig. 35). Method of graphical integration, with coefficient of dispersion assumed constant.

curve at ordinate e_0 is the field resistance line. Assume, further, that the initial main-exciter voltage is e_1, the maintenance of which requires a small bucking voltage from the pilot exciter. Suppose that some disturbance, such as a short-circuit, lowers the voltage of the a-c. generator so much that the pilot-exciter voltage goes to full boost in order to build up the voltage of the main exciter as rapidly as possible, and remains at full boost until ceiling voltage e_2 is reached. According to this assumption, E remains constant during the build-up process and, hence, the line $Ri - E$ is fixed. The process of graphical integration is conducted as already described except for the manner of determining Δe. That is, $1/\Delta e$ is plotted against e, as shown in Fig. 36b, and the area multiplied by T represents the time of build-up. In the case shown, the field resistance line is almost parallel to the straight part of the magnetization curve. As a result, Δe is almost constant, and the curve of e versus t is almost linear until saturation is reached.

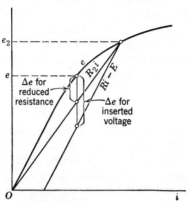

FIG. 37. Comparison of Δe for build-up caused by insertion of series voltage in shunt-field circuit of main exciter with Δe for build-up caused by reduction of the resistance of that circuit.

Figure 37 compares Δe for the excitation system being considered with Δe for a system previously considered, in which build-up was caused by reduction of the resistance of the shunt-field circuit of a self-excited exciter, the ceiling voltage being the same in both cases. It is clear that Δe is greater for insertion of series boosting voltage from the rotating amplifier than it is for reduction of the field resistance. Since the time constant is the same in both cases, the build-up is more rapid with the rotating amplifier.

Rapid build-down can also be obtained with the rotating amplifier, the line $Ri - E$ of Fig. 36a being elevated initially to maximum buck. However, the bucking voltage decreases as the alternating voltage comes near the correct value. A similar decrease of boost voltage occurs during build-ups in which correct alternating voltage is approached.

The calculation of exciter voltage versus time by the method of graphical integration has been outlined. Point-by-point calculation may be used instead, in which case eq. 52 is rewritten in the form

$$\Delta t = \frac{(\sigma N/k)\,\Delta e}{e + E - Ri} \qquad [56]$$

in which Δe is the change of e in time interval Δt. The point-by-point calculation is similar to that already described and illustrated.

Exciter with two or more field windings. We have discussed the calculation of build-up of exciter voltage in an exciter having combined self- and separate excitation voltages applied to the same field winding. Other types of exciters have two or more field windings, one of which is self-excited, while one or more others are separately excited. We will now discuss the two-field exciter with the aid of certain simplifying assumptions.[46] First, saturation will be neglected, with the result that the armature e.m.f. e is a linear function of the two field currents i_a and i_b, thus:

$$e = A_a R_a i_a + A_b R_b i_b \qquad [57]$$

where A_a and A_b are the steady-state voltage gains and R_a and R_b are the resistances of the field circuits. Second, it will be assumed that the same flux ϕ links both field windings. This is very nearly true because both are wound on the same pole cores. The applied voltages e_a and e_b are consumed in the resistive and inductive drops:

$$e_a = R_a i_a + N_a \frac{d\phi}{dt} \qquad [58]$$

$$e_b = R_b i_b + N_b \frac{d\phi}{dt} \qquad [59]$$

Solution of eqs. 57, 58, and 59 for $d\phi/dt$ yields:

$$\frac{d\phi}{dt} = \frac{A_a e_a + A_b e_b - e}{A_a N_a + A_b N_b} \qquad [60]$$

Assuming a constant coefficient of dispersion,

$$e = \frac{k\phi}{\sigma} \qquad [61]$$

we obtain:

$$\frac{de}{dt} = \frac{A_a e_a + A_b e_b - e}{(\sigma/k)(A_a N_a + A_b N_b)} = \frac{\Delta e}{T_a + T_b} \qquad [62]$$

The rate of increase of exciter armature voltage is, as before, equal to an accelerating voltage Δe divided by a time constant. The accelerating voltage is the difference between a linear combination of the voltages applied to the two field windings and the instantaneous armature voltage. *The time constant is the sum of the time constants*

*of the two field circuits separately** (including external resistance but
with external inductance assumed negligible). It is shown in Ref. 46
that the time constant of each field winding is approximately proportional to the volume of that winding; hence the sum of the time constants of two windings will be almost equal to the time constant of a
single field winding occupying the same space. Equation 62 also shows
that two applied field voltages are additive, very much as if they were
connected in series. Thus we see that it makes little difference in the
response of the machine whether the two voltages are applied to
separate windings or, in series, to the same winding.

If a more exact analysis is required, the build-up of exciter voltage
can be calculated point by point without the necessity of the two
simplifying assumptions which were made in the foregoing approximate
analysis.

If the self-excitation is furnished by a series field instead of a shunt
field, it is clear that the exciter cannot be considered to be unloaded:
the field circuit of the a-c. generator must be taken into account.

Response of loaded exciter. The terminal voltage of a loaded
exciter differs from the voltage of the unloaded exciter with the same
field current because of the effects of armature resistance (including
brush drop), armature inductance, and armature reaction. Of these,
resistance and reaction are the most important. The effect of armature
inductance is negligible at the low rates of change of armature current
which are encountered during build-up and build-down. Modern
exciters have interpoles and the brushes are set on neutral. Consequently there is no magnetizing or demagnetizing armature reaction.
There is, however, a cross-magnetizing armature reaction, which has
a demagnetizing effect unless the machine has a compensating winding.

The demagnetizing effect of cross-magnetizing armature reaction
can be explained as follows: The combined m.m.f. of field and armature
currents varies linearly from one side of a pole to the other. Over one
half of the width of the pole the armature m.m.f. augments the field
m.m.f., while over the other half the armature m.m.f. subtracts from
the field m.m.f. As a result, the flux density is increased on half the
area of each pole face and is decreased on the other half. However,
because of saturation, the decrease on one half exceeds the increase on
the other half, and there is a net decrease of flux.

The effect of both armature resistance and armature reaction is to
decrease the exciter response during build-up, especially that of a self-

*It was shown in Chapter XII that, for two coupled circuits having a little leak-
age, there is also a second, very short, time constant.

excited exciter. This fact will be demonstrated by the analysis which follows:

When a fault occurs on the armature circuit of the main (a-c.) generator, the field current of this generator is increased suddenly to an abnormally high value, which, flowing through the exciter armature, produces considerable resistance and reaction drop. This high value

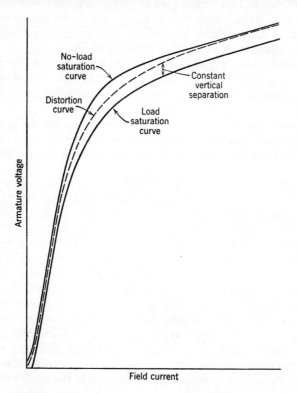

FIG. 38. Saturation curves for constant armature current.

of armature current may be assumed to remain substantially constant during most of the period of exciter build-up, not only because of the long time constant of the main-generator field but also because of the bolstering effect of the exciter build-up. By assumption of constant armature current during build-up, the analysis is facilitated.

If the armature current of the exciter is constant, the inductive drop is zero, the armature resistance drop and brush drop are constant, and the effect of armature reaction on the armature voltage is a function of saturation — hence of the field current. The combined effect of the several drops can be found by test. The results are plotted as a load saturation curve, or curve of armature terminal voltage versus field current under the condition of constant armature current (see Fig. 38). By addition of the constant resistance and brush drops to the ordinates of the load saturation curve, another curve is derived showing the internal voltage, or voltage generated by the air-gap flux, as a function of field current. The last curve is called the "distortion curve." Its abscissas exceed those of the no-load saturation curve by the amount of armature reaction. This amount is not constant, even though the armature current is constant, but varies with the curvature of the no-load saturation curve and is greatest in the vicinity of the knee.

Under the assumption of constant armature current, the voltage-time curve of a loaded exciter can be calculated by the method of graphical integration in a manner differing only in detail from that employed for an unloaded exciter. The load saturation curve and the distortion curve are used instead of the no-load saturation curve (Fig. 39). Specifically stated, the differences in procedure are as follows:

1. The variable of integration e is the internal armature voltage, which is now the ordinate of the distortion curve instead of that of the no-load saturation curve.

2. For a self-excited machine, the forcing voltage Δe is the difference between the armature terminal voltage (read on the load saturation curve) and the field Ri drop. For a value of e represented by DG in Fig. 39, the corresponding value of Δe is represented by EF. For a separately excited machine, Δe is represented by AF, as before. (It is assumed here that the *no-load* ceiling voltage AG is made the same for both kinds of excitation.)

3. Usually a curve of e versus t suffices. However, if a curve of exciter armature terminal voltage versus t is wanted it can be obtained by subtracting the constant armature-resistance and brush drops from e.

We are now able to deduce the effect of load upon exciter response during build-up. Let us consider first the self-excited machine. For the same field current i in Fig. 39, the values of Δe are CF at no load and EF at load. However, in using the method of graphical integration the comparison should be made for the same value of internal voltage e. On this basis Δe is $D'F'$ at no load and EF at load. On either basis, the effect of load is to reduce Δe noticeably. Since Δe appears in the denominator of the integrand, the integral (representing the time required for e to build up between specified limits) is increased by load.   In a separately excited machine Δe is $A'F'$ at no load and AF at load.   Because of armature reaction, load slightly reduces Δe and increases the time of build-up.

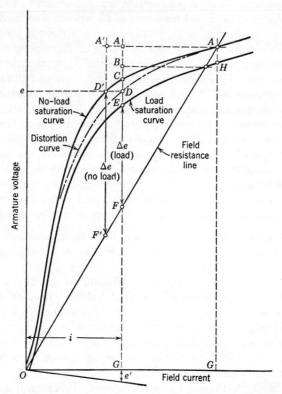

FIG. 39.   Quantities required for calculating the response of a loaded exciter by the method of graphical integration.

Thus, with either kind of excitation, the exciter response is decreased by load.   The effect is much greater in the self-excited exciter than in the separately excited one, however.

Besides reducing the response, load also reduces the ceiling voltage. That of the self-excited exciter is reduced from AG to BG (Fig. 39); that of the separately excited exciter, from AG to HG.

Calculation of field current of main generator during build-up of exciter.   Methods of calculating the field current of the main (a-c.) generator by point-by-point methods have been described in the last chapter. These methods assume that the exciter voltage is a known function of time. This function (the exciter voltage-time curve) can be found by methods given in this chapter. The simplest method is to calculate the voltage-time curve for no load and to assume that the result is valid also for the load condition. This assumption causes little error when applied to separately excited exciters. In the case of self-excited exciters it is advisable at least to take armature resistance into account while calculating the build-up curve. It is more accurate to include the effect of armature reaction also. The armature current of the exciter can be assumed constant, as already mentioned.

Regardless of which of these methods is used in calculating exciter build-up, the resistance of the armature of the exciter should be included in the value of total resistance of the field circuit of the main generator if the internal voltage of the exciter is used in this circuit. (An alternative way is to omit armature resistance and to use armature terminal voltage.)

The armature current of the exciter is not actually constant during build-up. The effect of its variation upon build-up can be taken into account, if desired, by means of a point-by-point solution in which both the exciter voltage and the field current of the main generator are calculated together. However, as such refinement is seldom, if ever, needed, the procedure will not be described. The assumption of constant exciter-armature current or the neglecting of armature resistance and reaction entirely has the advantage that it is possible to calculate the voltage-time curve of the exciter prior to, and independently of, the point-by-point calculation of main-generator field current.

Methods of increasing the response of an exciter.[13]   If the response of an existing exciter is not great enough, the following methods of increasing it should be considered:

1. *Providing separate excitation* for a self-excited machine.   In what follows, separate excitation is assumed.

2. *Increasing the ceiling voltage* by reducing the permanent external field-circuit resistance, if any, or by increasing the excitation voltage. The attainable ceiling voltage may be limited either by saturation or by commutation.

3. *Reducing the number of field turns in series* either by increasing the number of parallel paths or by providing a new field winding with larger conductor and fewer turns. If it is not desired also to increase the ceiling voltage, enough permanent external resistance

should be added to the field circuit to give the same field resistance per series turn, and hence the same total ampere-turns, as before.

4. *Increasing both the excitation voltage and the field resistance* in the same ratio so that the ceiling voltage is unchanged.

5. *Providing a new armature winding or a new armature wound for a higher voltage.* This is feasible only if the exciter has a greater capacity than required, because a higher voltage armature has a lower current rating and the collector-ring voltage of the main generator is not changed.

Methods 3 and 4 are similar in that they decrease the time constant of the exciter-field circuit without raising the ceiling voltage. The time constant of the field circuit of a separately excited exciter, as given by eqs. 17 and 29, is directly proportional to the number of turns N and inversely proportional to the excitation voltage E. Method 3 decreases N, whereas method 4 increases E.

Although the time required for the exciter voltage to build up from one given value of voltage to another varies inversely as the time constant, the nominal response of the exciter does not vary in the same way. If, for example, the time constant is halved, the exciter voltage will build up in 0.25 sec. to the value which it previously reached in 0.5 sec. During the second quarter-second, however, the voltage is nearer the ceiling value and rises more slowly than during the first quarter-second. Therefore, the nominal response, being defined for a time of 0.5 sec., is less than doubled.

In order to increase the nominal response to the desired value it may be necessary to increase the ceiling voltage. The required ceiling voltage can be estimated from eq. 65, which is derived from the following considerations: The maximum conceivable value of nominal response for a given ceiling voltage would be attained if the exciter voltage could rise instantly from the nominal collector-ring voltage to the ceiling voltage and then remain at the ceiling voltage. If E_c denotes the ceiling voltage and E_0 the nominal collector-ring voltage, the area under the voltage-time curve and above E_0 for 0.5 sec. is $A = 0.5(E_c - E_0)$. By eq. 50, the nominal response is

$$\left(\frac{\Delta e}{\Delta t}\right)_{\text{nom}} = \frac{8A}{E_0} = \frac{4(E_c - E_0)}{E_0} = 4\left(\frac{E_c}{E_0} - 1\right) \tag{63}$$

In practice, the greatest nominal response that can be attained is from 0.4 to 0.65 of this theoretical value. Use of the higher value gives

$$\left(\frac{\Delta e}{\Delta t}\right)_{\text{nom}} \approx 2.6\left(\frac{E_c}{E_0} - 1\right) \tag{64}$$

whence

$$E_c \approx E_0 \left[1 + 0.38 \left(\frac{\Delta e}{\Delta t} \right)_{\text{nom}} \right] \qquad [65]$$

This gives the required ceiling voltage approximately as a function of the desired nominal response.

REFERENCES

1. O. G. C. DAHL, *Electric Power Circuits: Theory and Applications*, Vol. II, *Power System Stability*. McGraw-Hill Book Co., New York, 1st ed., 1938. Chap. XV, "Analysis of Unloaded Exciters." Chap. XVI, "Analysis of Loaded Exciters." Chap. XVII, "Action of Voltage Regulators and Excitation Systems."

2. *Electrical Transmission and Distribution Reference Book*, by Central Station Engineers of the Westinghouse Electric and Manufacturing Company, East Pittsburgh, Pa., 1st edition, 1942. Chap. 7, "Machine Characteristics," by C. F. WAGNER, Part XIII, "Exciter Response," pp. 168–74. Chap. 8, "Power-System Stability," by R. D. EVANS, "Excitation Systems," pp. 201–4.

3. REINHOLD RÜDENBERG, "Fremd- und Selbsterregung von magnetisch gesättigten Gleichstromkreisen," *Wiss. Veröffentlichungen aus dem Siemens-Konzern*, vol. I, p. 179, 1920; also *Elektrische Schaltvorgänge*, Julius Springer, Berlin, 1923 and 1933. Solution by graphical integration.

4. F. L. MOON, "When May Alternator Field Rheostats be Omitted?" *Elec. Jour.*, vol. 14, pp. 47–50, February, 1917.

5. C. A. BODDIE, "Automatic Voltage Regulators," *Elec. Jour.*, vol. 14, pp. 75–84, February, 1917. Tirrill regulator with a-c. vibrating magnet.

6. J. H. ASHBAUGH, "The Extended Broad-Range Voltage Regulator," *Elec. Jour.*, vol. 22, pp. 559–61, November, 1925.

7. C. A. POWEL, "Quick-Response Excitation for Alternating-Current Synchronous Machinery," *Elec. Jour.*, vol. 24, pp. 157–62, April, 1927.

8. R. E. DOHERTY, "Excitation Systems: Their Influence on Short Circuits and Maximum Power," *A.I.E.E. Trans.*, vol. 47, pp. 944–56, July, 1928. Disc., pp. 969–74. Dynamic stability.

9. C. A. NICKLE and R. M. CAROTHERS, "Automatic Voltage Regulators: Application to Power Transmission Systems," *A.I.E.E. Trans.*, vol. 47, pp. 957–69, 1928. Disc., pp. 969–74. Contains an analysis of the vibrating type of regulator.

10. J. H. ASHBAUGH and H. C. NYCUM, "System Stability with Quick-Response Excitation and Voltage Regulators," *Elec. Jour.*, vol. 25, pp. 504–9, October, 1928.

11. R. H. PARK and E. H. BANCKER, "System Stability as a Design Problem," *A.I.E.E. Trans.*, vol. 48, pp. 170–94, January, 1929.

12. V. BUSH, "The Differential Analyzer: A New Machine for Solving Differential Equations," *Jour. Franklin Inst.*, vol. 212, pp. 447–88, October, 1931.

13. W. A. LEWIS, "Quick-Response Excitation," *Elec. Jour.*, vol. 31, pp. 308–12, August, 1934.

14. A. VAN NIEKERK, "Determining the Ratio of Exciter Response," *Elec. Jour.*, vol. 31, pp. 361–4, September, 1934.

15. C. R. HANNA, K. A. OPLINGER, and C. E. VALENTINE, "Recent Developments in Generator Voltage Regulation," *A.I.E.E. Trans.*, vol. 58, pp. 838–44, 1939. Disc., p. 844.

16. W. K. BOICE, S. B. CRARY, GABRIEL KRON, and L. W. THOMPSON, "The

Direct-Acting Generator Voltage Regulator," *A.I.E.E. Trans.*, vol. 59, pp. 149–56, March, 1940. Disc., pp. 156–7.

17. *American Standard Definitions of Electrical Terms*, American Institute of Electrical Engineers, New York, 1942. Definitions 10.95.440, 10.95.450, and 10.95.460.

18. C. CONCORDIA, "Steady-State Stability of Synchronous Machines as Affected by Voltage-Regulator Characteristics," *A.I.E.E. Trans.*, vol. 63, pp. 215–20, May, 1944. Disc., pp. 489–90.

19. E. L. HARDER and C. E. VALENTINE, "Static Voltage Regulator for Rototrol Exciter," *A.I.E.E. Trans. (Elec. Eng.)*, vol. 64, pp. 601–6, August, 1945.

20. H. A. P. LANGSTAFF, H. R. VAUGHAN, and R. F. LAWRENCE, "Application and Performance of Electronic Exciters for Large A-C. Generators," *A.I.E.E. Trans. (Elec. Eng.)*, vol. 65, pp. 246–54, May, 1946. Disc., pp. 515–20.

21. R. B. BODINE, S. B. CRARY, and A. W. RANKIN, "Motor-Driven Exciters for Turbine Alternators," *A.I.E.E. Trans. (Elec. Eng.)*, vol. 65, pp. 290–7, May, 1946. Disc., pp. 515–20.

22. J. B. MCCLURE, S. I. WHITTLESEY, and M. E. HARTMAN, "Modern Excitation Systems for Large Synchronous Machines," *A.I.E.E. Trans.*, vol. 65, pp. 939–45, 1946. Disc., pp. 1148–50. Summary of practice.

23. C. CONCORDIA, S. B. CRARY, and F. J. MAGINNISS, "Long-Distance Power Transmission as Influenced by Excitation Systems," *A.I.E.E. Trans.*, vol. 65, pp. 974–87, 1946. Disc., pp. 1175–7.

24. F. M. PORTER and J. H. KINGHORN, "The Development of Modern Excitation Systems for Synchronous Condensers and Generators," *A.I.E.E. Trans.*, vol. 65, pp. 1020–8, 1946. Disc., pp. 1156–9. Electronic pilot exciter, electronic main exciter, and Amplidyne pilot exciter.

25. G. DARRIEUS, "Long-Distance Transmission of Energy and the Artificial Stabilization of Alternating Current Systems," *C.I.G.R.E.*, 1946, Report 110.

26. E. L. HARDER, "Solution of the General Voltage Regulator Problem by Electrical Analogy," *A.I.E.E. Trans.*, vol. 66, pp. 815–25, 1947. Disc., p. 825.

27. C. L. KILLGORE, "Excitation Problems in Hydroelectric Generators Supplying Long Transmission Lines," *A.I.E.E. Trans.*, vol. 66, pp. 1277–82, 1947. Disc., pp. 1282–4.

28. A. W. KIMBALL, "Two-Stage Rototrol for Low-Energy Regulating Systems," *A.I.E.E. Trans.*, vol. 66, pp. 1507–11, 1947.

29. M. M. LIWSCHITZ, "The Multistage Rototrol," *A.I.E.E. Trans.*, vol. 66, pp. 564–8, 1947.

30. C. STEWART, "Automatic Voltage Control of Generators," *Jour. I.E.E.*, vol. 94, part IIA, pp. 39–48, May, 1947. Disc., pp. 60–5.

31. J. E. BARKLE and C. E. VALENTINE, "Rototrol Excitation Systems," *A.I.E.E. Trans.*, vol. 67, part I, pp. 529–34, 1948. Disc., p. 534.

32. C. LYNN and C. E. VALENTINE, "Main Exciter Rototrol Excitation for Turbine Generators," *A.I.E.E. Trans.*, vol. 67, part I, pp. 535–9, 1948. Disc., p. 539.

33. C. CONCORDIA, "Steady-State Stability of Synchronous Machines as Affected by Angle-Regulator Characteristics," *A.I.E.E. Trans.*, vol. 67, part I, pp. 687–90, 1948.

34. G. D. FLOYD and H. R. SILLS, "Generator Design to Meet Long Distance Transmission Requirements in Canada," *C.I.G.R.E.*, 1948, Report 131.

35. H. DAVID and J. FAVEREAU, "Stability of Alternators with Series Excitation Connected by a Long Line to a High-Power System," *C.I.G.R.E.*, 1948, Report 305.

36. W. A. LEWIS, "Excitation Requirements and Control of Reactive Power," *Proc. Midwest Power Conf.* (Chicago), vol. 10, pp. 145–56, 1948.

37. C. LYNN, "Rotating Regulator Exciters," *Proc. Midwest Power Conf.* (Chicago), vol. 10, pp. 157–67, 1948.

38. JAMES T. CARLETON, "The Transient Behavior of the Two-Stage Rototrol Main Exciter Voltage Regulating System as Determined by Electrical Analogy," *A.I.E.E. Trans.*, vol. 68, part I, pp. 59–63, 1949.

39. A. G. MELLOR and M. TEMOSHOK, "Excitation System Performance with Motor-Driven Exciters," *A.I.E.E. Trans.*, vol. 69, part I, pp. 321–7, 1950.

40. A. P. COLAIACO, A. A. JOHNSON, and J. E. REILLY, "Design and Test on Electronic Exciter Supplied from Common Shaft-Driven Generator," *A.I.E.E. Trans.*, vol. 69, part I, pp. 328–35, 1950. Disc., pp. 335–7.

41. A. H. PHILLIPS, W. H. LAMBERT, and D. R. PATTISON, "Excitation Improvement — Electronic Excitation and Regulation of Electric Generators as Compared to Conventional Methods," *A.I.E.E. Trans.*, vol. 69, part I, pp. 338–40, 1950. Disc., pp. 340–1.

42. E. L. HARDER, R. C. CHEEK, and J. M. CLAYTON, "Regulation of A-C Generators with Suddenly Applied Loads — Part II," *A.I.E.E. Trans.*, vol. 69, part I, pp. 395–405, 1950. Disc., pp. 405–6.

43. C. L. KILLGORE and N. G. HOLMDAHL, "Hydroelectric Generator Excitation Experience at Grand Coulee," *A.I.E.E. Trans.*, vol. 69, part II, pp. 855–60, 1950.

44. R. M. SAUNDERS, "Dynamoelectric Amplifiers," *Elec. Eng.*, vol. 69, pp. 711–6, August, 1950.

45. FRANK E. BOTHWELL, "Stability of Voltage Regulators," *A.I.E.E. Trans.*, vol. 69, part II, pp. 1430–3, 1950. Disc., p. 1433.

46. DIDIER JOURNEAUX, "Transient Operation of D-C Generators," *Allis-Chalmers Elec. Rev.*, vol. 15, no. 3, pp. 27–34, 3rd quarter, 1950.

47. C. CONCORDIA, "The Differential Analyzer as an Aid in Power System Analysis," *C.I.G.R.E.*, 1950, Report 311.

48. H. F. STORM, "Static Magnetic Exciter for Synchronous Alternators," *A.I.E.E. Trans.*, vol. 70, part I, pp. 1014–7, 1951.

49. H. G. FRUS, F. N. McCLURE, and W. H. FERGUSON, "Selection of Characteristics for Turbine-Generator Motor-Driven Exciters," *A.I.E.E. Trans.*, vol. 71, part III, pp. 176–82, January, 1952. Disc., pp. 182–3.

50. H. A. CORNELIUS, W. F. CAWSON, and H. W. CORY, "Experience with Automatic Voltage Regulation on a 115-Megawatt Turbogenerator," *A.I.E.E. Trans.*, vol. 71, part III, pp. 184–7, January, 1952.

51. G. K. KALLENBACH, F. S. ROTHE, H. F. STORM, and P. L. DANDENO, "Performance of New Magnetic Amplifier Type Voltage Regulator for Large Hydroelectric Generators," *A.I.E.E. Trans.*, vol. 71, part III, pp. 201–5, January, 1952. Disc., pp. 205–6.

52. F. M. PORTER and H. B. MARGOLIS, "Operating Experience with Shaft-Driven Exciters in Air and Hydrogen," *A.I.E.E. Trans.*, vol. 71, part III, pp. 758–67, October, 1952. Disc., pp. 767–8.

53. W. A. HUNTER and M. TEMOSHOK, "Development of a Modern Amplidyne Voltage Regulator for Large Turbine Generators," *A.I.E.E. Trans.*, vol. 71, part III, pp. 894–900, October, 1952. Disc., pp. 900–1.

54. CH. LAVANCHY, "A New Solution for the Regulation of Counter-Excitation Synchronous Compensators," *C.I.G.R.E.*, 1952, Report 331.

55. J. E. BARKLE, C. E. VALENTINE, and J. T. CARLETON, "Magamp Regulation

for Synchronous Machines," *Westinghouse Engineer*, vol. 12, pp. 204–7, November, 1952.

56. A. TUSTIN, *Direct Current Machines for Control Systems*, The Macmillan Company, New York, 1952.

57. J. T. CARLETON, P. O. BOBO, and W. F. HORTON, "A New Regulator and Excitation System," *A.I.E.E. Trans.*, vol. 72, part III, pp. 175–81, April, 1953. Disc., pp. 181–3.

58. L. F. LISCHER and R. B. GEAR, "Rotating Regulators Improve Light-Load Stability," *Electric Light and Power*. Part I, vol. 31, no. 12, pp. 106–11, October, 1953. Part II, vol. 31, no. 13, pp. 133–7, November, 1953.

59. MILAN VIDMAR, JR., "Comparison of Four Main Types of Rotary Exciters Employed in Modern Practice, with Regard to the Exciting Effectiveness," *C.I.G.R.E.*, 1954, Report 138.

60. R. DAVID and L. GATESOUPE, "Results of Recent Tests Regarding Different Systems of High Speed Excitation and De-excitation of Alternators," *C.I.G.R.E.*, 1954, Report 147.

PROBLEMS ON CHAPTER XIII

1. Represent the magnetization curve of Fig. 25 by the modified Fröhlich equation (eq. 12).

2. Obtain a formal solution of eq. 9 for separate excitation by substituting eq. 12 into it and integrating.

3. Having solved Probs. 1 and 2, work Example 1 by use of the formal solution obtained in Prob. 2. Compare results.

4. Repeat Prob. 2 for self-excitation.

5. Having solved Probs. 1 and 4, work Example 2 by use of the formal solution obtained in Prob. 4.

6. Find the voltage-time curve for build-down of the separately excited exciter of Example 1 from ceiling voltage to an ultimate value of one-third the ceiling voltage.

7. Repeat Prob. 6 for self-excitation.

8. Work Example 1 using the assumption of constant leakage inductance instead of constant coefficient of dispersion. The coefficient of dispersion is 1.15 only on the straight part of the magnetization curve. How much difference is there between the two assumptions in the time required for the armature voltage to build up to 250?

9. Find the nominal response of the separately excited exciter of Example 1. The nominal collector-ring voltage of the a-c. generator is 180 volts.

10. Find the nominal response of the self-excited exciter of Example 2. The nominal collector-ring voltage of the a-c. generator is 180 volts.

11. Work Example 1 by point-by-point calculation.

12. Work Example 2 by point-by-point calculation.

13. Work Example 3 by graphical integration.

14. Plot the voltage-time curves of the self-excited exciter of Example 2 from an initial voltage of 180 to the ceiling voltage obtained if all external resistance is removed from the field circuit. Compare the following two conditions: (*a*) no load, (*b*) constant load current of 150% of rated value.

The armature reaction at the knee of the no-load saturation curve amounts to 5% of the field current there, and elsewhere it is proportional to the curvature of the saturation curve. The full-load armature IR drop is 5% of rated voltage, and the brush drop is 2 volts.

15. In Example 3, what is the value of the constant corresponding to 2.6 in eq. 64?

16. It is proposed to reconnect the field winding of the separately excited exciter of Example 1 in two parallel circuits. How much permanent external resistance should be used in order to keep the ceiling voltage at 275 volts? What would the new value of nominal response be? Compare it with the original value calculated in Prob. 9. Nominal collector-ring voltage is 180.

17. Work Prob. 16 for three parallel circuits.

18. In order to obtain the same improvement in nominal response as in Prob. 16, but without reconnecting the field winding, what excitation voltage and what external resistance should be used? The ceiling voltage is to remain at 275 volts.

19. What voltage and current must be supplied by the pilot exciter when the main exciter is generating its ceiling voltage (a) in Prob. 16, (b) in Prob. 18?

20. It is proposed to reconnect the field winding of the separately excited exciter of Example 1 into two parallel circuits and, at the same time, to increase the ceiling voltage to 350. How much permanent external resistance should be used? What would the new value of nominal response be? (Compare it with the values obtained in Probs. 9 and 16.) Nominal collector-ring voltage is 180.

21. It is proposed to rewind the armature of the separately excited exciter of Example 1 in duplex wave. The field circuit would not be changed. What would the new ceiling voltage be? What would the nominal response be in building up from 180 volts?

22. Explain why a slow-speed exciter has a longer time constant than a high-speed exciter.

23. The exciter described in Example 1 is to be operated with combined self- and separate excitation, a rotating amplifier being connected in series with the shunt-field circuit. The resistance of this circuit is adjusted so that the no-load exciter armature voltage is 180 when the e.m.f. of the rotating amplifier is zero. Then the e.m.f. of the amplifier is changed to a value which will cause the no-load exciter voltage to build up to a ceiling value of 275 volts, this amplifier e.m.f. being held constant. Calculate and plot the curve of build-up of exciter voltage. Also calculate the nominal exciter response under these conditions. Compare the maximum power output of the rotating amplifier with that of the pilot exciter in Example 1.

CHAPTER XIV

DAMPER WINDINGS AND DAMPING

Almost all synchronous motors, synchronous condensers, and synchronous converters and many salient-pole synchronous generators are equipped with damper windings (also called amortisseur windings). In a few installations damper windings have been designed with regard to their effect upon system stability, but in most installations they have been provided for other purposes. Regardless of the reasons for their use, they affect stability to a greater or lesser extent.

Types of damper windings. There are two principal types of damper windings: (1) complete, or connected; (2) incomplete, nonconnected, or open. Both types consist of bars placed in slots in the pole faces and connected together at each end. The end conductors in the *complete damper winding* (Fig. 1a) are closed rings connecting the bars of all poles; whereas, in the *incomplete damper winding* (Fig. 1b), they are broken between poles. Thus, in the latter type, the damper winding of each pole is an independent grid. Complete dampers are similar to the squirrel-cage winding of an induction motor, except that the bars are not uniformly spaced, being omitted between the poles. The end rings sometimes have bolted joints between poles to facilitate the removal of a pole. Generator designers prefer incomplete dampers for mechanical reasons, particularly where the peripheral speed is high, because of the danger of damage to the unsupported connections between poles by high centrifugal force. Complete dampers, however, are electrically superior and are commoner now than incomplete dampers.

Damper windings may be classified also according to their resistance. *Low-resistance damper windings* produce their greatest torque at small slips; *high-resistance damper windings*, at large slips.

Occasionally a *double-deck damper winding* is used. This consists of a low-resistance, high-reactance damper, which is effective at small slips, and a high-resistance, low-reactance damper, which is effective at large slips. Double-deck dampers are used (like double squirrel-cage windings on induction motors) to improve the starting and pullin characteristics of synchronous motors. They have been used on a few

214

generators to improve stability by giving both positive-sequence damping and negative-sequence braking (both of which are discussed later in this chapter).[14]

Field collars have sometimes been used as substitutes for damper windings. A field collar is a heavy short-circuited copper loop placed

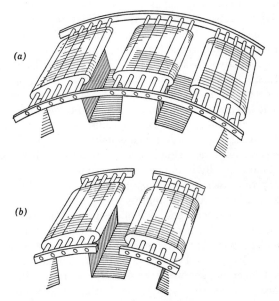

FIG. 1. Amortisseur windings or damper windings, (*a*) connected and (*b*) non-connected.

around the pole core near the outer end. Field collars can be used together with a single damper winding to give results similar to those given by a double-deck damper.

Damper windings are not used on turbogenerators, but the solid steel rotor cores of such machines provide paths for eddy currents and thus produce the same effects as dampers. Even in machines with laminated salient poles and no dampers, eddy currents in the pole faces have a very small damping effect.

Purposes of damper windings. The chief reasons for providing damper windings on salient-pole synchronous machines are the following:

1. *To provide starting torque* for synchronous motors, condensers, and converters.

2. *To suppress hunting.* This was the first application of dampers and the one for which they were named. Generators driven by reciprocating engines tend to hunt because of the pulsating torque of the engines. Motors driving loads of pulsating torque, such as compressors, likewise tend to hunt. Hunting from these causes is "forced" hunting. There is also a spontaneous hunting that occurs when synchronous machines are connected together by circuits having a high ratio of resistance to reactance.[8,9] This condition is likely to occur if the frequency is low, if the conductor size is small, or if the inductive reactance is partially cancelled by use of series capacitors. Both forced and spontaneous types of hunting are greatly decreased in amplitude by low-resistance dampers.

3. *To damp oscillations* started by aperiodic shocks, such as short circuits or switching. A possible cause of oscillations between generators in the same station is inequality of speeds of response of their several exciters. Oscillations from any of these causes are damped more rapidly if damper windings are added.

4. *To prevent distortion of voltage wave shape* caused by unbalanced loading; in other words, to suppress harmonics. Single-phase generators, phase balancers, and polyphase generators carrying poorly balanced load require heavy damper windings not only in order to suppress harmonics but also for other reasons (listed as items 5 and 6 below). Water-wheel generators without dampers may produce dangerous overvoltage during single-phase short circuits because of resonance between the capacitance of transmission lines and the inductance of the machines and lines at harmonic frequencies.[4,5,6] Dampers have been installed in some generators which did not originally have them in order to decrease the harmonic voltages to safe values.[7]

5. *To balance the terminal voltages* of the several phases during unbalanced loading, that is, to decrease the negative-sequence voltage. Damper windings decrease the negative-sequence reactance. The lower the negative-sequence impedance, the lower is the negative-sequence voltage.

6. *To prevent overheating of the pole pieces* of single-phase generators and phase balancers from eddy currents induced by sustained negative-sequence armature currents. The flux linkages of low-resistance dampers are nearly constant. Hence the dampers shield the pole pieces from variations of flux.

7. *To provide a braking torque on a generator during an unsymmetrical fault,* and thus to reduce the accelerating torque during the fault.

8. *To provide additional torque for synchronizing generators,* especially those which are synchronized automatically. The dampers are particularly helpful in case the generator is synchronized out of phase or somewhat off speed. They also help to pull the generator back into step after synchronism has been lost because of a fault.

9. *To reduce circuit-breaker recovery-voltage rates.*

10. *To reduce the stress on the insulation of the field winding* during current surges in the armature circuit, especially those which do not affect all poles alike, such as those due to internal faults.

Effect of damper windings on synchronous-machine constants. Damper windings affect the following synchronous-machine quantities: x_d'', x_q'', x_2, r_2, T_d'', and T_q'. The effects are discussed below and are illustrated numerically by Tables 1, 2, 3, and 4.

TABLE 1

CONSTANTS OF A SYNCHRONOUS GENERATOR AS AFFECTED BY TYPE
OF DAMPER WINDING[4]

(100 kva., 2,300 volts, 25.2 amp.)

Type	x_d''	x_q''	$\sqrt{x_d'' x_q''}$	x_q''/x_d''	r_{ad}''	r_{aq}''
No damper	0.260	0.577	0.388	2.22	0.028	0.105
Connected copper	0.157	0.146	0.151	0.93	0.036	0.047
Connected Everdur	0.171	0.157	0.164	0.92	0.063	0.111
Nonconnected copper	0.154	0.390	0.245	2.53	0.037	0.113

The constants are in per unit. They are test results, obtained by applying single-phase voltage to two armature terminals with the rotor stationary.

The conductivity of Everdur is approximately 6% of that of copper.

TABLE 2

CONSTANTS OF A SYNCHRONOUS CONDENSER AS AFFECTED BY TYPE
OF DAMPER WINDING[4]

(5,000 kva., 4,000 volts, 721 amp.)

Type	r_2		$x_2 = \frac{1}{2}(x_d'' + x_q'')$	
	Test	Calculated	Test	Calculated
No damper	0.045	0.040	0.75	0.69
Connected copper	0.026	0.029	0.195	0.215
Connected brass	0.045	0.044	0.195	0.215
Connected Everdur	0.12	0.125	0.20	0.215

The constants are in per unit.

TABLE 3

REACTANCES OF LARGE WATER-WHEEL GENERATOR
AS AFFECTED BY CONNECTED COPPER DAMPER WINDING[7]

(32.5 Mva., 0.8 power factor, 12 kv., three-phase,
60 cycles, 100 r.p.m., vertical shaft)
Calculated values

Per-Unit Reactance	Without Dampers	With Dampers	Per-Cent Reduction
x_l	0.22	0.22	0
x_d	1.15	1.15	0
x_q	0.73	0.73	0
x_d'	0.40	0.40	0
x_q'	0.73	0.73	0
x_d''	0.32	0.265	17.2
x_q''	0.73	0.29	60.3
x_2	0.48	0.28	41.7
x_0	0.14	0.123	12.1

TABLE 4

CALCULATED CONSTANTS OF WATER-WHEEL GENERATOR
AS AFFECTED BY INCOMPLETE DAMPER WINDING[12]

(9 Mva., 0.8 power factor, 13.8 kv., 60 cycles, 180 r.p.m.)
Reactances are in per unit, time constants in seconds.

Constant	Incomplete Damper and Top-Field Collar	Top-Field Collar Only, No Damper
x_d	0.91	0.91
x_d'	0.26	0.26
x_d''	0.14	0.177
x_q'	0.524	0.524
x_q'	0.524	0.524
x_q''	0.368	0.524
T_{d0}'	2.86	2.86
T_{d0}''	0.055	0.0136
T_{q0}''	0.044	—

Subtransient reactances in both axes of the rotor are decreased by
damper windings (see Tables 1, 3, and 4). A connected damper
decreases the quadrature-axis subtransient reactance x_q'' more than a
nonconnected damper does (see Table 1). Furthermore, the connected
damper makes x_q'' more nearly equal to the direct-axis subtransient
reactance x_d'' than the nonconnected damper can. The ratio x_q''/x_d''
can be made as low as 1.35 by a nonconnected damper, and much lower
by a connected damper.[2]

Negative-sequence reactance x_2, being the mean of x_d'' and x_q'', is decreased by damper windings.

Negative-sequence resistance r_2 may be high or low, depending upon the resistance of the damper windings (see Table 2). Negative-sequence impedance is discussed more fully in a later section of this chapter.

Subtransient time constants T_d'' and T_q'' depend upon the resistance and equivalent inductance of the dampers.

Effect of damper windings upon stability. The principal effects of damper windings upon power-system stability may be listed as follows:

1. Positive-sequence damping.
2. Negative-sequence braking during an unsymmetrical fault.
3. Effect of negative-sequence impedance upon positive-sequence electric power output of the machine during an unsymmetrical fault.

A lesser effect sometimes worth considering is:

4. D-c. braking.

Positive-sequence damping results from the torque caused by interaction of the damper currents with the positive-sequence (forward-rotating) magnetic field in the air gap. Except during starting or pulling out of step, the slip of the rotor with respect to the positive-sequence field is low and oscillatory. Positive-sequence damping causes the oscillations of the machine rotors, after an aperiodic shock that does not cause loss of synchronism, to decrease in amplitude and ultimately to die out entirely. Low-resistance amortisseurs greatly increase the amount of positive-sequence damping. Positive-sequence damping is present both during and after a fault. However, it is much more effective after clearing of a fault than during the fault because the positive-sequence voltage and flux are greater after clearing.

By absorbing energy from the oscillation, positive-sequence damping may prevent a machine which has survived the first swing from going out of step on the second or subsequent swings because of reduction of field flux linkage. However, the damping is not great enough to increase significantly the power that can be carried through the first swing. Its effect is almost always neglected in calculating power limits.

Negative-sequence braking results from the torque caused by interaction of the damper currents with the negative-sequence (backward-rotating) magnetic field in the air gap. Such a field is present in a polyphase machine only when an unbalance — usually an unsymmetrical short circuit — is present on the polyphase circuit to which the armature winding is connected. The slip of the rotor with respect to the negative-sequence field is $2 - s$, where s is the positive-sequence slip. Since s is small (except, as already noted, during starting and out-of-step operation), the negative-sequence slip is very nearly equal to 2. It never reverses, nor does the resulting torque reverse. The torque always retards the rotor, and hence may be called a "braking" torque. Its effect is therefore equivalent to a reduction of mechanical input torque. In a generator, which tends to speed up during a fault, the negative-sequence torque decreases the accelerating torque. On the other hand, in a motor, which tends to slow down during a fault, the negative-sequence torque increases the absolute value of accelerating torque (now a negative, or retarding, torque). It is apparent, then, that this braking effect is desirable in a generator but undesirable in a motor, a condenser, or a generator which acts as an equivalent motor. The braking effect is present only as long as an unsymmetrical fault is on the system. The greatest braking torque is afforded by high-resistance dampers, and very little, by low-resistance dampers. Thus the effect may be limited to generators by using high-resistance dampers on generators only.

In many respects negative-sequence braking is analogous to resistance grounding, which reduces the accelerating torque of a generator during ground faults. Both of these means of improving transient stability are less important now that high-speed fault clearing is generally used than they were when slower speeds were common. The higher the speed of clearing, the less important is the shock caused by the fault itself in comparison with the shock of opening the faulted line to clear the fault. This is true even if high-speed reclosing is employed.

Negative-sequence impedance. As already mentioned, a damper winding decreases the negative-sequence reactance of the machine on which it is installed and may either increase or decrease the negative-sequence resistance. In general, the negative-sequence impedance is lowered by a damper winding, especially by a low-resistance damper. Lowering the negative-sequence impedance of any machine on a network lowers the negative-sequence impedance of the network viewed from the point of fault, and thus also lowers the impedance of the fault shunt representing any type of short circuit except a three-phase short circuit. The effect is greater for a line-to-line short circuit than for any other type, and is greatest for a fault located near the machine equipped with the dampers. Usually a fault location near the principal equivalent generators is taken as the most severe one and the one used as a criterion of system stability. Lowering the impedance of the fault shunt weakens the tie between machines during the time that the fault is on the system, as indicated by an increase of the transfer reactance and a decrease of the amplitude of the sine terms in the power-angle equations; also, in the case of a two-machine system, by a decrease of the amplitude of the power-angle curve.

Thus, while an unsymmetrical fault is on the system the damper winding on a generator gives rise to two opposing effects: (1) braking torque, which is beneficial to stability, and (2) decrease of negative-sequence impedance, which is detrimental to stability. Which of these two effects predominates depends largely on the resistance of the damper winding. With a low-resistance damper, the decrease of nega-tive-sequence impedance usually predominates, while with a high-resistance damper the braking torque usually predominates. This is true because increasing the resistance of the damper both increases the negative-sequence impedance and increases the braking torque.

The more rapidly faults are cleared, the less important are both of these effects. The use of high-resistance dampers to increase the sta-bility limits of generators is therefore less important now than it was when slower clearing speeds were in general use.

Damper action explained by induction-motor theory. Inasmuch as a damper winding is similar to the squirrel-cage rotor winding of an induction motor, and the armature winding of a synchronous machine is like the stator winding of an induction motor, the various effects of the damper windings on stability (discussed above) can be analyzed — at least approximately — by induction-motor theory. This theory therefore will be briefly reviewed.

The induction motor is represented by an *equivalent T circuit* similar to that used for the transformer carrying a resistive load. See Fig. 2. The notation is explained in the caption of the figure. All quantities are for positive phase sequence. All rotor quantities are referred to the stator in magnitude, phase, and frequency. For example, I_r is the current which, if flowing in a stationary rotor winding having the same number of phases and the same effective number of turns as the stator winding and placed so that each rotor phase were exactly opposite the corresponding stator phase, would react magnetically on the stator in the same manner as does the actual rotor current flowing in the actual rotor winding.

A motor with stationary rotor is merely a polyphase transformer and can be represented by the equivalent circuit of a transformer. If the rotor is turning, it can be replaced by an equivalent stationary rotor, as will be explained.

The positive-sequence air-gap flux rotates at synchronous speed with respect to the stator and induces in the stator winding an e.m.f. of applied frequency f. The flux rotates at slip speed with respect to the rotor and induces in the rotor winding an e.m.f. of slip frequency sf.

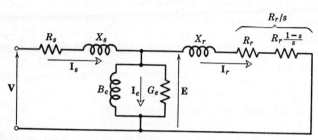

Fig. 2. Equivalent T circuit of induction motor for positive phase sequence.

R_s = stator resistance.
X_s = stator leakage reactance.
X_r = rotor leakage reactance at standstill (referred to stator).
R_r = rotor resistance (referred to stator).
s = slip.
B_e = exciting susceptance.
G_e = exciting conductance.
$\mathbf{I}_s$ = stator current.
$\mathbf{I}_r$ = rotor current (referred to stator).
$\mathbf{I}_e$ = exciting current.
$\mathbf{E}$ = e.m.f. induced in stator by air-gap flux
   = e.m.f. induced in rotor at standstill by air-gap flux (referred to stator).
$\mathbf{V}$ = stator terminal voltage.

The magnitude of the rotor e.m.f. is also proportional to the slip. At standstill ($s = 1$) it is (by definition) E; at slip s it is sE. The rotor leakage reactance is also proportional to the slip. At standstill it is X_r; at slip s it is sX_r. The rotor current is

$$\mathbf{I}_r = \frac{s\mathbf{E}}{R_r + jsX_r} \qquad [1]$$

Division of numerator and denominator by s puts eq. 1 in the form

$$\mathbf{I}_r = \frac{\mathbf{E}}{R_r/s + jX_r} \qquad [2]$$

Equation 2 is algebraically identical to eq. 1, but is open to a new and important physical interpretation, as follows: The current in the short-circuited rotor turning at slip s (eq. 1) is equal to the current which would flow in a stationary rotor if the rotor-circuit resistance were increased from R_r to R_r/s (eq. 2). The equivalent circuit of Fig. 2

accords with eq. 2 in that the rotor circuit of impedance $R_r/s + jX_r$ is connected across voltage **E**.

In the normal operation of an induction motor the slip is a small positive quantity, making resistance R_r/s in the equivalent rotor circuit much greater than the actual rotor resistance R_r. The additional resistance is $R_r(1 - s)/s$, shown in Fig. 2 as a separate resistor. The rotor input, which is received by induction from the stator, is

$$\frac{I_r^2 R_r}{s} \quad \text{watts per phase} \qquad [3]$$

but the rotor copper loss is only $I_r^2 R_r$ watts per phase. The difference,

$$I_r^2 R_r \frac{1 - s}{s} \quad \text{watts per phase} \qquad [4]$$

equal to the fictitious copper loss in the fictitious added resistor, is converted to mechanical power. It equals the mechanical output plus rotational losses.

Torque. Mechanical power is torque T times speed N, and the actual speed N of the motor is $(1 - s)$ times its synchronous speed N_s. Therefore,

$$P = NT = (1 - s)N_s T = I_r^2 R_r \frac{1 - s}{s} \quad \text{watts per phase} \qquad [5]$$

Hence the torque is

$$T = \frac{I_r^2 R_r}{N_s s} \quad \text{watts per phase per unit of speed} \qquad [6]$$

If this same torque were developed at synchronous speed, the mechanical power would be

$$N_s T = I_r^2 \frac{R_r}{s} \quad \text{watts per phase} \qquad [7]$$

The torque at any speed may be expressed in terms of the power it would produce at synchronous speed. The unit of torque so defined is the "synchronous watt."

$$T = I_r^2 \frac{R_r}{s} \quad \text{synchronous watts per phase} \qquad [8]$$

The torque in synchronous watts is equal to the rotor input in watts. Equation 8 also gives the torque in per unit if I_r and R_r are in per unit.

In order to find an equation for torque as a function of slip, suppose that either the stator terminal voltage V or other voltages in the network to which the motor is connected are constant. The network to the left of the E in Fig. 2 can then be replaced by the equivalent circuit of Thévenin's theorem. Let the constant e.m.f. of this circuit be V',

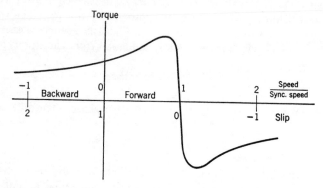

FIG. 3. Torque of an induction motor as a function of speed or slip.

and the impedance, $R_s' + jX_s'$. These combine with the rotor impedance, $R_r/s + jX_r$, to form a simple series circuit in which the rotor current $\mathbf{I}_r$ flows. Accordingly, the scalar value of the rotor current is given by

$$I_r{}^2 = \frac{(V')^2}{(R_s' + R_r/s)^2 + (X_s' + X_r)^2} \qquad [9]$$

This value, when substituted in eq. 8, gives the following expression for torque:

$$T = \frac{(V')^2\, R_r/s}{(R_s' + R_r/s)^2 + (X_s' + X_r)^2} \qquad [10]$$

A curve of T versus slip s is shown in Fig. 3. By taking the derivative of T with respect to R_r/s, we find that maximum torque occurs at the slip

$$s_m = \frac{R_r}{\sqrt{(R_s')^2 + (X_s' + X_r)^2}} \qquad [11]$$

Substitution of eq. 11 into eq. 10 gives the value of maximum torque as

$$T_m = \frac{(V')^2}{2[R_s' + \sqrt{(R_s')^2 + (X_s' + X_r)^2}]} \qquad [12]$$

At speeds above synchronous, the slip is negative. Under this condition, both the mechanical power (given by eq. 5) and the torque (given by eq. 6 or 8) become negative, that is, a retarding torque. The machine is then an induction generator.

If a synchronous machine with dampers hunts or swings, the slip is alternately positive and negative. The torque is likewise alternately positive and negative, and always tends to bring the speed back to synchronous speed.

Negative-sequence applied voltage causes a wave of air-gap flux to rotate backward at synchronous speed. If the slip of the rotor with respect to the positive-sequence field is s, the slip with respect to the negative-sequence field is $2 - s$. The positive-sequence slip of a synchronous machine is normally so small that the negative-sequence slip may be taken as 2 without appreciable error. Equation 10 and Fig. 3 show that for this condition the torque is positive though the speed is negative. In other words, the torque opposes the rotation; it is a braking torque. Equation 4 shows that for $s = 2$ the mechanical power output,

$$I_r^2 R_r \frac{1-2}{2} = -\tfrac{1}{2} I_r^2 R_r \quad \text{watts per phase} \qquad [13]$$

is negative (that is, it is actually input) and is equal to half the rotor copper loss, $I_r^2 R_r$. The other half of the rotor copper loss is supplied electrically via the stator terminals. Thus there is at the same time both electric and mechanical power input, all of which goes into losses, principally copper losses. The mechanical power input is equal to the electric power input to the rotor (air-gap power) and is a definite fraction of the input to the stator.

The negative-sequence rotor currents have a frequency $(2 - s)f$, or very nearly $2f$, where f is the stator frequency. In a synchronous machine such currents flow both in the field winding and in the damper windings if damper windings are provided, otherwise, in the field winding and in the field pole faces.

The influence of rotor-circuit (damper) resistance R_r on damping torque can be shown by plotting curves of torque versus slip for various values of R_r. It is apparent from eq. 10 that, if R_r and s are changed proportionally, the torque is unchanged. Therefore the effect of increasing the rotor resistance is to increase the abscissas of the torque-slip curve in direct proportion to the rotor resistance. See Fig. 4. The slip at which maximum torque occurs is directly proportional to rotor resistance (eq. 11), but the maximum torque itself is independent of rotor resistance (eq. 12).

In order to give high damping torque at small values of slip, the dampers should have as low a resistance as possible. In order to give high negative-sequence braking torque, the dampers should have a much higher resistance, such that maximum torque occurs at or near $s = 2$. A damper which is designed for one of these purposes is poorly suited for the other purpose.

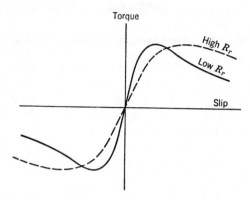

FIG. 4.   Effect of rotor-circuit resistance on torque-slip curve.

Negative-sequence impedance of a machine may be found by putting $s = 2$ in the equivalent circuit of Fig. 2 and reducing this circuit to a single impedance $r_2 + jx_2$ at the stator terminals. Obviously, the negative-sequence resistance r_2 depends greatly upon the rotor resistance R_r (also see Table 2). If the exciting admittance is neglected in comparison with the rotor admittance, as it can be at $s = 2$, then

$$r_2 \approx R_s + \tfrac{1}{2}R_r \qquad [14]$$

Calculation of damping. Although induction-motor theory has been used above in a qualitative explanation of damping in synchronous machines, it does not necessarily follow that the same theory is accurate enough to be used for the calculation of damping. Induction-motor theory assumes constant slip and a symmetrical rotor with only one set of windings. (A symmetrical rotor is one in which there is no difference between the direct- and quadrature-axis circuits.) A synchronous machine, even though equipped with damper windings, has an unsymmetrical rotor, with a field winding on only one axis, and the slip of the machine varies during the disturbances considered in stability studies. Nevertheless, induction-motor theory is considered applicable to the calculation of negative-sequence braking. For the calculation of positive-sequence damping, however, synchronous-machine theory is invoked.

Calculation of negative-sequence braking. The slip of the rotor with respect to the negative-sequence field is very nearly 2. Its value may be taken as 2 with little error, even though the machine is actually swinging or starting to pull out of step, because the torque is nearly independent of slip in this vicinity (see Fig. 3).

If the rotor circuits in the two axes are unlike (that is, if $x_d'' \neq x_q''$ or if $T_{d0}'' \neq T_{q0}''$), then the negative-sequence torque pulsates at twice the rated frequency. This fluctuation is so rapid compared with the frequency of electromechanical swings that the average torque, as calculated by induction-motor theory, can be used with negligible error in stability calculations. By eq. 13, the mechanical power corresponding to this torque is

$$P_b = \tfrac{1}{2}I_{r2}^2 R_r \qquad [15]$$

(Since the speed is substantially constant, the torque is directly proportional to the mechanical power. At normal speed, power and torque are numerically equal if expressed in watts and synchronous watts, respectively, or if both are expressed in per unit, as is more usual in stability work).

In eq. 15 I_{r2} is the negative-sequence rotor current, and R_r is the rotor resistance. Since the negative-sequence rotor current is directly proportional to the negative-sequence stator (armature) current I_{s2}, we may write:

$$P_b = K_b I_{s2}^2 \qquad [16]$$

where K_b is a constant. If exciting admittance, represented by the shunt branch of Fig. 2, is neglected, as is permissible for the negative-sequence circuit, then $I_{r2} \approx I_{s2}$ and also, from eq. 14, $R_r \approx 2\,(r_2 - r_1)$, where r_1 is the positive-sequence resistance, equal to the armature resistance R_s. With these substitutions made, eq. 15 becomes:

$$P_b \approx I_{s2}^2(r_2 - r_1) \qquad [17]$$

This form is convenient for computing the negative-sequence braking power of synchronous machines because the positive- and negative-sequence resistances of the machines are usually given rather than the rotor resistance. The negative-sequence armature current, which is present only during unsymmetrical faults, can be calculated by the method of symmetrical components, as explained in Chapter VI, Vol. I. It can be measured on a calculating board if the negative-sequence network is set up. An expression, such as eq. 16 or 17, giving the torque in terms of negative-sequence current, is preferable to one like eq. 10, giving the torque in terms of the voltage, because the former is simpler and because the negative-sequence current of the machine is just as easy to compute or to measure as the negative-sequence voltage is.

The negative-sequence torque is always a retarding or braking torque. It therefore has the same effect on the angular motion of the rotor as a decrease of mechanical input torque. In the calculation of swing curves, negative-sequence damping may be handled as a reduction of the input.

When damper action was neglected, the accelerating power was taken as the difference between the mechanical power input and the electric power output (both being internal values):

$$P_a = P_i - P_u \qquad [18]$$

When negative-sequence braking is taken into account, another term is included. Thus

$$P_a = P_i - P_b - P_u \qquad [19]$$

where P_b is the braking power. The term P_u, as before, represents only the positive-sequence power output.

The reason that negative-sequence electric power does not appear in eq. 19 will be shown by the following "balance sheet" of power. The mechanical power input at the shaft is consumed in the following ways:

1. Rate of increase of kinetic energy.
2. Positive-sequence power output at terminals.
3. Negative-sequence power output at terminals.
4. Positive-sequence stator copper loss.
5. Negative-sequence stator copper loss.
6. Half of negative-sequence rotor copper loss.
7. Other half of negative-sequence rotor copper loss.
8. Rotational loss.

Item 3 is actually a negative quantity; that is, there is a negative-sequence input at the armature terminals. This input supplies the losses of items 5 and 6. Hence, items 3, 5, and 6 add to zero and may be dropped from the list. Item 1 is P_a. Item 2 plus item 4 is P_u, the power supplied by the machine to the positive-sequence network, the latter including the armature resistance. Item 7 is P_b, the braking power. The shaft input less item 8 is P_i. Thus eq. 19 is justified.

Negative-sequence braking can be neglected except in machines having a high-resistance damper winding. It exists, even in such machines, only during the existence of an unbalanced fault.

EXAMPLE 1 229

Example 1

A hydroelectric station is delivering rated load at unity power factor and at normal voltage to a receiving system which may be considered as an infinite bus. Between the hydroelectric station and the receiving system is a double-circuit high-voltage transmission line having a positive-sequence reactance of 0.40 per unit and a zero-sequence reactance of 0.75 per unit on

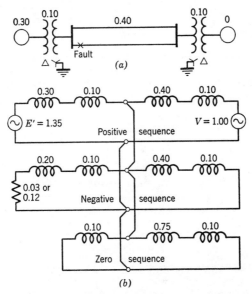

Fig. 5. (a) One-line diagram and (b) sequence networks of the power system of Example 1.

a base equal to the rating of the station. (See Fig. 5a.) The transformers at each end of the line have a reactance of 0.10 per unit on the same base. They are connected in Δ on the low-voltage side and in Y, with solidly grounded neutral, on the high-voltage side. The generators have the following per-unit constants:

$$x_d' = 0.30 \qquad r_1 = 0.005$$

$$x_2 = 0.20 \qquad H = 3.0$$

With low-resistance dampers,

$$r_2 = 0.03$$

but, with high-resistance dampers,

$$r_2 = 0.12$$

Calculate the initial accelerating power of the generators for each type of damper during a two-line-to-ground fault adjacent to the high-voltage sending-end bus, and again for a line-to-line fault at the same place. Neglect the effect of all resistance except the negative-sequence resistance of the generators.

Solution. *Prefault condition.* Assume that the voltage behind x_d' is constant. The initial value of this voltage is

$$\mathbf{E}' = \mathbf{V} + jx\mathbf{I} \qquad (a)$$
$$= 1.00 + j0.9 \times 1.00$$
$$= 1.35 \underline{/42.0°}$$

Two-line-to-ground fault. The sequence networks are shown in Fig. 5b, connected to represent a two-line-to-ground fault. The reduction of the network is shown in Fig. 6. In Fig. 6a the identity of the negative-sequence path through the generators is preserved. The current in this branch must

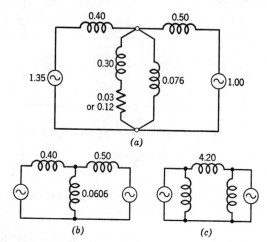

Fig. 6. Reduction of the network of Fig. 5 (Example 1).

be found in order to calculate the negative-sequence braking torque. The resistance of this branch has two values, one for each type of damper. However, as this resistance has a negligible effect on the positive-sequence power, it is omitted in the further reduction of the fault shunt, as shown in Fig. 6b. In Fig. 6c the T circuit has been changed into a π, whose architrave reactance is 4.20 per unit. The initial positive-sequence power output of the generators while the fault is present is, accordingly,

$$P_u = \frac{E'V}{X}\sin\delta = \frac{1.35 \times 1.00}{4.20}\sin 42.0° \qquad (b)$$
$$= 0.321 \times 0.669 = 0.215 \text{ per unit}$$

EXAMPLE 1   231

The initial mechanical input is the same as before the fault, or 1.000 per unit. The initial accelerating power, with negative-sequence braking neglected, is therefore (by eq. 18):

$$P_a = P_i - P_u = 1.000 - 0.215 = 0.785 \text{ per unit} \qquad (c)$$

The negative-sequence braking torque will now be calculated for each type of damper. The initial voltage across the fault shunt is almost independent of the negative-sequence resistance. Let it be called $\mathbf{V}_f$. Then application of Kirchhoff's current law to Fig. 6b yields:

$$\frac{1.35 \,\underline{/42.0°} - \mathbf{V}_f}{j0.40} + \frac{1.00 \,\underline{/0} - \mathbf{V}_f}{j0.50} - \frac{\mathbf{V}_f}{j0.0606} = 0 \qquad (d)$$

$$\mathbf{V}_f \left(\frac{1}{0.40} + \frac{1}{0.50} + \frac{1}{0.0606} \right) = \frac{1.35 \,\underline{/42.0°}}{0.40} + \frac{1.00 \,\underline{/0}}{0.50}$$

$$21.0\mathbf{V}_f = 3.37 \,\underline{/42.0°} + 2.00 \,\underline{/0}$$
$$= 2.00 + 2.50 + j2.26$$

$$21.0V_f = \sqrt{(4.50)^2 + (2.26)^2} = 5.04$$

$$V_f = 0.240 \text{ per unit}$$

The negative-sequence current in the generators with high-resistance dampers is:

$$I_2 = \frac{0.240}{\sqrt{(0.12)^2 + (0.30)^2}} = \frac{0.240}{0.323} = 0.743 \text{ per unit}$$

With low-resistance dampers it is:

$$I_2 = \frac{0.240}{\sqrt{(0.03)^2 + (0.30)^2}} = \frac{0.240}{0.301} = 0.797 \text{ per unit}$$

The negative-sequence braking torque with high-resistance dampers is (by eq. 17):

$$P_b = I_2{}^2(r_2 - r_1) = (0.743)^2(0.120 - 0.005)$$
$$= 0.063 \text{ per unit}$$

and with low-resistance dampers:

$$P_b = (0.797)^2(0.030 - 0.005) = 0.016 \text{ per unit}$$

The accelerating power with high-resistance dampers is (by eq. 19):

$$P_a = (P_i - P_u) - P_b = 0.785 - 0.063 = 0.722 \text{ per unit}$$

With low-resistance dampers, it is:

$$P_a = 0.785 - 0.016 = 0.769 \text{ per unit}$$

Line-to-line fault. The connections of the sequence networks for representing this type of fault are as shown in Fig. 5, except that the zero-sequence network is omitted. The reduction of the networks proceeds as in Fig. 6, except that the shunt reactance shown as 0.076 per unit in Fig. 6a becomes 0.50 per unit; that shown as 0.0606, Fig. 6b, becomes 0.187 with resistance neglected; and the architrave reactance shown as 4.20 per unit, Fig. 6c, becomes 1.97 per unit. The last substitution, when made in eq. b, gives the positive-sequence electrical output as $1.35 \times 0.669/1.97 = 0.458$ per unit. Therefore the accelerating power with dampers neglected is $1.000 - 0.458 = 0.542$ per unit. The second substitution, made in eq. d, yields:

$$9.83 \ V_f = 5.04$$

$$V_f = 0.513 \text{ per unit}$$

With high-resistance dampers,

$$I_2 = \frac{0.513}{0.323} = 1.59 \text{ per unit}$$

$$P_b = (1.59)^2 \times 0.115 = 0.290 \text{ per unit}$$

$$P_a = 0.542 - 0.290 = 0.252 \text{ per unit}$$

With low-resistance dampers

$$I_2 = \frac{0.513}{0.301} = 1.70 \text{ per unit}$$

$$P_b = (1.70)^2 \times 0.025 = 0.073 \text{ per unit}$$

$$P_a = 0.542 - 0.073 = 0.469 \text{ per unit}$$

A *summary of results* is given in Table 5. From these results we may conclude that the high-resistance dampers are more effective than the low-

TABLE 5

SUMMARY OF RESULTS, EXAMPLE 1
NEGATIVE-SEQUENCE BRAKING POWER

Type of Fault	Accelerating Power in Per Unit		
	Dampers Neglected	Low-Resistance Dampers	High-Resistance Dampers
Two-line-to-ground	0.785	0.769	0.722
Line-to-line	0.542	0.469	0.252

resistance dampers in producing negative-sequence braking and that such braking is present to a much greater extent during a line-to-line fault than during a two-line-to-ground fault. However, as faults not involving ground are of infrequent occurrence on steel-tower, high-voltage transmission lines, and as two-line-to-ground faults are usually assumed in calculations of stability limits, not much advantage can be taken of the effectiveness of high-resistance dampers on line-to-line faults. The use of high-speed switching, moreover, reduces the benefits of dampers in producing negative-sequence braking.

Calculation of d-c. braking. For three-phase faults at or very near the armature terminals of a machine, the d-c. components of short-circuit armature current persist long enough to have an appreciable effect. The d-c. components of armature current induce in the rotor circuits currents of fundamental frequency, which give rise to a braking torque similar to that caused by negative-sequence armature currents. The d-c. braking torque (or power), like the negative-sequence braking torque, decreases the accelerating torque, and may be considered as all or part of P_b in eq. 19.

Although the rotor currents induced by direct armature currents are of fundamental frequency, whereas those induced by negative-sequence armature currents are of twice fundamental frequency, nevertheless for a given magnitude of armature current the magnitudes of the various rotor currents are substantially the same in the two cases, being determined mainly by the reactances. There is, however, this important difference: that whereas in the negative-sequence case *half* the rotor copper loss was supplied mechanically and therefore produced braking torque, in the d-c. case *all* the rotor copper loss is supplied mechanically. This loss, expressed in per unit, is $I_r{}^2 R_r$, or twice the value given by eq. 15. Using the same value of R_r as before, we get for the d-c. braking power twice the value given by eq. 17, namely:

$$P_b \approx 2 I_s{}^2 (r_2 - r_1) \qquad [20]$$

Here I_s is the *effective* value of the armature currents, which we can imagine to be polyphase currents of very low frequency, whose instantaneous values equal the direct armature currents. The *crest* value of these polyphase currents corresponds to the *total* direct current, that is, to the value of d-c. component that would exist in one phase of the armature if the switching angle were such as to give this component its maximum value. As stated in Chapter XII, for an unloaded machine the total direct current is initially equal to the initial crest value of the a-c. component of armature short-circuit current and decays exponentially with time constant T_a. If the total instantaneous d-c. component of armature current is denoted by i_{dc}, the expression for d-c. braking power becomes

$$P_b \approx i_{dc}{}^2 (r_2 - r_1) \qquad [21]$$

Note that as i_{dc} decreases exponentially P_b also decreases.

For types of fault other than three-phase and for faults not very near the armature terminals, i_{dc} decays so rapidly that its braking effect is negligible.

Calculation of positive-sequence damping. The slip of the rotor with respect to the positive-sequence armature voltage is small and varies both in magnitude and sign. Equation 10 and Fig. 4 show that at small slips the torque of an induction machine is almost directly proportional to the slip. In the practical calculation of positive-sequence damping, therefore, the damping torque — and likewise the damping power — are assumed to be proportional to the slip. However, because of the difference between the direct and quadrature axes, the constant of proportionality depends upon the angular position of the rotor. These two features appear in an equation, derived by Park[10] and quoted in modified form by Dahl,[1] for the damping power of a synchronous machine connected to an infinite bus through series reactance. In the derivation, the following assumptions were made:

1. No resistance in armature circuit.
2. No resistance in field circuit.
3. Small slip.
4. Damping action caused by only one set of rotor windings (the damper windings).

The equation for damping power is:

$$P_D = E^2 s\omega \left[\frac{(x_d{}' - x_d{}'')T_{d0}{}''}{(x_e + x_d{}')^2} \sin^2 \delta + \frac{(x_q{}' - x_q{}'')T_{q0}{}''}{(x_e + x_q{}')^2} \cos^2 \delta \right] \quad [22]$$

where P_D = instantaneous damping power in per unit.

E = voltage of infinite bus in per unit.

s = slip in per unit (see discussion in next paragraph).

$\omega = 2\pi \times$ rated frequency.

$x_d{}'$, $x_d{}''$, $x_q{}'$, $x_q{}''$ = machine reactances in per unit, as previously defined (Chapter XII).

x_e = external reactance in per unit in series with armature.

$T_{d0}{}''$, $T_{q0}{}''$ = open-circuit subtransient time constants in the direct and quadrature axes, respectively, both expressed in seconds.

δ = angle by which the machine leads the angle of the infinite bus.

In stability calculations it is preferable to take P_D and s as positive when there is induction generator action, even though to do so is contrary to the usual conventions of induction-motor theory.   Then, in eq. 22,

$$s = \frac{1}{360f} \cdot \frac{d\delta}{dt} \qquad [23]$$

where f is the frequency of the infinite bus in cycles per second and $d\delta/dt$ is in electrical degrees per second.

Derivation of equation.   The rigorous derivation of eq. 22 is too long and complicated to be given here, but a derivation based on induction-machine theory and leading to the same result will be presented.   It must first be assumed that the rotor is symmetrical (that is, alike on both axes) and that the field windings are closed but not excited.*

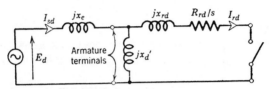

FIG. 7.   Direct-axis equivalent circuit of synchronous machine, for calculation of positive-sequence damping.   The quadrature-axis circuit is similar.

In order to apply induction-machine theory, we must next establish an equivalent circuit similar to Fig. 2 but with its constants expressed in terms of the usual synchronous-machine reactances and time constants.   The three sets of windings (armature, field, and damper) are inductively coupled, somewhat like the windings of a three-circuit transformer.   However, since we wish to find the damper current I_r due to the armature voltage E, we can set up an equivalent T circuit in which the identity of the armature and damper circuits only is preserved, while the identity of the field circuit is lost, even though the presence of the field circuit affects the impedance of the common branch of the T, much as the eddy-current paths do in the equivalent T circuit of a two-winding transformer or machine.   Such a circuit is shown in Fig. 7.   As discussed in Chapter XII, the reactance of either series arm ("leakage reactance") can be made zero by proper choice of the arbitrary ratio of transformation.   Let the armature leakage reactance of the machine itself be set equal to zero in this manner, leaving only the external reactance x_e in the series arm.   The impedance seen from the armature terminals, with the field winding short-circuited and the damper winding open, is the transient reactance $x_d{}'$.   Conse-

---

*It can be shown that the excitation does not affect the damping torque if the armature resistance is negligible.

quently, the shunt arm of the equivalent T circuit is x_d'. By analogy with the equivalent circuit of the induction motor, the damper branch of the equivalent circuit has a resistance R_{rd}/s, where R_{rd} is the damper resistance (referred to the armature) and s is the slip. At large slips R_{rd}/s is negligibly small, and the impedance seen from the armature terminals is the subtransient reactance x_d''. Therefore, the damper leakage reactance x_{rd} must have a value such that, in parallel with x_d', it gives a reactance x_d''. Thus,

$$x_d'' = \frac{x_{rd} x_d'}{x_{rd} + x_d'} \qquad [24]$$

whence

$$x_{rd} = \frac{x_d' x_d''}{x_d' - x_d''} \qquad [25]$$

Now that the equivalent circuit has been established, expressions will be found for the stator and rotor currents. The former is

$$I_s = \frac{E}{jx_e + \dfrac{(R_{rd}/s + jx_{rd})(jx_d')}{R_{rd}/s + j(x_{rd} + x_d')}} \qquad [26]$$

which, at small slip, becomes

$$I_s \approx \frac{E}{j(x_e + x_d')} \qquad [27]$$

The latter is

$$I_r = I_s \frac{jx_d'}{R_{rd}/s + j(x_{rd} + x_d')}$$

$$\approx I_s \frac{jx_d'}{R_{rd}/s} \qquad [28]$$

which, upon substitution of eq. 27, becomes

$$I_r \approx \frac{Ex_d'}{(x_e + x_d')R_{rd}/s} \qquad [29]$$

The damping power (by eq. 5) is

$$P_D = I_r^2 R_{rd} \frac{1-s}{s} = \frac{E^2(x_d')^2(1-s)s}{(x_e + x_d')^2 R_{rd}} \qquad [30]$$

The factor $(1 - s)$ may be discarded because, by assumption, s is very small. The damper resistance R_{rd} will be replaced by an expression involving the direct-axis subtransient open-circuit time constant T_{do}''. Since the resistance of the field circuit is neglected, this time constant is the ratio of the equivalent inductance of the damper winding to the resistance of the damper winding, the equivalent inductance being determined with the field winding closed and the armature winding open (because we want the open-circuit time constant). According to the equivalent circuit (Fig. 7), the reactance corresponding to the equivalent inductance of the damper is $x_{rd} + x_d'$. By eqs. 24 and 25, it may be written also as

$$x_{rd} + x_d' = \frac{x_{rd}x_d'}{x_d''} = \frac{(x_d')^2}{x_d' - x_d''} = x \qquad [31]$$

Hence the time constant is

$$T_{d0}'' = \frac{L}{R_{rd}} = \frac{x}{\omega R_{rd}} = \frac{(x_d')^2}{\omega(x_d' - x_d'')R_{rd}} \qquad [32]$$

from which

$$R_{rd} = \frac{(x_d')^2}{\omega(x_d' - x_d'')T_{d0}''} \qquad [33]$$

By use of this expression for R_{rd}, eq. 30 becomes:

$$P_D = \frac{E^2(x_d' - x_d'')\omega T_{d0}'' s}{(x_e + x_d')^2} \qquad [34]$$

If the rotor is unsymmetrical, the damping power fluctuates at twice the slip frequency between the value given by eq. 34 and that given by a similar equation containing the corresponding quadrature-axis constants. The resultant fluctuating damping power is found by substituting for E in eq. 34 and in the corresponding quadrature-axis equation its direct- and quadrature-axis components, namely:

$$E_d = E \sin \delta \qquad [35a]$$

$$E_q = E \cos \delta \qquad [35b]$$

Thus, the direct-axis damping power is:

$$P_{Dd} = \frac{E^2 \sin^2 \delta \ (x_d' - x_d'')\omega T_{d0}'' s}{(x_e + x_d')^2} \qquad [36a]$$

The quadrature-axis damping power is:

$$P_{Dq} = \frac{E^2 \cos^2 \delta \ (x_q' - x_q'')\omega T_{q0}'' s}{(x_e + x_q')^2} \qquad [36b]$$

The total damping power is the sum of eqs. 36, which is eq. 22.

Effect of armature resistance. In large machines with effective damper windings, the effect of armature resistance is usually negligible. When it is not negligible, its effect is to decrease the damping torque, and in extreme cases the net damping may be negative, leading to sustained hunting. Approximate equations for damping torque, taking both saliency and armature resistance into account, are given by Liwschitz.[13]

Extension to multimachine system. Although eq. 22 was derived for one machine connected to an infinite bus, its use can be extended first to a system of two finite machines and then to a multimachine system.

First consider two finite machines. In calculating the damping power of one machine, the other machine can be represented (at least approximately) by a constant e.m.f. in series with a constant reactance. According to Thévenin's theorem, the latter machine and the intervening network, viewed from the terminals of the former machine, can be replaced by an equivalent e.m.f. and impedance in series. The equivalent e.m.f. then takes the place of the voltage E of the infinite bus in eq. 22, while the equivalent impedance (in which the resistance is usually small compared with the reactance) takes the place of the external reactance x_e. The damping power of the other machine can be computed in similar fashion, using new values of E and x_e.

In a multimachine system a similar procedure can be followed. In calculating the damping of any one machine, the remainder of the system, viewed from the terminals of that machine, is replaced by an equivalent e.m.f. and impedance, according to Thévenin's theorem, and these are used as E and x_e, respectively, in eq. 22. The equivalent e.m.f. and impedance may be found on an a-c. calculating board, as follows: The machine whose damping is being calculated is disconnected from the rest of the system, and the open-circuit voltage of the system is measured in both magnitude and phase. It is the equivalent e.m.f. **E**. The equivalent impedance can be found by dividing **E** by the short-circuit current of the system (not including the machine in question).

In the course of a point-by-point determination of swing curves, **E** is read at each step. It varies both in phase and in magnitude. The slip s is calculated by eq. 23, taking δ as the *difference* of angles of the machine in question and of **E**, and replacing $d\delta/dt$ by $\Delta\delta/\Delta t$. In order that $\Delta\delta/\Delta t$ may represent the slip at the particular instant of time for which P_D is being calculated, $\Delta\delta$ should be taken as the average for the intervals immediately preceding and immediately following the instant. However, as $\Delta\delta$ for the latter interval depends upon P_D, and therefore cannot be calculated until after P_D has been calculated, it must be estimated by extrapolation. Then, if the estimated value of $\Delta\delta$ does not agree with the value calculated from the accelerating power and inertia constant, successive approximations can be made until satisfactory agreement is reached.

The calculation of damping power in a multimachine system is probably less rigorous than in a two-machine system because in the multimachine system the magnitude of E may vary, because of the relative swinging of the several machines comprising the remainder of the system. This variation of E is a departure from the idea of an infinite bus, as assumed in the derivation of eq. 22.

Accelerating power. After the damping power P_D has been computed, as just described, it is taken into account as an additional component of positive-sequence electric output power; hence it diminishes the accelerating power. The expression for accelerating power (replacing eqs. 18 and 19) is:

$$P_a = P_i - P_b - P_D - P_u \qquad [37]$$

where, as before, P_i is the mechanical power input; P_b, the negative-sequence braking power; P_u, the positive-sequence synchronous power output; and, in addition, P_D is the positive-sequence damping power output.

Flow of damping power in the positive-sequence network. When damping occurs, the positive-sequence power output of the machine is the algebraic sum of the damping power and the synchronous power (calculated as though the machine had no damper windings). If the former is much smaller than the latter, it may be sufficiently accurate to solve the positive-sequence network as though only the synchronous components of power existed. Then cognizance of the damping power would be taken only in the calculation of accelerating power (eq. 37). From the values of accelerating power of every machine of the system, the new angular positions of the machines would be calculated, and the network again solved taking only synchronous power into account.

If, however, the damping power should be as great as 5% or 10% of the synchronous power, it might affect conditions in the network sufficiently to warrant taking it into account in the network solution.

The circuit of Fig. 7 gives a clue as to how damping power can be represented on an a-c. calculating board if saliency is neglected. To the usual representation of a synchronous machine, consisting of the transient reactance in series with the voltage behind transient reactance, there is added a parallel branch. When the machine is running slow, the added branch may consist merely of a resistance R_{rd}/s, adjusted to absorb an amount of power equal to the calculated

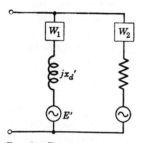

FIG. 8. Representation of a synchronous machine by two phase shifters: one to supply or absorb synchronous power P_u, as usual; the other to supply or absorb damping power P_D. Wattmeter W_1 reads P_u; W_2 reads P_D.

negative (accelerating) damping power. However, when the machine is running fast, a *source* of power is required to represent the damping power; and the only practical source is one of the phase shifters ordinarily used to represent generators. Then two phase shifters are used to represent one synchronous machine, as shown in Fig. 8. The phase shifter that supplies (or absorbs) synchronous power is adjusted, as usual, to have the proper voltage (usually constant) behind transient reactance at the proper angular position δ, as calculated for each step. The phase shifter that supplies (or absorbs) damping power is adjusted to have a power output equal to the calculated damping power and to have unity

power factor, or no reactive power. These adjustments are readily made with the aid of a wattmeter-varmeter. Unity power factor is assumed because, in Fig. 7, $R_{rd}/s \gg x_{rd}$.

EXAMPLE 2

A 60-cycle salient-pole synchronous generator having the following constants:

Reactances in per unit

$$x_d = 1.15 \qquad x_d' = 0.37 \qquad x_d'' = 0.24$$
$$x_q = 0.75 \qquad x_q' = 0.75 \qquad x_q'' = 0.34$$

Time constants in seconds

$$T_{d0}' = 5.0 \qquad T_{d0}'' = 0.035 \qquad T_{q0}'' = 0.035$$

is delivering a current of 1.00 per unit at a power factor of 0.91, lagging, to an infinite bus having a voltage of 1.00 per unit. A three-phase short circuit occurring at the terminals of the generator is cleared in 0.20 sec. without disconnecting the generator from the bus. Calculate and plot a swing curve, taking into account both field decrement and damping. Compare the curve with those obtained in Example 8, Chapter XII, in which damping was neglected.

NOTE: The generator constants, the prefault conditions, the fault, and the time of clearing are the same as in Example 8.

EXAMPLE 2   241

Solution. There is no damping during the fault. Consequently, when the fault is cleared, 0.20 sec. after its occurrence, conditions are the same as in Example 8 with field decrement taken into account; namely,

$$\delta = 106.0°$$

$$E_q' = 1.04 \text{ per unit}$$

The swing curve after 0.20 sec. is calculated, as before, from the relation (eq. e of Example 8):

$$\Delta^2\delta = 10.8 P_a \tag{a}$$

where now, taking damping into account,

$$P_a = P_i - P_u - P_D = 0.91 - (P_u + P_D) \tag{b}$$

The synchronous power is calculated as before, by eq. g of Example 8:

$$P_u = 2.70 E_q' \sin\delta - 0.685 \sin 2\delta \tag{c}$$

Herein E_q' may be assumed to be the same as it was in Example 8, Table 12, since it was found to decrease at a fairly constant rate (Fig. 44, Chapter XII), which will not be affected by the damping. The damping power is calculated from eqs. 22 and 23:

$$P_D = \frac{E^2 \times 2\pi f \Delta\delta}{360 f \Delta t}\left[\frac{(x_d'-x_d'')T_{d0}''}{(x_e+x_d')^2}\sin^2\delta + \frac{(x_q'-x_q'')T_{q0}''}{(x_e+x_q')^2}\cos^2\delta\right]$$

$$= \frac{(1.00)^2 \times 2\pi\Delta\delta}{360 \times 0.05}\left[\frac{(0.37-0.24)0.035}{(0+0.37)^2}\sin^2\delta + \frac{(0.75-0.34)0.035}{(0+0.75)^2}\cos^2\delta\right]$$

$$= (0.0116 \sin^2\delta + 0.0089 \cos^2\delta)\Delta\delta$$

$$= (0.0102 + 0.0014 \cos 2\delta)\Delta\delta \tag{d}$$

Since the fluctuation of damping power with δ is small, it will be sufficiently accurate to use the average value,

$$P_D = 0.0102\Delta\delta \tag{e}$$

taking $\Delta\delta$ as the average value for the time intervals immediately preceding and following the instant for which P_D and P_a are to be computed.

The swing calculations are carried out in Table 6.

The swing curve is plotted as curve c in Fig. 9. Curves a and b are plotted from the results of Example 8, Chapter XII, in which damping is neglected. Comparison of the three curves shows that the beneficial effect of damping almost compensates for the detrimental effect of field decrement even though the fault lasts for more than two-thirds of the time required for the machine to swing to its maximum angular displacement from the bus. Consequently, the assumptions of constant flux linkage and negligible damping lead to but little error. If the fault had been cleared sooner, damping probably would have been more effective in reducing the amplitude of swing.

TABLE 6

Computation of Swing Curve After Clearing of Fault — Damping and Field Decrement Taken into Account (Example 2)

t (sec.)	E_q' (p.u.)	$\sin \delta$	$\sin 2\delta$	$2.70 E_q'$ $\sin \delta$	-0.685 $\sin 2\delta$	P_u (p.u.)	$\Delta\delta$ (est.)	P_D (p.u.)	P_a (p.u.)	$\Delta^2\delta$ (deg.)	$\Delta\delta$ (deg.)	δ (deg.)
0.20−	1.04					0		0	0.91		34.4	
0.20+	1.04	0.961	−0.530	2.70	+0.36	3.06	30.8	0.31	−2.46			
0.20 avg.	1.04								−0.78	− 8.4		106.0
0.25	1.02	0.743	−0.994	2.04	+0.68	2.72	15.2	0.15	−1.96	−21.2	26.0	132.0
0.30	0.99	0.686	−0.998	1.83	+0.68	2.51	− 4.0	−0.04	−1.56	−16.8	4.8	136.8
0.35	0.96	0.823	−0.935	2.13	+0.64	2.77	−21.0	−0.21	−1.65	−17.8	−12.0	124.8
0.40											−29.8	95.0

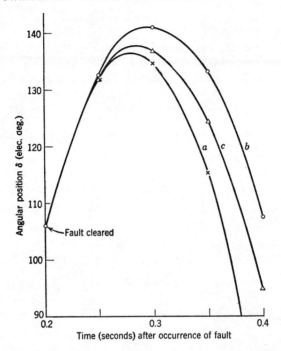

FIG. 9. Effect of damping upon swing curves (Example 2). (*a*) Damping and field decrement neglected (constant flux linkage). (*b*) Damping neglected, but decrement taken into account. (*c*) Damping and decrement taken into account.

Power-angle curve with damping included. The electric power output of a synchronous machine consists, as has already been pointed out, of two components: synchronous power P_u, which is a function of the angular position of the machine relative to the other machines, and induction-generator or damping power P_D, which is a function of the relative angular velocity. The ordinary power-angle curve of a two-machine system is a curve of P_u versus angular difference δ and is a single-valued function of δ. The operating point moves along this curve, its position being a function of time, and, if the motion is oscillatory, the two extreme points, reached in each oscillation, are so placed that the net area between the curve of P_u and the horizontal line P_i is zero. The effect of damping may be shown in the power-angle curve by adding P_D to the ordinates, thus showing the total electric power output $P_u + P_D$ as a function of δ. The new curve lies above the old one when δ is increasing and below it when δ is decreasing, and forms a spiral of approximately elliptical form, as shown in Fig. 10.   Each successive oscillation is smaller, and the curve converges on the point of equilibrium, which is the intersection of the curve of P_u and the horizontal line of P_i.   The principle of equal areas still applies: the net area between the curve of $P_u + P_D$ and the line P_i is zero at the extreme values of δ, where the velocity is zero — points $B, D, G, J,$ and M in Fig. 10.   Area $ABC =$ area CDE; area $DEF =$ area FGH; area $GHI =$ area IJK; and area $JKL =$ area LMN.

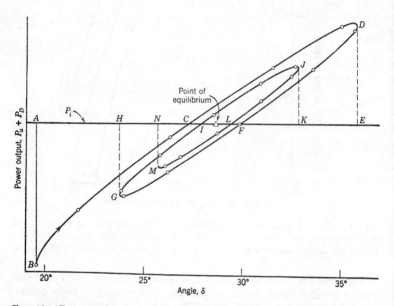

FIG. 10.   Power-angle curve with damping included.   (Plotted from data of Ref. 11.   The marked points are for equal intervals of time.)

Heating effect of rotor currents.[20-24]   When a synchronous machine is subjected to an unbalanced short circuit, negative-sequence currents are induced in the rotor.   Because of the high frequency of these currents, they are confined to paths near the surface of the rotor, such as the damper windings and pole faces of a salient-pole machine or the slot wedges of a round-rotor machine, with the retaining rings acting as end connections between wedges.   These paths have a relatively high resistance and much heat is developed in them.   If the currents are sustained for more than a few seconds, the heat may cause damage: the slot wedges of turbogenerators may be heated to a temperature where they lose their mechanical strength to resist the high centrifugal forces and fail in shear, or the retaining rings may expand from heat and part contact with the rotor body, thus giving rise to arcing at the shrink fits between rings and rotor body. Experience has shown that the machine will not be injured if $\int I_2{}^2 dt$ does not exceed 30, I_2 being the negative-sequence current in per-unit and t, the time in seconds.

REFERENCES

1. O. G. C. Dahl, *Electric Power Circuits: Theory and Applications*, Vol. II, "Power System Stability," McGraw-Hill Book Co., Inc., New York, 1938. Chap. XIX, "Damper Windings and Their Effect."

2. *Electrical Transmission and Distribution Reference Book*, by Central Station Engineers of the Westinghouse Electric & Manufacturing Co., East Pittsburgh, Pa., 1st edition, 1942, pp. 141–5, 160–3, 200–1.

3. C. F. Wagner, "Damper Windings for Water-Wheel Generators," *A.I.E.E. Trans.*, vol. 50, pp. 140–51, March, 1931. Disc., pp. 151–2.

4. C. F. Wagner, "Unsymmetrical Short Circuits on Water-Wheel Generators Under Capacitive Loading," *Elec. Eng.*, vol. 56, pp. 1385–95, November, 1937.

5. C. F. Wagner, "Overvoltages on Water-Wheel Generators," *Elec. Jour.*, vol. 35, pp. 321–5 and 351–4, August and September, 1938.

6. Edith Clarke, C. N. Weygandt, and C. Concordia, "Overvoltages Caused by Unbalanced Short Circuits — Effect of Amortisseur Windings," *A.I.E.E. Trans.*, vol. 57, pp. 453–66, August, 1938. Disc., pp. 466–8.

7. R. B. George and B. B. Bessesen, "Generator Damper Windings at Wilson Dam," *A.I.E.E. Trans.*, vol. 58, pp. 166–71, April, 1939. Disc., pp. 171–2. Installation of dampers on generator which had been in service 12 years without dampers in order to decrease harmonic overvoltages during unsymmetrical short circuits with capacitive loading.

8. C. A. Nickle and C. A. Pierce, "Stability of Synchronous Machines: Effect of Armature Circuit Resistance," *A.I.E.E. Trans.*, vol. 49, pp. 338–50, January, 1930. Disc., pp. 350–1.

9. C. F. Wagner, "Effect of Armature Resistance Upon Hunting of Synchronous Machines," *A.I.E.E. Trans.*, vol. 49, pp. 1011–24, July, 1930. Disc., pp. 1024–6.

10. R. H. Park, "Two-Reaction Theory of Synchronous Machines," Part I, *A.I.E.E. Trans.*, vol. 48, pp. 716–27, July, 1929. Disc., pp. 727–30. Part II, *A.I.E.E. Trans.*, vol. 52, pp. 352–4, June, 1933. Disc., pp. 354–5.

11. S. B. Crary and M. L. Waring, "Torque-Angle Characteristics of Synchronous Machines Following System Disturbances," *A.I.E.E. Trans.*, vol. 51, pp. 764–73, September, 1932. Disc., pp. 773–4.

12. F. A. Hamilton, Jr., "Field Tests to Determine the Damping Characteristics of Synchronous Generators," *A.I.E.E. Trans.*, vol. 51, pp. 775–9, September, 1932.

13. M. M. Liwschitz, "Positive and Negative Damping in Synchronous Machines," *A.I.E.E. Trans.*, vol. 60, pp. 210–3, May, 1941.

14. Roger Coe and H. R. Stewart, "Generator Stability Features Fifteen Mile Falls Development," *Elec. Jour.*, vol. 28, pp. 139–43, March, 1931.

15. C. Concordia and G. K. Carter, "Negative Damping of Electrical Machinery," *A.I.E.E. Trans.*, vol. 60, pp. 116–9, March, 1941. Disc., p. 752.

16. WILLIAM L. RINGLAND, "Damper Windings for Waterwheel and Diesel Engine Driven Generators," *Proc. Midwest Power Conference* (Chicago), vol. 8, pp. 89–94, 1946.

17. LEE A. KILGORE and EUGENE C. WHITNEY, "Spring and Damping Coefficients of Synchronous Machines and Their Application," *A.I.E.E. Trans.*, vol. 69, part I, pp. 226–9, 1950. Disc., pp. 229–30.

18. CHARLES CONCORDIA, "Synchronous Machine Damping Torque at Low Speeds," *A.I.E.E. Trans.*, vol. 69, part II, pp. 1550–3, 1950.

19. CHARLES CONCORDIA, "Synchronous Machine Damping and Synchronizing Torques," *A.I.E.E. Trans.*, vol. 70, part I, pp. 731–7, 1951.

20. A. WUST and J. DISPAUX, "The Operation of Turbo-Alternators under Unbalanced or Out-of-Step Conditions," *C.I.G.R.E.*, 1952, Report 106.

21. R. F. LAWRENCE and R. W. FERGUSON, "Generator Negative-Sequence Currents for Line-to-Line Faults," *A.I.E.E. Trans.*, vol. 72, part III, pp. 9–16, February, 1953.

22. M. D. ROSS and E. I. KING, "Turbine-Generator Rotor Heating During Single-Phase Short Circuits," *A.I.E.E. Trans.*, vol. 72, part III, pp. 40–5, February, 1953.

23. P. L. ALGER, R. F. FRANKLIN, C. E. KILBOURNE, and J. B. McCLURE, "Short-Circuit Capabilities of Synchronous Machines for Unbalanced Faults," *A.I.E.E. Trans.*, vol. 72, part III, pp. 394–403, June, 1953. Disc., pp. 403–4.

24. E. I. POLLARD, "Effects of Negative-Sequence Currents on Turbine-Generator Rotors," *A.I.E.E. Trans.*, vol. 72, part III, pp. 404–6, June, 1953. Disc., p. 406.

25. TH. LAIBLE, "The Effect of Solid Poles and of Different Forms of Amortisseur on the Characteristics of Salient-Pole Alternators," *C.I.G.R.E.*, 1950, Report 111.

PROBLEMS ON CHAPTER XIV

1. Work Example 1 for a line-to-ground fault.

2. In Example 1 find the critical clearing time of a two-line-to-ground fault with and without negative-sequence braking of the generator due to high-resistance dampers.

3. Find the transient stability limit of the system of Example 1 with and without negative-sequence braking if a two-line-to-ground fault near the sending end is cleared in 0.1 sec.

4. In Example 1 find the value of r_2 that gives maximum negative-sequence braking power during (a) a two-line-to-ground fault at the sending end of the transmission line and (b) a line-to-line fault at the same location. Can the accelerating power be made zero in either case? Assume that x_2 is not affected by varying r_2.

5. Find the initial value in per unit of the d-c. braking torque produced in a typical turbogenerator due to a three-phase short-circuit on the armature terminals. Also find the torque 0.05 sec. later.

6. Work Example 2 taking into account the variation of positive-sequence damping due to saliency.

7. Work Example 2 neglecting saliency and field decrement. Carry out the swing curve for several cycles of swing and find the percentage decrease in amplitude of swing per cycle.

CHAPTER XV

STEADY-STATE STABILITY

Preceding chapters of this book have been devoted almost entirely to *transient stability*, which, as will be recalled, is the ability of the synchronous machines of a power system to remain in synchronism after a specified sudden, severe, unrepeated shock (usually a short circuit). This chapter discusses *steady-state stability*, which is the ability of synchronous machines to remain in synchronism after a very minute disturbance. Small disturbances are always present in a power system; for example, there are gradual changes in load, manual or automatic changes of excitation, irregularities in prime-mover input, and so forth. Obviously these small disturbances cannot cause loss of synchronism unless the system is operating at, or very near, its *steady-state stability limit*. This limit is the greatest power that can be transmitted on a specified circuit, under specified operating conditions in the steady state, without loss of synchronism. The steady-state stability limit of a circuit is greater than the transient stability limit of the same circuit under the same operating conditions.

Importance of steady-state stability. A knowledge of steady-state stability limits is important for the following reasons:

1. *A system can be operated above its transient stability limit but not above its steady-state limit.* When so operated it is stable as long as no fault occurs, or even if a fault does occur provided the fault is sufficiently less severe than that for which the transient limit was calculated. Since most faults on long overhead transmission lines are caused by lightning, it might well be considered prudent to operate such a line above its transient stability limit during fair weather and to reduce the load below the transient limit before the onset of a thunderstorm. Moreover, lines can be built that are virtually lightningproof,* and such lines can be operated prudently above their transient limits even during storms.

*While no line is completely immune to lightning, the severity of the lightning stroke (as measured by its current) required to flash over the line insulation depends upon such features of the line design as shielding due to ground wires, tower-footing resistance, spacing of line and ground conductors, and flashover voltage of line insulators. As the severity of lightning strokes varies greatly, the probability of flashover can be greatly reduced by improvement in these features of design.

Another instance of circuits operated above their transient stability limits is the following: Some generating stations feeding into metropolitan areas over long transmission lines were formerly operated sectionalized, each generator, or group of generators, being connected to the load area over a separate transmission circuit.[6] In the event of a fault on any main circuit, that circuit and the associated generators were disconnected. As automatic reclosing was not used, the transient stability limit was zero. This mode of operation was dictated by slow fault clearing, which would have caused loss of synchronism between the metropolitan system and the entire remote station if the latter were not sectionalized. The advent of faster relays and breakers has rendered this type of operation unnecessary and undesirable. (See Study 3, Chapter VII, Vol. I.)

In the several cases just described where lines are operated above the transient limits for a fault on the main line, the practical stability limit is largely determined by faults on other, more remote, perhaps lower voltage circuits which, in the aggregate, are faulted much more frequently than the main circuits. In many cases, however, the limits so determined are fairly close to the steady-state limits of the main circuits and may be approximated by subtracting a reasonable margin from the steady-state limit.

Tie lines interconnecting two large power systems are often designed for a normal power transfer which is small compared with the capacity of the systems. Unless the power flow on such lines is carefully controlled, steady-state pullout is likely to occur. Automatic control for tie-line loads is available and is widely used. This control utilizes impulses transmitted over communication circuits to the governors of the prime movers.

2. *The transient-stability limit can be raised by increasing the speed of clearing faults but cannot exceed the steady-state stability limit* of the final circuit (that is, with the faulted circuit disconnected unless high-speed reclosing is employed). The great improvements which have been made in relaying and circuit breaking (discussed in Vol. II) have already greatly raised the transient stability limits of many power systems and are available for raising those of others. Further improvements, particularly in the speeds of circuit breakers, may confidently be expected. Nevertheless, the steady-state stability limit of any system represents a "ceiling" which cannot be exceeded through improvements in relays and breakers but which is fixed primarily by the impedances of lines, generators, and other apparatus. When very short clearing times are used, the transient stability

limit, calculated on the basis of constant field flux (constant voltage behind transient reactance), may even exceed the steady-state limit with the faulted circuit switched out, calculated on the basis of constant field current (constant voltage behind saturated synchronous reactance) of value determined by the prefault condition. This is possible because the transient reactance of a synchronous machine is considerably smaller than its saturated synchronous reactance (discussed in a later section of this chapter). In such a case the system would actually be unstable — though probably not on the first swing — unless voltage regulators were used to prevent the transient field current from decaying too much. If, on the other hand, the calculated transient limit were below the steady-state limit, it would be concluded that the system was stable. This conclusion rests on the supposition that the amplitude of swings is decreased by damping fast enough to make up for the field decrement. The use of voltage regulators gives assurance of stability. When fast clearing is used (say 6 cycles or under) it is advisable to check the steady-state stability limits as well as the transient limits, lest an erroneous conclusion be reached on the basis of the latter alone. The same reasoning applies to the switching out of an unfaulted line.

Historically, steady-state stability was studied first. Then, as it was recognized that short circuits were the most severe hazard to stable operation, attention was directed to transient stability and its improvement. More recently, progress of the art of power-system protection has again directed attention to steady-state stability, though not to the disregard of transient stability. As mentioned above, the principal factors which again direct attention to steady-state stability are: (1) increased fault-clearing speeds, which make the transient limits closely approach the steady-state limits, and (2) increased reliability of transmission lines and other equipment, which makes faults less frequent and therefore makes it less dangerous to risk instability in the event of a fault. To this list might be added (3) improved methods of system operation and out-of-step relaying, which make the disturbance due to loss of synchronism less severe than formerly.

Transmission lines not exceeding 200 miles in length usually have rated loads well below the steady-state stability limit. At lengths of 300 miles or more steady-state stability may be a limiting factor.[16]

The steady-state stability limit, as defined above, is the maximum power that can be transmitted in the steady state without loss of synchronism. This definition needs to be made more precise.

In the first place, where should the power be measured? If a line has any loss, the maximum power at the sending end of the line is greater than the maximum power at the receiving end and occurs at a different angular separation. From a practical standpoint, however, the *received* power is more important than the sent power and, therefore, is to be understood even though not stated explicitly. There is no advantage in sending more power into the line if so doing does not increase the received power but only increases the losses.

In the second place, what is the nature of the disturbance that ultimately causes loss of synchronism if the stability limit is exceeded? The disturbance is taken as a *slow, sustained increase in load*. The rate of increase of load should be slow compared with the natural frequencies of mechanical oscillation of the machines and also compared with the rate of change of field flux in the machines. As a result, the slow change in load is accompanied by a slow adjustment of the angular displacements of the machine rotors, without oscillation, *but there is no change in the field currents*.

In the third place, what cognizance should be taken of the manual or automatic control of frequency and voltage? Any increase of load changes the system frequency and decreases the terminal voltages of the machines. After each small increment of load the generator inputs are assumed to be adjusted so as to maintain constant frequency and the field currents are assumed to be increased so as to maintain constant terminal voltages.* It is important to note that the increase of field currents occurs *after* the increase of load, as it would with manual control of the voltage. If the increase of field current should occur simultaneously with the increase of load, as it could if suitable voltage regulators were used, the stability limit would be increased significantly. The limit under this condition is called the *dynamic stability limit* or the *steady-state stability limit with automatic devices*; this is discussed briefly in Chapter XIII and also later in the present chapter. Unless otherwise specified, the steady-state stability limit is understood to be the static limit, that is, the limit with hand control.

To summarize the conditions just discussed: *The steady-state stability limit of a particular circuit of a power system may be defined as the maximum power at the receiving end of the circuit that can be transmitted without loss of synchronism if the load is increased in very small steps*

*In some cases other operating conditions may be specified than constant terminal voltage; for example, constant voltage at a point other than the machine terminals, or terminal voltage varying with load in a specified manner, or constant field current during large changes in load. The important point is that the operating conditions of the power system assumed in the analysis should agree with those that are likely to be used in actual operation of the system.

and if the field currents are changed after each increment of load so as to restore the normal operating conditions (usually constant terminal voltages).

This definition suffices for a two-machine system. For a multi-machine system, additional stipulations are necessary as to how the power is to be supplied and absorbed. Such stipulations are not included in any general definition but are decided upon in each individual stability study in accordance with the contemplated operating conditions.

Two-machine system with negligible losses. The type of power system whose steady-state stability limit can be found most simply consists of two synchronous machines, a generator and a motor, connected through a network of pure reactances. Because no power is lost in pure reactances, the electrical output of the generator is always equal to the electrical input of the motor. One power-angle curve can therefore be used to show how the power transmitted from the generator to the motor depends upon the angular separation of the rotors of the two machines, or upon the phase difference of the two internal voltages (behind saturated or equivalent synchronous reactances), under the condition of constant field currents (constant internal voltages). The equation of this curve is

$$P = \frac{E_1 E_2}{x} \sin \delta \qquad [1]$$

where P = power transmitted from machine 1 to machine 2.

   E_1 = internal voltage of machine 1.

   E_2 = internal voltage of machine 2.

   x = transfer reactance between the internal voltages; that is, the reactance of the architrave of the equivalent π circuit to which the reactive network, including the machine reactances, can be reduced.

   δ = angle by which E_1 leads E_2.

If the internal voltages are constant, the maximum power occurs at $\delta = 90°$ and is

$$P_m = \frac{E_1 E_2}{x} \qquad [2]$$

The system is stable at any value of power less than P_m, provided $\delta < 90°$. This may be shown as follows: Suppose that the shaft load on the motor is increased, thus causing the mechanical output to exceed the electrical input. There is then a net retarding torque, causing the motor to slow down and thereby to increase the angle δ. As δ

increases, the electrical input of the motor increases until it equals the mechanical output. At the same time the electrical output of the generator increases and for a while exceeds the mechanical input. There is then a net retarding torque on the generator. The frequency drops until it is corrected by the governor increasing the mechanical input of the generator. The system then operates in the steady state at the new load. The load can be increased in this manner in small steps until the maximum power given by eq. 2 is reached at $\delta = 90°$. Any further increase in mechanical power of either machine cannot be balanced by a corresponding increase in electric power. There is, therefore, an accelerating torque on the generator or a retarding torque on the motor, either of which increases δ. An increase of δ beyond 90° decreases the electric power. Both the accelerating torque of the generator and the retarding torque of the motor increase, δ increases rapidly, and synchronism is lost. The steady-state stability limit evidently is reached at $\delta = 90°$.

In the case just considered, the field currents of the machines were assumed constant. If the field currents are constant while the load is varied over a wide range, the terminal voltages of the machines will vary considerably. Usually it is desired that the terminal voltages have specified values, which are held as the load is increased, so that when the stability limit is reached the voltages still have the specified values. Nevertheless, as already explained, the voltage regulation is assumed to be so slow that pullout occurs under the condition of constant field current instead of constant terminal voltage. Accordingly, the angle δ between the internal voltages is 90° at pullout. Calculation is required to find the magnitudes of the internal voltages when the angle between them is 90° and the terminal voltages have their specified values. This calculation may be carried out by a cut-and-try process, which will now be illustrated, or graphically, as described later.

Example 1

Find the steady-state stability limit of a system (Fig. 1) consisting of a generator of equivalent reactance 0.60 unit connected to an infinite bus through a series reactance of 1.00 unit. The terminal voltage of the generator is held at 1.10 units and the voltage of the infinite bus, at 1.00 unit.

Solution. The vector diagram is that of Fig. 2. If the voltage of the infinite bus is taken as reference, the terminal voltages are

$$\mathbf{V}_1 = 1.10 \underline{/\theta}$$
$$\mathbf{V}_2 = 1.00 \underline{/0}$$

where θ is the angle between them.

EXAMPLE 1 **253**

Assume $\theta = 30°$. Then the current is

$$\mathbf{I} = \frac{\mathbf{V}_1 - \mathbf{V}_2}{jx_e} = \frac{1.10\underline{/30°} - 1.00\underline{/0}}{j1.00} = \frac{0.95 + j0.55 - 1.00}{j1.00}$$

$$= \frac{j0.55 - 0.05}{j1.00} = 0.55 + j0.05$$

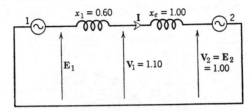

FIG. 1. Circuit of two-machine reactance system the steady-state stability limit of which is found in Example 1.

The internal voltage of the generator is

$$\mathbf{E}_1 = \mathbf{V}_1 + jx_1\mathbf{I} = 0.95 + j0.55 + j0.60(0.55 + j0.05)$$
$$= 0.95 + j0.55 + j0.33 - 0.03$$
$$= 0.92 + j0.88 = 1.27\underline{/44°}$$

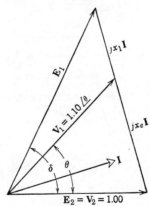

FIG. 2. Vector diagram of two-machine reactance system the steady-state stability limit of which is found in Example 1.

The angle between internal voltages is

$$\delta = 44°$$

and the transmitted power is

$$P = \frac{E_1 E_2}{x}\sin \delta = \frac{1.27 \times 1.00}{1.60}\sin 44° = 0.55$$

The power can be computed also from the reference voltage and the in-phase current:

$$P = 1.00 \times 0.55 = 0.55$$

The power-angle curve (power versus δ) is shown as A in Fig. 3. The maximum power with this value of excitation is $1.27 \times 1.00/1.60 = 0.79$. However, as the power is increased the excitation must also be increased.

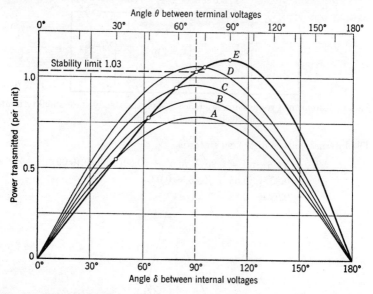

Fig. 3. Power-angle curves of the two-machine reactance system the steady-state stability limit of which is found in Example 1. Curves A, B, C, D are for constant excitation; curve E, for constant terminal voltage.

Next assume $\theta = 45°$.

$$\mathbf{I} = \frac{1.10\,\underline{/45°} - 1.00\,\underline{/0}}{j1.00} = \frac{0.78 + j0.78 - 1.00}{j1.00}$$

$$= \frac{-0.22 + j0.78}{j1.00} = 0.78 + j0.22$$

$$\mathbf{E_1} = 0.78 + j0.78 + j0.60(0.78 + j0.22)$$
$$= 0.78 + j0.78 + j0.47 - 0.13$$
$$= 0.65 + j1.25 = 1.41\,\underline{/62.5°}$$

$$\delta = 62.5°$$

$$P = 1.00 \times 0.78 = 0.78$$

EXAMPLE 1   255

The power-angle curve is shown as B in Fig. 3. The maximum power with this value of excitation is $1.41 \times 1.00/1.60 = 0.88$. However, the excitation should be further increased.

Next assume $\theta = 60°$.

$$\mathbf{I} = \frac{1.10 \underline{/60°} - 1.00 \underline{/0}}{j1.00} = \frac{0.55 + j0.95 - 1.00}{j1.00}$$

$$= \frac{-0.45 + j0.95}{j1.00} = 0.95 + j0.45$$

$$\mathbf{E}_1 = 0.55 + j0.95 + j0.60(0.95 + j0.45)$$
$$= 0.55 + j0.95 + j0.57 - 0.27$$
$$= 0.28 + j1.52 = 1.54 \underline{/79.5°}$$

$$\delta = 79.5°$$

$$P = 1.00 \times 0.95 = 0.95$$

The power-angle curve is shown as C in Fig. 3. The maximum power with this value of excitation is $1.54 \times 1.00/1.60 = 0.96$.

Next assume $\theta = 75°$.

$$\mathbf{I} = \frac{1.10 \underline{/75°} - 1.00 \underline{/0}}{j1.00} = \frac{0.28 + j1.06 - 1.00}{j1.00}$$

$$= \frac{-0.72 + j1.06}{j1.00} = 1.06 + j0.72$$

$$\mathbf{E}_1 = 0.28 + j1.06 + j0.60(1.06 + j0.72)$$
$$= 0.28 + j1.06 + j0.64 - 0.43$$
$$= -0.15 + j1.70 = 1.70 \underline{/95°}$$

$$\delta = 95°$$

$$P = 1.00 \times 1.06 = 1.06$$

The power-angle curve is shown as D in Fig. 3. The maximum power with this value of excitation is $1.70 \times 1.00/1.60 = 1.06$.

The system would be unstable with $\theta = 75°$ because $\delta > 90°$.

In Fig. 3, curve E is the locus of constant terminal voltages of the specified value. The power at $\delta = 90°$, read from this curve, is the steady-state stability limit. It is 1.03 per unit.

The value of θ at the stability limit is 70°. If θ could be increased to 90° without instability, the maximum power at the specified terminal voltages would be

$$P = \frac{V_1 V_2}{x_e} = \frac{1.10 \times 1.00}{1.00} = 1.10 \text{ per unit}$$

This is the crest value of curve E of Fig. 3. If curve E had been plotted against θ, the angle between terminal voltages, it would have been sinusoidal; but, being plotted against δ, the angle between internal voltages, it is distorted.

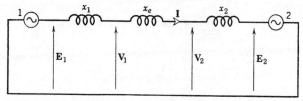

FIG. 4. Two synchronous machines connected through external reactance x_e.

Clarke diagram for two-machine series reactance system. The cut-and-try process illustrated in Example 1 can be avoided through use of a graphical construction devised by Miss Clarke.[1] The construction will be discussed now for two machines connected through

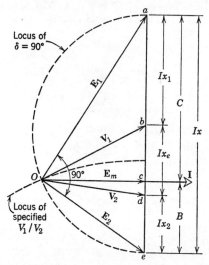

FIG. 5. Vector diagram of the circuit of Fig. 4 (Clarke diagram).

series external reactance, as in Fig. 4. In the next section the diagram will be extended to the case of two machines connected through any reactance network, and, later, to the case of series impedance having a resistance component.

Figure 5 is a vector diagram of the circuit of Fig. 4. The current vector is drawn horizontally; consequently, the Ix drops are drawn vertically. The several voltage vectors radiating from point O differ by the appropriate Ix drops. In order to represent conditions at the steady-state stability limit, the diagram must be drawn so that V_1 and V_2 have their assigned values and so that E_1 and E_2 are 90° apart. Furthermore, the several Ix drops must be proportional to the corresponding reactances since the current I is the same in all reactances of the series circuit.

The construction is carried out in the following way:

1. Lay off segments Ix_1, Ix_e, and Ix_2 along a straight line, making them proportional to the given values of x_1, x_e, and x_2, respectively, to any convenient scale.

2. With $I(x_1 + x_e + x_2) = Ix$ as diameter, construct a semicircle (shown by a dotted line in Fig. 5). Any point O lying on this semicircle meets the requirement that E_1 lead E_2 by 90°. This fact arises from the theorem of geometry that any angle inscribed in a semicircle is a right angle.

3. Construct a portion of the locus of constant ratio V_1/V_2 (also shown by a dotted line in Fig. 5). If $V_1 = V_2$, this locus is the perpendicular bisector of Ix_e. If $V_1 \neq V_2$, the locus can be proved to be a circle whose center is on the vertical line of Ix drops or an extension thereof. However, the easiest way to construct it probably is to locate several points on it by intersections of arcs struck with centers at the heads of vectors $\mathbf{V}_1$ and $\mathbf{V}_2$ and radii in the specified ratio V_1/V_2.

4. The intersection of this locus with the semicircle is point O. Vectors $\mathbf{E}_1$, $\mathbf{V}_1$, $\mathbf{V}_2$, and $\mathbf{E}_2$ may now be drawn.

5. The scale of the diagram is set by the specified values of V_1 and V_2.

6. The scale having been found, the power (which is the same at all points of the circuit) can be calculated. Two simple ways of calculating it are the following:

   a. Measure the lengths of vectors $\mathbf{E}_1$ and $\mathbf{E}_2$. Then

$$P_m = \frac{E_1 E_2}{x_1 + x_e + x_2} = \frac{E_1 E_2}{x} \qquad [3]$$

   b. Measure E_m, the perpendicular from O to Ix. It represents the in-phase component of each of the four voltages. It also represents the lowest voltage at any point on the line between machines, at which point the power factor is unity. Also measure the diameter of the circle, $Ix = I(x_1 + x_e + x_2)$ and divide it by the total reactance x in order to find the current I. Then

$$P_m = E_m I \qquad [4]$$

For values of V_1/V_2 differing greatly from 1.00, the locus of constant V_1/V_2 will not intersect the semicircle. The lack of an intersection indicates that no power can be transmitted stably with the assumed values of terminal voltage.

EXAMPLE 2

Solve Example 1 by use of the Clarke diagram.

Solution. As shown in Fig. 6, lay off $AB = Ix_1 = 0.60$ unit and $BF = Ix_2 = 1.00$ unit. With the midpoint C of line AF (0.80 unit from each end) as center, draw a semicircle AOF of radius 0.80 unit. Construct the locus $DGHOK$ by locating points G, H, K by intersections of arcs having centers at B and F. For point K, the radii are 1.10 from B and 1.00 from F; for point H, they are 0.83 and 0.75; for point G, 0.55 and 0.50. The intersection of this locus with the semicircle is point O. Draw OA, OB, and OF, representing $\mathbf{E}_1$, $\mathbf{V}_1$, and $\mathbf{V}_2 = \mathbf{E}_2$, respectively. Measure OF. It is 0.83 unit of length and represents 1.00 unit of voltage. Therefore, the scale is 1 unit of length = 1.21 units of voltage. Measure OA. It is 1.38 units of length and therefore represents a voltage of $1.38 \times 1.21 = 1.67$ units.

The steady-state stability limit is therefore

$$P_m = \frac{1.67 \times 1.00}{1.6} = 1.04 \text{ units}$$

This agrees well with the value (1.03) found in Example 1.

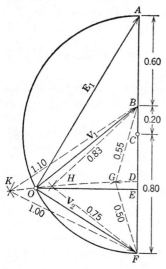

FIG. 6. Clarke diagram for determination of the steady-state stability limit of the system of Fig. 1 (Example 2).

Extension of Clarke diagram to cover any reactance network. Any network of pure reactances, through which power is transmitted from one synchronous machine to another, can be reduced to an equivalent series-reactance circuit similar to the one considered in the last section. First the portion of the network outside the machines is reduced to an equivalent π, which will be composed of pure reactances if the original network was. As the machines themselves can be represented by their internal voltages and reactances (their resistances being negligible), we now have a pure-reactance network of the form shown in Fig. 7. (The shunt branches are shown as capacitive, though they may equally well be inductive.) This circuit could be further reduced, say, to an equivalent π connecting the internal voltages. However, this will not be done because it is necessary to preserve the identity of the terminals of the machines, where the voltages are specified. The internal points, on the other hand, need not be preserved. Further reduction is therefore accomplished by an application, from Miss Clarke,[1] of Thévenin's theorem to the portions of the network to the left and right of architrave reactance x_e. Thévenin's theorem states that a two-terminal

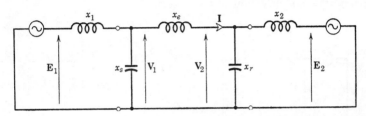

Fig. 7. Reactance network between the terminals of two machines reduced to an equivalent π.

linear network can be replaced by an e.m.f. and an impedance in series without affecting conditions outside the network. The impedance of Thévenin's equivalent circuit is equal to the input impedance of the original network with its internal e.m.f.'s short-circuited. Therefore, in our case, the Thévenin's impedance at the generator end is the reactance of the parallel combination of the generator reactance x_1 and the shunt reactance x_s, or

$$x_1' = \frac{x_1 x_s}{x_1 + x_s} \qquad [5]$$

Similarly, the Thévenin reactance at the motor end is

$$x_2' = \frac{x_2 x_r}{x_2 + x_r} \qquad [6]$$

The e.m.f. of Thévenin's theorem is the open-circuit voltage at the terminals of the network. At the generator end, this is the voltage across x_s with x_e disconnected, or

$$\mathbf{E_1}' = \frac{x_s}{x_1 + x_s}\,\mathbf{E_1} = \frac{x_1'}{x_1}\,\mathbf{E_1} \qquad [7]$$

Similarly, at the motor end the equivalent e.m.f. is

$$\mathbf{E_2}' = \frac{x_r}{x_2 + x_r}\,\mathbf{E_2} = \frac{x_2'}{x_2}\,\mathbf{E_2} \qquad [8]$$

The circuit of Fig. 7 is thus reduced to the equivalent series circuit of Fig. 8. If E_1 and E_2 are constant, E_1' and E_2' are also constant. The maximum power that can be transmitted over the circuit of Fig. 8 for constant values of E_1' and E_2' (corresponding to constant field currents) occurs when $\mathbf{E}_1'$ leads $\mathbf{E}_2'$ by 90°. This value of power is also the maximum value for the circuit of Fig. 7. Since the system is stable for all values of power up to the maximum, the value so found is the steady-state stability limit of the system.

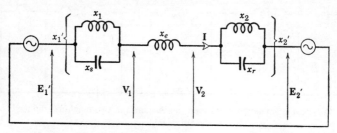

Fig. 8. The circuit of Fig. 7 reduced to a series circuit by use of Thévenin's theorem.

The Clarke diagram therefore can be used as before except that x_1, x_2, E_1, and E_2 are replaced by x_1', x_2', E_1', and E_2', respectively (eqs. 5 through 8), and x_e now represents the architrave reactance of the equivalent π circuit of the external network. The actual internal voltages and currents of the machines can be calculated if desired. However, they are not needed for calculating the stability limit, for it can be calculated in terms of the equivalent quantities, thus:

$$P_m = \frac{E_1' E_2'}{x_1' + x_e + x_2'} \qquad [9]$$

where E_1' and E_2' at 90° phase difference are determined by means of the Clarke diagram.

Example 3

A generator having an internal reactance (equivalent synchronous reactance) of 0.60 per unit feeds power to an infinite bus over a transmission line, the equivalent π of which has an architrave impedance of $j1.0$ and pillars of $-j5.0$ each. The terminal voltage of the generator and the voltage of the infinite bus are both held at 1.0 per unit. Find the steady-state stability limit.

Solution. The Thévenin reactance of the generator (eq. 5) is

$$x_1' = \frac{0.60(-5.0)}{0.60 - 5.00} = \frac{-3.0}{-4.4} = 0.68$$

From a Clarke diagram, similar in form to Fig. 6, but with $AB = 0.68$, $BC = 0.16$, and $CF = 0.84$, and with OD the perpendicular bisector of BF, E_1' is found to be 1.53 per unit. The stability limit is (eq. 9)

$$P_m = \frac{1.53 \times 1.00}{0.68 + 1.00} = 0.91 \text{ per unit}$$

Equation for steady-state stability limit of two-machine reactance system. As an alternative to the graphical construction described in an earlier section, an algebraic equation based on the Clarke diagram can be used to find the steady-state stability limit. This equation will now be derived.

The general plan of the derivation is to express the internal voltages, E_1 and E_2, in terms of the given terminal voltages, V_1 and V_2, and the reactances, and then to use eq. 3 for maximum power.

Refer to the vector diagram, Fig. 5. From the relations between the sides of a right triangle, the in-phase component E_m of the several voltage vectors can be written in the following four ways, using successively triangles Oac, Obc, Odc, and Oec:

$$E_m^2 = E_1^2 - C^2 \tag{10}$$

$$= V_1^2 - (C - Ix_1)^2 \tag{11}$$

$$= V_2^2 - (B - Ix_2)^2 \tag{12}$$

$$= E_2^2 - B^2 \tag{13}$$

From eqs. 10 and 11,

$$\begin{aligned} V_1^2 &= E_1^2 - C^2 + (C - Ix_1)^2 \\ &= E_1^2 - C^2 + C^2 - 2CIx_1 + I^2x_1^2 \\ &= E_1^2 - 2CIx_1 + I^2x_1^2 \end{aligned} \tag{14}$$

Similarly, from eqs. 12 and 13,

$$V_2^2 = E_2^2 - 2BIx_2 + I^2x_2^2 \tag{15}$$

Now BI, CI, and I^2 in eqs. 14 and 15 must be expressed in terms of voltages and reactances. From right triangle Oae,

$$E_1^2 + E_2^2 = I^2x^2 = (C + B)(C + B) \tag{16}$$

From eqs. 10 and 13,

$$E_1^2 - E_2^2 = C^2 - B^2 = (C + B)(C - B) \tag{17}$$

Add eqs. 16 and 17 and divide by 2, obtaining

$$E_1^2 = C(C + B) = CIx \tag{18}$$

Subtract eq. 17 from eq. 16 and divide by 2, obtaining

$$E_2{}^2 = B(C + B) = BIx \qquad [19]$$

From eq. 18,

$$CI = \frac{E_1{}^2}{x} \qquad [20]$$

From eq. 19,

$$BI = \frac{E_2{}^2}{x} \qquad [21]$$

From eq. 16,

$$I^2 = \frac{E_1{}^2 + E_2{}^2}{x^2} \qquad [22]$$

Substitution of eqs. 20, 21, and 22 into eq. 14 gives:

$$V_1{}^2 = E_1{}^2 - 2E_1{}^2 \frac{x_1}{x} + E_1{}^2 \left(\frac{x_1}{x}\right)^2 + E_2{}^2 \left(\frac{x_1}{x}\right)^2$$

$$= E_1{}^2 \left(1 - \frac{x_1}{x}\right)^2 + E_2{}^2 \left(\frac{x_1}{x}\right)^2$$

$$V_1{}^2 x^2 = E_1{}^2 (x - x_1)^2 + E_2{}^2 x_1{}^2$$

$$= E_1{}^2 (x_e + x_2)^2 + E_2{}^2 x_1{}^2 \qquad [23]$$

A similar substitution into eq. 15 gives:

$$V_2{}^2 x^2 = E_1{}^2 x_2{}^2 + E_2{}^2 (x_e + x_1)^2 \qquad [24]$$

Simultaneous solution of eqs. 23 and 24 yields:

$$E_1{}^2 = \frac{[V_1{}^2 (x_e + x_1)^2 - V_2{}^2 x_1{}^2] x^2}{(x_e + x_1)^2 (x_e + x_2)^2 - x_1{}^2 x_2{}^2} \qquad [25]$$

$$E_2{}^2 = \frac{[V_2{}^2 (x_e + x_2)^2 - V_1{}^2 x_2{}^2] x^2}{(x_e + x_1)^2 (x_e + x_2)^2 - x_1{}^2 x_2{}^2} \qquad [26]$$

Hence

$$E_1 E_2 = x^2 \frac{\sqrt{\begin{array}{c} V_1{}^2 V_2{}^2 [(x_e + x_1)^2 (x_e + x_2)^2 + x_1{}^2 x_2{}^2] \\ - V_1{}^4 x_2{}^2 (x_e + x_1)^2 - V_2{}^4 x_1{}^2 (x_e + x_2)^2 \end{array}}}{(x_e + x_1)^2 (x_e + x_2)^2 - x_1{}^2 x_2{}^2} \qquad [27]$$

Substitution of eq. 27 into eq. 3 gives:

$$P_m = \frac{E_1 E_2}{x} = x \frac{\sqrt{\begin{array}{c} V_1{}^2 V_2{}^2 [(x_e + x_1)^2 (x_e + x_2)^2 + x_1{}^2 x_2{}^2] \\ - V_1{}^4 x_2{}^2 (x_e + x_1)^2 - V_2{}^4 x_1{}^2 (x_e + x_2)^2 \end{array}}}{(x_e + x_1)^2 (x_e + x_2)^2 - x_1{}^2 x_2{}^2} \qquad [28]$$

EXAMPLE 4   263

The denominator may be rewritten as

$$[(x_e + x_1)(x_e + x_2) + x_1 x_2][(x_e + x_1)(x_e + x_2) - x_1 x_2]$$
$$= [x_e^2 + x_1 x_e + x_2 x_e + 2 x_1 x_2][x_e^2 + x_1 x_e + x_2 x_e]$$
$$= [x_e(x_e + x_1 + x_2) + 2 x_1 x_2][x_e(x_e + x_1 + x_2)]$$
$$= (x_e x + 2 x_1 x_2) x_e x$$

giving

$$P_m = \frac{\sqrt{\begin{array}{c} V_1^2 V_2^2[(x_e + x_1)^2(x_e + x_2)^2 + x_1^2 x_2^2] \\ - V_1^4 x_2^2(x_e + x_1)^2 - V_2^4 x_1^2(x_e + x_2)^2 \end{array}}}{x_e(x_e x + 2 x_1 x_2)} \qquad [29]$$

This is the desired equation. Some values of V_1 and V_2 which differ too greatly make the radicand zero or negative, showing that no power can be transmitted stably at such voltages.

Considerable simplification results if the voltages are equal. Putting $V_1 = V_2 = V$ and simplifying, we get

$$P_m = \frac{V^2 \sqrt{(x_e + 2 x_1)(x_e + 2 x_2)}}{x_e x + 2 x_1 x_2} \qquad [30]$$

Equations 29 and 30 can be applied to any reactance network by use of the method given in the last section.

EXAMPLE 4

Check the results of Examples 1 (or 2) and 3 by means of eqs. 29 and 30.
Solution. *Example 1 or 2.* Data:

$$V_1 = 1.10, \qquad V_2 = 1.00, \qquad x_1 = 0.60, \qquad x_e = 1.00, \qquad x_2 = 0.$$

Use eq. 29.

$$V_1^2 V_2^2 = 1.21, \qquad V_1^4 = 1.46, \qquad V_2^4 = 1.00$$
$$x_e + x_1 = 1.60, \qquad x_e + x_2 = 1.00$$
$$(x_e + x_1)^2(x_e + x_2)^2 + x_1^2 x_2^2 = (1.60)^2 \times (1.00)^2 - 0 = 2.56$$
$$x_2^2(x_e + x_1)^2 = 0$$
$$x_1^2(x_e + x_2)^2 = (0.60)^2 \times (1.00)^2 = 0.36$$
$$x = x_1 + x_e + x_2 = 1.60$$
$$x_e(x_e x + 2 x_1 x_2) = 1.00(1.00 \times 1.60 + 0) = 1.60$$
$$P_m = \frac{\sqrt{1.21 \times 2.56 - 1.46 \times 0 - 1.00 \times 0.36}}{1.60}$$
$$= \frac{\sqrt{3.10 - 0.36}}{1.60} = \frac{\sqrt{2.74}}{1.60} = 1.04 \text{ per unit}$$

This agrees with the previous results.

Example 3. Data:

$$V_1 = V_2 = V = 1.00, \qquad x_1' = 0.68, \qquad x_e = 1.00, \qquad x_2 = 0.$$

Use eq. 30.

$$P_m = \frac{(1.00)^2 \sqrt{(1.00 + 2 \times 0.68)1.00}}{1.00 \times 1.68 + 0} = \frac{\sqrt{2.36}}{1.68}$$

$$= 0.92 \text{ per unit}$$

This value agrees well with the previous result (0.91).

Two-machine system with losses. Power-angle curves. Although every actual circuit has losses, the methods developed in the preceding sections of this chapter for circuits without losses furnish useful and relatively simple approximations, the accuracy of which depends upon the amount of loss. Nevertheless, methods of finding the steady-state stability limits, taking losses into consideration, should be developed not only for use where losses are high but also for establishing the accuracy of the approximate methods.

The theory of steady-state stability of circuits with resistance is complicated by the following facts: (1) Maximum power at the sending end exceeds the maximum power at the receiving end and occurs at a different angular separation of the two machines. (2) The maximum stable angle depends upon the relative inertias of the machines and upon governor action.

Let the power-angle curves of the two machines be considered first. The network, including the reactances of the machines, can be reduced to an equivalent π connecting the two internal points of the machines and the neutral point. The method of doing this was described in Chapter III. Let the following notation be used:

$\mathbf{Y}_{12} = Y_{12} \underline{/\theta_{12}} = \mathbf{Y}_{21} = Y_{21} \underline{/\theta_{21}} =$ mutual admittance of terminals 1 and 2

$\mathbf{Y}_{11} = Y_{11} \underline{/\theta_{11}} =$ self-admittance of terminal 1 (sending end)

$\mathbf{Y}_{22} = Y_{22} \underline{/\theta_{22}} =$ self-admittance of terminal 2 (receiving end)

$\mathbf{y}_{12} = y_{12} \underline{/-\theta_{12}} =$ admittance of architrave of π, also called the transfer admittance

$\mathbf{y}_{01} =$ admittance of pillar of π at sending end

$\mathbf{y}_{02} =$ admittance of pillar of π at receiving end

$\theta_{12} =$ angle of transfer, or architrave, impedance

$\mathbf{E}_1 = E_1 \underline{/\delta_1} =$ internal voltage of machine 1 (the generator)

$\mathbf{E}_2 = E_2 \underline{/\delta_2} =$ internal voltage of machine 2 (the motor)

$\delta = \delta_1 - \delta_2 =$ the angle by which $\mathbf{E}_1$ leads $\mathbf{E}_2$

The terminal admittances have the following values in terms of the admittances of the elements of the equivalent π circuit:

$$\mathbf{Y}_{12} = \mathbf{Y}_{21} = -\mathbf{y}_{12} = y_{12} \underline{/180° - \theta_{12}}$$

$$\mathbf{Y}_{11} = \mathbf{y}_{01} + \mathbf{y}_{12}$$

$$\mathbf{Y}_{22} = \mathbf{y}_{02} + \mathbf{y}_{12}$$

Hence

$$\Theta_{12} = \Theta_{21} = 180° - \theta_{12}$$

The power input to the network at the sending end is, by eqs. 17 of Chapter III, Vol. I,

$$\begin{aligned}
P_1 &= E_1{}^2 Y_{11} \cos \Theta_{11} + E_1 E_2 Y_{12} \cos (\Theta_{12} - \delta_1 + \delta_2) \\
&= E_1{}^2 Y_{11} \cos \Theta_{11} + E_1 E_2 Y_{12} \cos (180° - \theta_{12} - \delta) \\
&= E_1{}^2 Y_{11} \cos \Theta_{11} + E_1 E_2 Y_{12} \cos (\delta + \theta_{12} - 180°) \quad [31]
\end{aligned}$$

and the input at the receiving end (output if negative) is

$$\begin{aligned}
P_2 &= E_2 E_1 Y_{21} \cos (\Theta_{21} - \delta_2 + \delta_1) + E_2{}^2 Y_{22} \cos \Theta_{22} \\
&= E_2{}^2 Y_{22} \cos \Theta_{22} + E_1 E_2 Y_{12} \cos (180° - \theta_{12} + \delta) \\
&= E_2{}^2 Y_{22} \cos \Theta_{22} - E_1 E_2 Y_{12} \cos (\delta - \theta_{12}) \quad [32]
\end{aligned}$$

With fixed magnitudes of internal voltages E_1 and E_2, the first term of the last line of each equation is constant while the second term is a cosine function of δ. By eq. 31, maximum output of machine 1 (the generator) occurs at $\delta = 180° - \theta_{12} = \delta_{m1}$. By eq. 32, maximum input of machine 2 (the motor) occurs at $\delta = \theta_{12} = \delta_{m2}$.

Here θ_{12} is the angle of the architrave impedance. If this impedance consists of pure inductive reactance (as in the case previously considered), $\theta_{12} = 90°$ and both maxima occur at $\delta = 90°$. If the architrave impedance consists of positive resistance and inductive reactance, θ_{12} is less than $90°$; then maximum sent power occurs at a value of δ greater than $90°$, and maximum received power, at a value of δ less than $90°$. Power-angle curves for this case are plotted in Fig. 9. The loss in the line is also plotted versus δ. Another possibility is that the architrave impedance has negative resistance. This can occur, for example, if there is a shunt resistance, as shown on the circuit diagram of Fig. 10. When the T circuit shown there is converted to a π, the architrave impedance is

$$jX + jX + \frac{(jX)(jX)}{R} = -\frac{X^2}{R} + j2X$$

the real part of which is negative. With negative resistance and inductive reactance, θ_{12} lies between $90°$ and $180°$. Consequently,

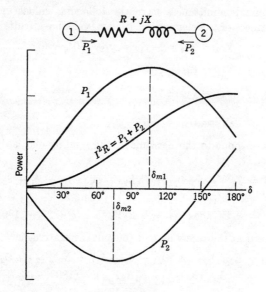

Fig. 9. Power-angle curves of two machines connected through series resistance and inductive reactance.

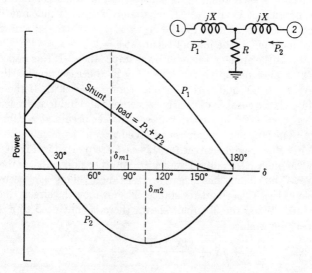

Fig. 10. Power-angle curves of two machines connected through reactance with an intermediate shunt resistance load.

maximum sent power occurs at δ less than $90°$, and maximum received power, at δ greater than $90°$. The power-angle curves for this case are given in Fig. 10. The power consumed by the load is also shown. With either series or shunt resistance, the maximum received power $(-P_2)$ is less than the maximum sent power (P_1).

Two-machine system with losses. Effect of inertia. Consider a *generator of finite inertia feeding power to an infinite bus through series impedance with resistance.* The power-angle curves for constant excitation are shown in Fig. 9. The output of the generator is shown by curve P_1; the power received at the infinite bus, by $-P_2$. If the power input to the generator is slowly increased, the generator voltage is advanced in phase, thus increasing the angular separation δ. The output of the generator increases so as to equal its input until P_1 reaches its maximum value at $\delta = \delta_{m1} = 180° - \theta_{12} > 90°$. Therefore, the system is stable for all positive values of δ less than δ_{m1}. However, maximum power is received by the infinite bus at $\delta = \delta_{m2} = \theta_{12} < 90° < \delta_{m1}$. Therefore, by definition, the steady-state stability limit is the maximum value of received power, $-P_2$, and this occurs at $\delta = \delta_{m2}$. The system is stable at this angle.

Next consider a *motor of finite inertia receiving power from an infinite bus through series impedance.* The curves of Fig. 9 again apply. Now P_1 is the output of the infinite bus, and $-P_2$ is the input of the motor. Let the shaft load on the motor be slowly increased. The motor voltage is retarded in phase, thus increasing δ, and the input of the motor increases so as to equal its output, until $-P_2$ reaches its maximum value at $\delta = \delta_{m2}$. If the motor load is further increased, synchronism is lost.

In both of the preceding cases the stability limit is the maximum value of $-P_2$, which occurs at $\delta = \delta_{m2} = \theta_{12}$, which is less than $90°$. In the case of the finite motor synchronism is lost if δ exceeds this angle, but in the case of the finite generator δ can increase from δ_{m2} to δ_{m1}, with an accompanying increase in generator output P_1, before synchronism is lost. The generator therefore is more stable when operating at the stability limit than the motor is.

Next consider a *generator and a motor both of finite, and not necessarily equal, inertias.* It would be expected that the maximum stable value of δ would be greater than δ_{m2} but less than δ_{m1}, and that the exact value would depend upon the relative inertias of the two machines, being near δ_{m2} if the inertia of the generator were high compared with that of the motor, and near δ_{m1} if the reverse were true. This expectation is borne out by the equivalent power-angle curve of a two-machine system, derived in Chapter IV, Vol. I. By eq. 26 of that chapter, the maximum of this curve occurs at

$$\delta = \delta_c = \tan^{-1}\left(\frac{M_1 + M_2}{M_1 - M_2} \tan\theta_{12}\right) \qquad [33]$$

where M_1 and M_2 are the inertia constants of the two machines. The critical angle δ_c is always between the angles of maximum sent and received power:

$$\theta_{12} = \delta_{m2} < \delta_c < \delta_{m1} = 180° - \theta_{12} \qquad [34]$$

It approaches δ_{m2} if $M_1 \gg M_2$, and approaches δ_{m1} if $M_1 \ll M_2$.

In each of the three cases considered above, all of which are for positive series resistance, the steady-state stability limit is reached at $\delta = \delta_{m2}$. However, it appears that δ can increase beyond δ_{m2} up to a value δ_c before synchronism is lost. Thus at maximum received power there is a margin of stability which depends upon the relative inertias, being greatest when machine 2 (the motor) is an infinite bus.

The situation is somewhat different *if the series resistance is negative.* The power-angle curves are given in Fig. 10. Here the maximum sent power is reached at a smaller value of δ than that for maximum received power ($\delta_{m1} < \delta_{m2}$). It is therefore necessary to investigate whether the system is stable at values of δ between δ_{m1} and δ_{m2}.

If the motor is an infinite bus, the generator pulls out of step at δ_{m1}, before $-P_2$ reaches its maximum value. The stability limit is then the value of $-P_2$ at $\delta = \delta_{m1}$. If, however, the generator is an infinite bus, the motor pulls out of step at δ_{m2}, where $-P_2$ is greatest. The stability limit is greater for the infinite generator than for the infinite motor.

If both machines are finite, the system would appear to be stable for all values of δ up to δ_c computed from eq. 33 and lying between δ_{m1} and δ_{m2}. The stability limit would then be the value of received power at $\delta = \delta_c$. The received power would be less than its maximum value but greater than its value at $\delta = \delta_{m1}$.

Two-machine system with losses. Effect of governor action. The foregoing discussion has shown that a two-machine system is stable without doubt for all positive values of δ less than δ_{m1} or δ_{m2}, whichever is smaller. Furthermore, the discussion of the effect of inertia has indicated that the system would be stable at even larger values of δ, up to δ_c given by eq. 33. This increased range of stable angle increases the stability limit if the series resistance is negative, but not if it is positive, though in the latter case the margin of stability is increased.

These conclusions were drawn from the equivalent power-angle curve, which was based upon the assumption that the mechanical power of both machines remained constant. For consistency with this assumption, the disturbance used as a test of stability would consist of a small angular displacement, which might be caused by a momentary small increase of mechanical power of either machine. A sustained increase of mechanical power, however, can lead to different results, depending upon the manner in which the increase is applied and upon the resulting governor action tending to maintain the frequency of the system.

Let us investigate the stability of a two-machine system with negative transfer resistance (due to positive shunt resistance) when the angular separation δ is between δ_{m1} and δ_c. Instead of using the equivalent power-angle curve of the system, we shall use the individual acceleration curves of the two machines, which are plots of acceleration versus δ. The acceleration of machine 1 (the generator) is

$$\frac{d^2\delta_1}{dt^2} = \frac{P_{i1} - P_{u1}}{M_1} = \frac{P_{a1}}{M_1} \qquad [35]$$

where P_{i1} = mechanical power input.
P_{u1} = electric power output.
P_{a1} = accelerating power.
M_1 = inertia constant.

A similar relation holds for machine 2 (the motor). Hence each of the two acceleration curves is derived from the corresponding power-angle curve of Fig. 10 by first subtracting it from the mechanical input, which is assumed constant, and then dividing the result by the inertia constant. The acceleration curves so obtained are shown in Fig. 11 for $M_1 \gg M_2$. Only a small range of δ near 90° is shown. In the steady state neither machine is accelerating. Therefore the two acceleration curves intersect on the horizontal axis (point a). For stability without governor action, curve 2 must have a greater slope than curve 1. At values of $\delta < \delta_{m1}$, the slope of curve 2 is positive and that of curve 1 is negative. For δ between δ_{m1} and δ_{m2}, both curves have positive slopes, but that of curve 2 is greater than curve 1 up to δ_c, where the slopes become equal. In Fig. 11, point a represents stable steady-state operation at an angle between δ_{m1} and δ_c. Now let the shaft load of the motor be increased by a small amount. This lowers the motor characteristic from 2 to $2'$. Initially the motor has a retardation ab, which tends to increase δ. When δ reaches point c, the intersection of curves 1 and $2'$, both machines have small and equal accelerations cd. Therefore δ does not change immediately, but the system frequency slowly increases until the governor decreases the mechanical input of the generator. This lowers curve 1, causing the operating point of both machines to reach stable equilibrium at point e. In this instance, governor action tends to decrease δ and therefore does not cause instability.

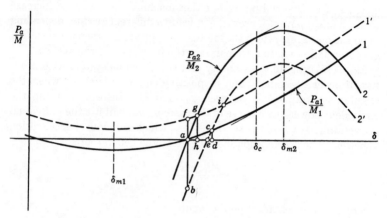

Fig. 11. Acceleration curves of two-machine system with negative transfer resistance.

In practice, most "two-machine" systems consist not of a generator and a motor but rather of two generators (or groups of generators) one of which (no. 2) has a local load supplied partly from the adjacent generator and partly over a transmission line from the distant generator (no. 1). Machine 2, together with its local load, constitutes an "equivalent motor." Both generators have governors. The power transmitted from one to the other can be increased either as described before or in the opposite order, thus: The governor of machine 1 is first adjusted to increase the mechanical input, which we will assume to be held constant thereafter. This shifts the acceleration curve upward from 1 to 1′. Machine 1 has an initial acceleration af. Angle δ increases to the abscissa of point g, the intersection of curves 1′ and 2. Here both machines have equal accelerations gh. The frequency increases. The governor of machine 2 thereupon decreases the mechanical input, an action which is equivalent to increasing the mechanical output of the equivalent motor and which lowers the motor characteristic from 2 to 2′. If there were no further governor action the machines would reach equilibrium at point i, the intersection of curves 1′ and 2′. However, here the acceleration of both machines is even greater than before. The governor of machine 2 therefore continues to lower curve $2'$ until it no longer intersects curve $1'$, whereupon synchronism is lost. With this method of increasing the load, governor action tends to increase δ and causes instability.

The conclusion is that with δ in the range between δ_{m1} and δ_c the system may be either stable or unstable under the condition of small sustained increase of load, taking governor action into consideration, depending upon how the increase of load is accomplished.

The same kind of reasoning leads to a similar conclusion regarding the stability of a two-machine system with positive transfer resistance. In the range of δ from δ_{m2} to δ_c, the system may be either stable or unstable. It is unstable if the shaft load of the motor is increased first, but is stable if the input of the generator is increased first. As already noted, however, these facts do not alter the stability limit which occurs at $\delta = \delta_{m2}$.

It has been assumed that the governor of one machine is set for constant mechanical power and that the governor of the other machine then maintains frequency. If both governors tend to maintain frequency, the maximum stable angle would appear to depend upon the relative sensitivity of the two governors.

Two-machine system with losses. Conservative criterion for stability. To summarize the conclusions reached in the last two sections: If δ_{m1} is greater than δ_{m2} (as it is when the transfer resistance is positive), the steady-state stability limit is the maximum received power and occurs at $\delta = \delta_{m2}$. If δ_{m1} is less than δ_{m2} (as it is when the transfer resistance is negative), the stability limit is less than the maximum received power and occurs at an angle between δ_{m1} and δ_c, depending upon governor action. The larger of these angles, δ_c, lies between δ_{m1} and δ_{m2}, the exact value depending upon the relative inertias of the two machines.

Because of the uncertainty that usually exists regarding whether load will always be increased in the same manner, *it is advisable to take the steady-state stability limit of a two-machine system as the value of received power at* $\delta = \delta_{m1}$ *or* δ_{m2}, *whichever is smaller*. (This value of δ is either θ_{12} or $180° - \theta_{12}$, whichever is smaller, θ_{12} being the angle of the transfer impedance.) This limit is a conservative one. In some cases there will be a small margin either in the value of δ or in the values of both δ and received power. Nevertheless, it may be considered accurate enough for all practical purposes because a fairly large variation in δ in the range between δ_{m1} and δ_{m2} produces a relatively small percentage change in received power. Furthermore, the practical operating power limit is usually set considerably below the calculated steady-state stability limit (say at 75% of the latter) to allow for power variations caused by changes of loads or by remote faults.

At values of δ smaller than both δ_{m1} and δ_{m2}, the curve of P_1 versus δ has positive slope, while that of P_2 has negative slope. Since $\delta = \delta_1 - \delta_2$ by definition, the operation is stable if both

$$\frac{\partial P_1}{\partial \delta_1} > 0 \quad \text{and} \quad \frac{\partial P_2}{\partial \delta_2} > 0 \qquad [36]$$

These derivatives are called *synchronizing-power coefficients*. A conservative criterion for stability, applicable to multimachine systems as well as two-machine systems, is that the synchronizing-power coefficients of all machines be positive. In other words, if any one machine is advanced in phase while the others are constant in phase, its electrical output should increase (or its electrical input should decrease); conversely, if any machine is retarded in phase, its electrical output should decrease (or its electrical input should increase). If each machine meets this test, the system is stable. In making the test, one keeps the internal voltages constant (representing constant field currents). If the system is found to be stable, the angular separation is increased and the internal voltages are increased so as to keep the terminal voltages at their specified values; as a result the power is increased. The test for stability is made again, and the procedure is repeated until instability is indicated by one of the synchronizing-power coefficients becoming negative. In this manner the steady-state stability limit is found. The stability limit of a system of any number of machines can be determined advantageously by following the described procedure on an a-c. calculating board. The stability limit of some two-machine systems can also be found graphically as described in the next section.

Clarke diagram for two-machine system with resistance. In an earlier section the Clarke diagram was described for a two-machine system having inductive reactance without resistance. The stability limit of such a system was reached when the angular separation δ between internal voltages reached 90°, which angle was inscribed in a semicircle. According to the conservative stability criterion discussed in the last section, the effect of resistance is to change the value of δ at which the stability limit is reached from 90° to a smaller value, equal to either θ_{12} or $180° - \theta_{12}$, whichever is smaller, where θ_{12} is the angle of the transfer impedance between internal voltages. In what follows this angle will be called simply θ_{12}, which value holds when the transfer resistance is positive. Use will be made of the theorem of geometry that any angle inscribed in a circular arc of central angle $360° - 2\theta_{12}$ is θ_{12}.

The vector diagram of the system of Fig. 12, in which the two machines are connected through external series impedance $r_e + jx_e$, is shown in Fig. 13. At the stability limit the angle between E_1 and

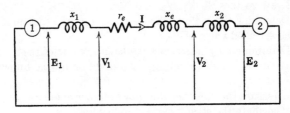

Fig. 12.   Two synchronous machines connected through external impedance $r_e + jx_e$.

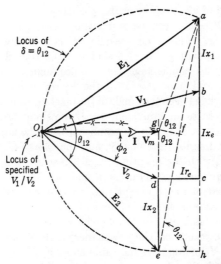

Fig. 13.   Vector diagram of the system of Fig. 12 (Clarke diagram).

E_2 is $\theta_{12} = \tan^{-1}(x_{12}/r_{12}) = \tan^{-1}[(x_1 + x_e + x_2)/r_e]$. The diagram is constructed so as to meet both this requirement and the required values of V_1 and V_2 by means of the following procedure:

1. With vector $\mathbf{I}$ as reference, lay off Ix_1, Ix_e, Ir_e, and Ix_2 to any convenient scale.

2. Draw the vector sum ae.

3. Draw fg, the perpendicular bisector of ae.

4. Extend *ed* until it intersects *fg* at *g*.

5. With *g* as center, draw circular arc *aOe*.

6. Construct part of the locus of constant ratio V_1/V_2 as described for the Clarke diagram of a reactance system. The intersection of this locus and circular arc *aOe* is point *O*.

7. Draw vectors E_1, V_1, V_2, and E_2.

8. Determine the scale of the diagram from the measured length and the specified value of V_1 or V_2.

9. Determine I by measuring the length of one of the Ix vectors, converting the length to voltage, and dividing by the known value of x.

10. Measure the receiving-end power-factor angle ϕ_2.

11. Calculate the steady-state stability limit as

$$P_2 = V_2 I \cos \phi_2 \quad \text{or} \quad V_m I \qquad [37]$$

The method of locating the center *g* of arc *aOe* so that the length of the arc is $360° - 2\theta_{12}$ can be verified as follows: Angle *aeh* is $\theta_{12} = \tan^{-1}[(Ix_1 + Ix_e + Ix_2)/Ir_e]$. Angle *egf* equals angle *aeh* because they are corresponding parts of similar right triangles *egf* and *aeh*. Likewise angle *agf* equals angle *egf*. Hence angle *ega* is $2\theta_{12}$, arc *aOe* is $360° - 2\theta_{12}$, and angle *aOe* is θ_{12}, the desired angle.

If the network between terminals of the machines has shunt branches, it can be reduced to an equivalent π. If the shunt branches of the π are purely reactive, they can be paralleled with the adjacent machine reactances, as described previously, and the Clarke diagram can then be constructed with the resulting parallel reactances x_1' and x_2' used in place of the machine reactances x_1 and x_2. The equivalent circuit is then like that of Fig. 8 except that r_e is inserted in series with x_e. The Clarke diagram of this equivalent circuit gives the maximum received power (stability limit) at point E_2' of this figure. Since no power is lost in reactance, the power there is the same as at point V_2. The power at V_2 of Fig. 8 is the same as at V_2 of Fig. 7 because the circuits are equivalent here; and, since no power is lost in the shunt reactance x_r, the power at the terminals of machine 2 (at the right of x_r, Fig. 7) is the same as that at E_2' of Fig. 8. A circuit with shunt capacitive reactances arises if a transmission line between the machines is represented by a nominal or equivalent π.

If the shunt branches of the π have resistance, however, the Clarke diagram is no longer applicable because the loss in x_r of Fig. 7 does not equal the loss in x_r of Fig. 8 for the same values of V_2 and I, and hence the power inside the equivalent machine (at E_2', Fig. 8) is no longer equal to the power of the actual machine (at E_2, Fig. 7). In this case

EXAMPLE 5   275

the stability limit can be calculated by successive trials. First the network *including machine reactances* is reduced to a π in order to find the angle θ_{12} of the transfer impedance. Then, using the specified values of V_1 and V_2 and an assumed angle between them, the vector values of $\mathbf{E}_1$ and $\mathbf{E}_2$ are calculated. By trial, the angle between $\mathbf{V}_1$ and $\mathbf{V}_2$ is found that gives angle θ_{12} between $\mathbf{E}_1$ and $\mathbf{E}_2$. The received power under this condition is the steady-state stability limit.

No algebraic equation has been derived for the steady-state stability limit of a two-machine system with resistance.

EXAMPLE 5

By use of the Clarke diagram, find the steady-state stability limit of a system like that described in Example 1 except that the external circuit has a resistance of 0.3 unit.

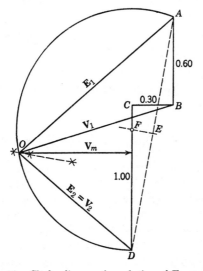

Fig. 14. Clarke diagram for solution of Example 5.

Solution. The diagram is constructed in Fig. 14, with $AB = 0.60$ unit, $BC = 0.30$ unit, and $CD = 1.00$ unit. Line AD is drawn, and its perpendicular bisector EF is constructed. With F as center, arc AOD is drawn. Three points on the locus $V_1/V_2 = 1.1$ are found as the intersections of arcs struck with points B and D as centers. Thus point O is located. From O, vectors $\mathbf{E}_1$, $\mathbf{V}_1$, and $\mathbf{V}_2$ are drawn to points A, B, and D, respectively, and $\mathbf{V}_m$ is drawn perpendicular to CD. The scale of the diagram is established by measuring V_2, which is found to be 1.05 units of length and represents 1.00 unit of voltage. Hence one unit of length represents 0.952 unit of voltage. As a check, V_1 is also measured. It is 1.16 units of length, representing 1.10 units of voltage. $1.10/1.16 = 0.948$. Use the average, 0.950. V_m measured 0.815 unit of length; hence it represents $0.815 \times 0.950 = 0.775$ unit of voltage. The current I is found as follows: $CD = Ix_e = 1.00$ unit of length = 0.95 unit of voltage. $I = Ix_e/x_e = 0.95/1.00 = 0.95$ unit of current. The steady-state stability limit is the received power, $V_m I = 0.775 \times 0.95 = 0.74$ per unit.

Multimachine system. The conservative criterion for steady-state stability, described earlier in this chapter for a two-machine system, is also applicable to a system having any number of machines. Each machine in turn is tested for stability by advancing the angular position δ of its internal voltage (the magnitude of this voltage being kept constant) and noting whether the electric power output of the machine increases or decreases. If it increases — that is, if

$$\frac{\partial P_n}{\partial \delta_n} > 0 \qquad [38]$$

machine n is stable. If every machine is stable, the system is stable.

In applying the test for stability to each machine of a multimachine system, one must make an assumption concerning the division of incremental power among the remaining machines. The following three different assumptions have been proposed:

1. That the relative angular positions of the remaining machines be constant.

2. That the power outputs of all but two machines remain constant while the angular displacement between these two is altered.

3. That, when the angular position of one machine is altered, the accompanying change of power be divided among the remaining machines in accordance with their prime-mover characteristics (or load characteristics, in case of motors).

The choice between the three foregoing assumptions rests upon convenience and upon judgment as to which best represents the actual or contemplated operating conditions.

Criteria based on assumptions 2 and 3 have been formulated mathematically (assumption 2 in Ref. 8, assumption 3 in Ref. 9, both being discussed also in Chapter 3 of Ref. 20 and in Chapter VIII of Ref. 14). However, the amount of algebraic work increases rapidly with the number of machines.

By far the simplest method of investigating a multimachine system is to use an a-c. calculating board. In testing a machine for stability by means of the a-c. board, the power source representing this machine is advanced in phase. The treatment of the other machines during the test depends upon which assumption is used. Assumption 1 (that the other machines have fixed phase) is the easiest to apply on the calculating board. If this assumption is used, the power sources representing the remaining machines need not be touched (unless their inherent voltage regulation is poor). If assumption 2 or 3 is used, the other power sources must be readjusted in phase so as either to keep the power constant or to divide the power increment in the manner decided upon. This may be done by trial without much difficulty.

In many studies it is sufficient to determine whether or not a system is stable for a particular operating condition. In some studies, however, it is required to find the steady-state stability limit of a particular machine or line. Before this can be done, the operating conditions must be decided upon. If the stability limit of a machine (or station) is wanted, how are increments of power of this machine to be divided among the remaining machines (or stations)? If the stability limit of a line is wanted, how are the increments of sending-end power to be supplied by the various generators and how are the increments of receiving-end power to be absorbed by the various motors or other loads?

The answers to these questions depend upon the expected operating practice and are often dictated by other considerations than stability. Among the considerations are: relative economy of generating stations, expected extremes of water supply for hydro stations, best sites for new generating plant or for enlargement and rehabilitation of old plants, maintenance of proper voltage at substations, thermal load limit of cables, expected growth of loads, provision of spinning reserve against sectionalization of the system by faults or by instability, and so on.

Having decided upon how the increased amounts of power are to be supplied and consumed, the stability limit of a line or machine is found by increasing the power in steps. At each step the operating conditions are adjusted appropriately (to give the right values of voltage, to avoid overloading of circuits, and so on) and the system is then tested for stability. The stability limit lies between the highest value of received power for which the system is found to be stable and the lowest value of received power for which the system is found to be unstable.

In testing for stability, it is not usually necessary to test every machine at every step, but only those which appear to be weakest or those whose angular separation is greatest.

Representation of synchronous machines. The methods of calculation presented in the preceding part of this chapter are based on the assumption that the power system is a linear network, that is, one representable by constant voltages and constant impedances. The components of the power system which depart most from linearity are the synchronous machines and the loads.

Let us first consider the synchronous machines. Their reactances constitute a large part of the transfer impedances of the network, and it is important, therefore, to use values that are at least approximately correct. A synchronous machine in the steady state is represented by its synchronous reactance and excitation voltage. These quantities are affected by saliency and by saturation.

Effect of saliency. The steady-state power-angle equation of a salient-pole machine was given in Chapter XII as eq. 235 and, with resistance neglected, as eq. 237. The power-angle curve was shown in Fig. 36 of that chapter. The equations and curve contain a fundamental component and a second harmonic. The second harmonic, called reluctance power, is proportional to the square of the terminal voltage and to $x_d - x_q$. When round-rotor theory is used for a salient-pole machine, x_q is assumed to be equal to x_d, whence it follows that the reluctance power is zero. The effect of the reluctance power is to increase the maximum power and to decrease the angle at which it occurs.

Usually pullout occurs with the excitation voltage much higher than the terminal voltage, and under these conditions the effect of reluctance power on the stability limit is small. However, in the case of an underexcited synchronous condenser with normal terminal voltage, the reluctance power considerably increases the stability limit. It is even possible for such a machine to operate stably with reversed field current.

With strong excitation, saliency can be neglected with little error — and that on the safe side. In general, the effect of saturation is much more important than that of saliency.

EXAMPLE 6

Find the stability limit of a salient-pole synchronous motor for which $x_d = 1.2$ per unit and $x_q = 0.9$ per unit when the motor is operated from an infinite bus of voltage 1.00 per unit. The excitation voltage of the motor is (a) 1.5, (b) 0.5 per unit. Neglect resistance and saturation. Find the error which would be caused in each case by neglecting saliency.

Solution. (a) Use eq. 237 of Chapter XII, which gives power as a function of angle δ.

$$P = \frac{E_q V}{x_d} \sin \delta + V^2 \frac{x_d - x_q}{2 x_d x_q} \sin 2\delta$$

$$= \frac{1.5 \times 1.0}{1.2} \sin \delta + (1.0)^2 \frac{1.2 - 0.9}{2 \times 1.2 \times 0.9} \sin 2\delta$$

$$= 1.25 \sin \delta + 0.14 \sin 2\delta \qquad (a)$$

Find the maximum value of P by trial.

If $\delta = 90°$, $P = 1.25 \times 1.00\ \ + 0.14 \times 0\ \ \ \ = 1.25.$

If $\delta = 80°$, $P = 1.25 \times 0.985 + 0.14 \times 0.34 = 1.27.$

If $\delta = 70°$, $P = 1.25 \times 0.940 + 0.14 \times 0.40 = 1.23.$

The stability limit is approximately 1.27 per unit. Round-rotor theory gives 1.25 per unit. The error caused by neglecting saliency is -1.5%.

(b) With $E_q = 0.5$, the first term of eq. a is one-third of its previous value.

$$P = 0.42 \sin \delta + 0.14 \sin 2\delta \tag{b}$$

By trial, $P_m = 0.49$ at $\delta \approx 65°$. Round-rotor theory gives 0.42. The error is -14%.

Effect of saturation. An unsaturated nonsalient-pole synchronous machine is represented in the steady state by its unsaturated synchronous reactance x_d, which is constant, and its excitation voltage E_q, which is constant if the field current is constant. A saturated synchronous machine can be represented similarly by a reactance and an e.m.f., but these are not constant. However, if properly chosen, they may be assumed constant during small changes in load such as are assumed to occur in the test for steady-state stability. The reactance of a saturated machine has been variously called "adjusted," "equivalent," or "saturated" synchronous reactance. The last two terms will be used here with somewhat different significances.

The saturated and equivalent synchronous reactances are smaller than the unsaturated reactance, and the stability limit computed with saturation neglected and the excitation voltage assumed constant is smaller than the true stability limit with saturation present and constant field current. The values of saturated and equivalent synchronous reactance vary with the saturation. The value of equivalent reactance usually lies within the range 0.4 to 0.8 of the unsaturated synchronous reactance.

Several methods of finding the values of saturated or equivalent synchronous reactance have been advanced by various writers.[7,10,12] These methods differ in their simplicity and in their accuracy.

An accurate way of representing a saturated nonsalient-pole machine by means of a reactance and an e.m.f. was given by Putman.[3] Both the reactance and the e.m.f. vary with saturation, being functions of the voltage E_l behind armature leakage reactance (or, more accurately, of the voltage E_p behind Potier reactance). The manner in which these quantities vary with E_p can be deduced from the vector diagram,

Fig. 15, which is much like that of Fig. 62 of Chapter XII. The following notation is used:

I = armature current
V_t = armature terminal voltage
r_a = armature resistance
x_p = Potier reactance

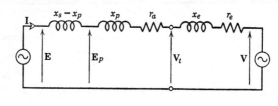

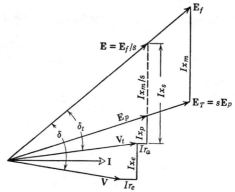

FIG. 15. Vector diagram of cylindrical-rotor synchronous machine with saturation.

E_p = voltage behind Potier reactance
E_T = voltage that would exist behind Potier reactance if there were no saturation and if field and armature currents were unchanged

$$s = E_T/E_p = \text{saturation factor*} = 1 + \frac{\text{m.m.f. for iron}}{\text{m.m.f. for air gap}} = AC/AB$$

in Fig. 19
x_d = unsaturated synchronous reactance
$x_m = x_d - x_p$ = reactance equivalent to the armature reaction if there were no saturation
E_f = armature voltage which would be induced by field current I_f if there were no saturation

*In Refs. 3, 10, and 12 the saturation factor is denoted by k instead of by s. However, k is deemed misleading for a quantity which is not constant.

EXAMPLE 7   281

It is clear from the vector diagram that the terminal conditions would be the same if the saturated machine were replaced by an equivalent unsaturated machine having an e.m.f.

$$\mathbf{E} = \frac{\mathbf{E}_f}{s} \qquad [39]$$

and a synchronous reactance

$$x_s = x_p + \frac{x_m}{s} = x_p + \frac{x_d - x_p}{s} \qquad [40]$$

Equations 39 and 40 give the saturated values of the excitation voltage and of the synchronous reactance, respectively. Furthermore, the load angle δ_t between the excitation voltage and the terminal voltage is the same for the equivalent machine of Fig. 15 as for the actual machine.

When a saturated machine is represented according to eqs. 39 and 40, it must be borne in mind that s varies with E_p and hence with load. Therefore, in plotting a power-angle curve for constant field current, variation of s must be taken into account. Kingsley[12] has devised a method of obtaining the power-angle curve of a saturated cylindrical-rotor machine connected through series impedance to an infinite bus. His method, which is based on eqs. 39 and 40, together with means for finding the values of s and related quantities, is illustrated in Example 7, which follows. Example 7 is taken from Ref. 12 with permission.

Example 7

A cylindrical-rotor synchronous generator whose open-circuit and short-circuit characteristics are shown in Fig. 16 and whose armature resistance and Potier reactance are, respectively, 0.022 per unit and 0.105 per unit transmits power through external series impedance of $0.092 + j0.436$ per unit to an infinite bus of voltage 1.00 per unit. The generator is operated at constant excitation of 1.61 per unit. Calculate and plot the air-gap power of the generator and the power received by the infinite bus as functions of the angle δ between the excitation voltage and the voltage of the infinite bus.

Solution. Let the following notation be used (see Fig. 15):

$\mathbf{I}$ = current
$\mathbf{V} = V\underline{/0}$ = voltage of infinite bus
$\mathbf{E}_p$ = voltage behind Potier reactance
$\mathbf{E}_f = E_f\underline{/\delta}$ = unsaturated value of excitation voltage
$\mathbf{E} = \mathbf{E}_f/s$ = saturated value of excitation voltage
s = saturation factor
P_a = air-gap power of the generator
P_b = power delivered to the infinite bus

r_e = external resistance
r_a = armature resistance
$r = r_e + r_a$ = total series resistance
x_e = external reactance
x_p = Potier reactance of armature
x_d = unsaturated synchronous reactance

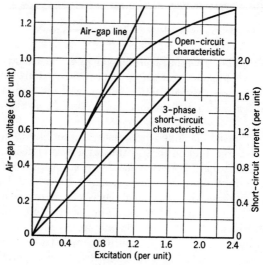

FIG. 16.   Open-circuit and short-circuit characteristics of a cylindrical-rotor synchronous machine (Example 7).   (From Ref. 12, with permission.)

$x_m = x_d - x_p$ = reactance equivalent to armature reaction when there is no saturation
$x_s = x_p + x_m/s$ = saturated synchronous reactance
$x = x_e + x_s$ = total series reactance, saturated value
$\mathbf{Z} = Z \underline{/90° - \alpha} = r + jx = (r_e + r_a) + j(x_e + x_s)$
$\mathbf{Z}_c = Z_c \underline{/90° - \alpha_c} = (r_e + r_a) + j(x_e + x_p)$
$\alpha = \tan^{-1}(r/x)$
$\alpha_c = \tan^{-1}[(r_e + r_a)/(x_e + x_p)]$
δ = angle by which $\mathbf{E}$ leads $\mathbf{V}$

For the case considered in this example, the following circuit parameters (all expressed in per unit) are given:

$$V = 1.00 \qquad r_a = 0.022 \qquad r_e = 0.092$$
$$E_f = 1.61 \qquad x_p = 0.105 \qquad x_e = 0.436$$

and several other quantities, which are independent of saturation, are readily calculated.

EXAMPLE 7   283

From the curves of Fig. 16 at an excitation of 1.2 per unit, the open-circuit voltage on the air-gap line is 1.2 per unit and the short-circuit current is 1.24 per unit. Hence

$$x_d = \frac{1.20}{1.24} = 0.970$$

$$x_m = x_d - x_p = 0.970 - 0.105 = 0.865$$

$$r = r_e + r_a = 0.092 + 0.022 = 0.114$$

$$x_e + x_p = 0.436 + 0.105 = 0.541$$

$$Z_c = \sqrt{(r_e + r_a)^2 + (x_e + x_p)^2} = \sqrt{(0.114)^2 + (0.541)^2} = 0.553$$

$$\alpha_c = \tan^{-1} \frac{r_e + r_a}{x_e + x_p} = \tan^{-1} \frac{0.114}{0.541} = \tan^{-1} 0.210 = 11.9°$$

In terms of the notation given above, the power-angle equations **31 and 32** for the case of series impedance may be rewritten as follows:

$$P_a = \frac{EV}{Z} \sin(\delta - \alpha) + \frac{E^2 r}{Z^2} \qquad (a)$$

$$P_b = \frac{EV}{Z} \sin(\delta + \alpha) - \frac{V^2 r}{Z^2} \qquad (b)$$

Upon substitution of $E = E_f/s$ (eq. 39), eqs. a and b become:

$$P_a = \frac{E_f V}{sZ} \sin(\delta - \alpha) + \frac{E_f^2 r}{(sZ)^2} \qquad (c)$$

$$P_b = \frac{E_f V}{sZ} \sin(\delta + \alpha) - \frac{V^2 r}{Z^2} \qquad (d)$$

In eqs. c and d, sZ, α, and Z^2 are variables dependent upon saturation, which varies with δ even though E_f and V are constant. Hence, to determine the values of these quantities to be used in eqs. c and d, it is necessary to express the Potier voltage E_p (which determines the saturation) as a function of δ. This may be done as follows:

From Fig. 15,

$$\mathbf{E}_p = \mathbf{V} + \mathbf{Z}_c \mathbf{I} \qquad (e)$$

and

$$\mathbf{I} = \frac{\mathbf{E} - \mathbf{V}}{\mathbf{Z}} \qquad (f)$$

Hence

$$\mathbf{E}_p = \mathbf{V} + \mathbf{Z}_c \frac{\mathbf{E} - \mathbf{V}}{\mathbf{Z}} = \frac{\mathbf{Z}_c \mathbf{E} + (\mathbf{Z} - \mathbf{Z}_c)\mathbf{V}}{\mathbf{Z}} \qquad (g)$$

Since

$$\mathbf{E} = \frac{\mathbf{E}_f}{s} \qquad (h)$$

and

$$\mathbf{Z} - \mathbf{Z}_c = \frac{jx_m}{s} \qquad (i)$$

$$\mathbf{Z}\mathbf{E}_p = \mathbf{Z}_c \frac{\mathbf{E}_f}{s} + j\frac{x_m}{s}\mathbf{V} \qquad (j)$$

Hence

$$s\mathbf{Z}\mathbf{E}_p = \mathbf{Z}_c\mathbf{E}_f + jx_m\mathbf{V}$$
$$= Z_cE_f\underline{/\delta + 90° - \alpha_c} + x_mV\underline{/90°} \qquad (k)$$

The right-hand side of eq. k is the sum of two vectors differing in phase by an angle $(\delta - \alpha_c)$. Hence, by the law of cosines, the magnitude of the vector sum is given by

$$(sZE_p)^2 = (Z_cE_f)^2 + (x_mV)^2 + 2Z_cx_mE_fV \cos(\delta - \alpha_c) \qquad (l)$$

which, for the case under consideration, becomes:

$$(sZE_p)^2 = (0.553 \times 1.61)^2 + (0.865 \times 1.00)^2$$
$$+ 2 \times 0.553 \times 0.865 \times 1.61 \times 1.00 \cos(\delta - 11.9°)$$
$$= 1.54 + 1.54 \cos(\delta - 11.9°) \qquad (m)$$

From eq. l or m, for any assumed value of δ, the corresponding value of $(sZE_p)^2$ can be calculated. This quantity is a function of E_p, as are also variables sZ, α, and Z^2, which appear in eqs. c and d. By assuming various values of E_p, these values can be calculated, and curves can be drawn showing sZ, α, and Z^2 as functions of $(sZE_p)^2$. The values read from the curves can then be substituted in eqs. c and d to find P_a and P_b for any value of δ.

The construction of the auxiliary curves will be illustrated for one assumed value of E_p, namely $E_p = 1.00$.

The saturation factor s is defined as the abscissa of the open-circuit characteristic divided by the abscissa of the air-gap line. For $E_p = 1.00$, from Fig. 16,

$$s = \frac{1.19}{1.00} = 1.19$$

$$x_s = x_p + \frac{x_m}{s} = 0.105 + \frac{0.865}{1.19} = 0.105 + 0.726 = 0.831$$

$$x = x_e + x_s = 0.436 + 0.831 = 1.27$$

$$Z = \sqrt{r^2 + x^2} = \sqrt{(0.114)^2 + (1.27)^2} = 1.27$$

$$Z^2 = 1.61$$

$$sZ = 1.19 \times 1.27 = 1.51$$

$$(sZE_p)^2 = (1.51 \times 1.00)^2 = 2.28$$

$$\alpha = \tan^{-1}(r/x) = \tan^{-1}(0.114/1.27) = \tan^{-1} 0.090 = 5.1°$$

EXAMPLE 7   285

By carrying through similar calculations for several other assumed values of E_p, points can be calculated for plotting the auxiliary curves of Fig. 17.

By use of the auxiliary curves, points on the power-angle curves can be calculated. The following calculations for one assumed value of δ illustrate the method:

Let $\delta = 60°$. From eq. m,

$$(sZE_p)^2 = 1.54 + 1.54 \cos (60.0° - 11.9°)$$
$$= 1.54 + 1.54 \cos 48.1° = 2.57$$

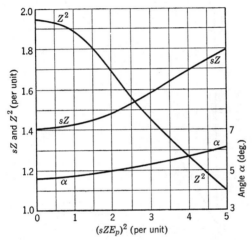

Fig. 17. Auxiliary curves for Example 7. (From Ref. 12, with permission.)

From the curves of Fig. 17 at abscissa 2.57, the following quantities are read:

$$sZ = 1.54, \qquad \alpha = 5.2°, \qquad Z^2 = 1.55$$

Substitution of these values and of $\delta = 60°$ into eqs. c and d gives:

$$P_a = \frac{1.61 \times 1.00}{1.54} \sin (60° - 5.2°) + \frac{(1.61)^2 \times 0.114}{(1.54)^2} = 0.980$$

$$P_b = \frac{1.61 \times 1.00}{1.54} \sin (60° + 5.2°) - \frac{(1.00)^2 \times 0.114}{1.55} = 0.876$$

The complete power-angle curves are plotted in Fig. 18. This figure also shows test results. The agreement is good, the calculated values of power being, at the worst, about 0.02 per unit below the test results.

The maxima of the curves are:

$$P_{a(\text{max})} = 1.24 \text{ per unit}$$

$$P_{b(\text{max})} = 1.02 \text{ per unit}$$

These maxima can be found, if desired, without plotting the complete power-angle curves. To find $P_{a(\max)}$ assume an approximate value of α, substitute $\delta = 90° + \alpha$ into eq. l, and compute $(sZE_p)^2$. From the auxiliary curve, read sZ and substitute it into eq. c, also putting $\sin(\delta - \alpha) = 1$. Similarly, $P_{b(\max)}$ is found by putting $\delta = 90° - \alpha$ in eq. l, computing $(sZE_p)^2$, reading sZ and Z^2 from the auxiliary curves, and substituting their values into eq. d, also putting $\sin(\delta + \alpha) = 1$.

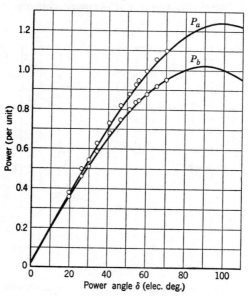

FIG. 18. Power-angle curves for Example 7 by calculation and by test. Test points are shown by small circles. (From Ref. 12, with permission.)

Equivalent synchronous reactance. For general use in stability studies, it is preferable to use, instead of the saturated synchronous reactance and excitation voltage, which vary with load as illustrated in the foregoing example, a reactance and an e.m.f. which are constant during small changes in load, even though their values depend upon the initial operating condition. Such quantities are called *equivalent synchronous reactance* and *equivalent excitation voltage*. If they are used, it is possible to apply the test for stability, previously discussed, that the synchronizing power $dP/d\delta$ be positive.

The problem may be thought of as that of finding the constant e.m.f. and reactance of an unsaturated machine which, for small changes of load, is equivalent to a given saturated machine. The two machines are equivalent if, for given terminal conditions **V** and **I**, the same change of **V** occurs for the same small change of **I**. In other words, the derivative dV/dI (or its reciprocal) should be the same for both machines.

For present purposes consider the point behind Potier reactance as the terminal. Then the external network (including Potier reactance) is not affected by saturation. The relation between voltage and current of the saturated machine is

$$\mathbf{E}_p = \frac{\mathbf{E}_f}{s} - \frac{jx_m}{s}\mathbf{I} \qquad [41]$$

and of the equivalent unsaturated machine

$$\mathbf{E}_p = \mathbf{E}_f' - jx_m'\mathbf{I} \qquad [42]$$

where $\mathbf{E}_f$, $\mathbf{E}_f'$, x_m, and x_m' are constant, while s is a function of E_p,

The derivative $dI/d\mathbf{E}_p$ will be found for each machine, and the two expressions will be equated to find reactance x_m'. For the saturated machine, from eq. 41,

$$s\mathbf{E}_p = \mathbf{E}_f - jx_m\mathbf{I}$$

$$\mathbf{I} = \frac{\mathbf{E}_f - s\mathbf{E}_p}{jx_m}$$

$$\frac{d\mathbf{I}}{d\mathbf{E}_p} = -\frac{1}{jx_m}\frac{d(s\mathbf{E}_p)}{d\mathbf{E}_p} \qquad [43]$$

For the equivalent unsaturated machine, from eq. 42,

$$\mathbf{I} = \frac{\mathbf{E}_f' - \mathbf{E}_p}{jx_m'}$$

$$\frac{d\mathbf{I}}{d\mathbf{E}_p} = -\frac{1}{jx_m'} \qquad [44]$$

Equate eqs. 43 and 44 and solve for x_m', obtaining

$$x_m' = x_m \frac{d\mathbf{E}_p}{d(s\mathbf{E}_p)} \qquad [45]$$

The equivalent synchronous reactance is

$$x_{eq} = x_p + x_m' = x_p + (x_d - x_p)\frac{d\mathbf{E}_p}{d(s\mathbf{E}_p)} \qquad [46]$$

The real derivative, $dE_p/d(sE_p)$, equals the slope of the no-load saturation curve if the latter is regarded as a plot of E_p against sE_p (Fig. 19); or, for any other scale of abscissas, the derivative equals the slope of the no-load saturation curve at ordinate E_p divided by the slope of the air-gap line.

However, in eq. 46 $\mathbf{E}_p$ is complex, and the value of the derivative varies with the phase angle between $\mathbf{E}_p$ and $d\mathbf{E}_p$, as illustrated in Fig. 20 for a finite increment $\Delta\mathbf{E}_p$. In Fig. 20a, $\Delta\mathbf{E}_p$ is in phase with $\mathbf{E}_p$. Here the derivative

$$\frac{d\mathbf{E}_p}{d(s\mathbf{E}_p)} = \frac{dE_p}{d(sE_p)} \qquad [47]$$

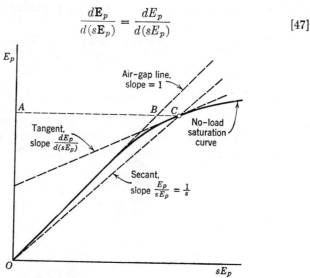

FIG. 19. The slopes of the tangent and the secant through the operating point of the no-load saturation curve are the minimum and maximum values, respectively, of the magnitude of the derivative $d\mathbf{E}_p/d(s\mathbf{E}_p)$ which appears in eq. 46 for equivalent synchronous reactance.

which is real and has a magnitude which, as already stated, is equal to the slope of the saturation curve. In Fig. 20c, on the other hand, $\Delta\mathbf{E}_p$ is in quadrature with $\mathbf{E}_p$. The saturation factor s is the same before and after addition of the increment $\Delta\mathbf{E}_p$, the two triangles are similar, and the derivative is now

$$\frac{d\mathbf{E}_p}{d(s\mathbf{E}_p)} = \frac{E_p}{sE_p} = \frac{1}{s} \qquad [48]$$

It is again real, but its magnitude is greater than in Fig. 20a and is represented geometrically by the slope of the secant through the operating point on the saturation curve (Fig. 19). In Fig. 20b, $\Delta\mathbf{E}_p$ is neither in phase with nor in quadrature with $\mathbf{E}_p$. There is some change in saturation, but not so much as there was in Fig. 20a for the same absolute value of $|\Delta\mathbf{E}_p|$. The two triangles are not similar; $\Delta(s\mathbf{E}_p)$ is not parallel to $\Delta\mathbf{E}_p$, and hence the derivative in eq. 46 is complex.

Consequently, the equivalent reactance given by that equation is complex; or, in other words, the equivalent impedance is not a pure reactance. Its resistance component is usually neglected, however. The magnitude of the derivative in *b* lies between the two extremes of *a* and *c*. Hence the equivalent synchronous reactance lies between the extremes

$$x_{eq(min)} = x_p + (x_d - x_p) \frac{\text{slope of no-load saturation curve}}{\text{slope of air-gap line}} \quad [49]*$$

and

$$x_{eq(max)} = x_p + \frac{x_d - x_p}{s} \quad [50]$$

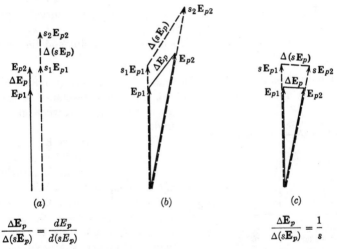

$$\frac{\Delta \mathbf{E}_p}{\Delta(s\mathbf{E}_p)} = \frac{d E_p}{d(s E_p)} \qquad\qquad \frac{\Delta \mathbf{E}_p}{\Delta(s\mathbf{E}_p)} = \frac{1}{s}$$

FIG. 20. Showing the effect of phase on the derivative $d\mathbf{E}_p/d(s\mathbf{E}_p)$.

For the same degree of saturation, the minimum value of equivalent reactance occurs when the saturation is varying most rapidly; the maximum, when the saturation is not varying. Both are smaller than the unsaturated synchronous reactance x_d.

The angle between $\mathbf{E}_p$ and $\Delta \mathbf{E}_p$, and hence the value of equivalent synchronous reactance, for given initial values of $\mathbf{E}_p$ and $\mathbf{I}$ depends upon the external network, including all other machines, and upon the nature of the small change of load (which, in testing for stability, is usually an increase in angular displacement). This dependence may

*Equation 49 is similar to the expressions for equivalent reactance given by Clarke[2] and Kilgore.[11]

be readily appreciated if the external network is represented by an impedance $\mathbf{Z}_{ext}$ and an e.m.f. $\mathbf{E}_{ext}$ according to Thévenin's theorem, as shown in Fig. 21.

A full investigation of the dependence of x_{eq} upon the parameters of this circuit is difficult. However, at or near pullout, a reactance given by the average of eqs. 49 and 50 is approximately correct and is recommended for general use in steady-state stability studies. This average value is

$$x_{eq(\text{avg})} \approx x_p + (x_d - x_p) \frac{\sqrt{S_{tan}\, S_{sec}}}{S_{ag}} \qquad [51]$$

where x_p = Potier reactance.

x_d = unsaturated direct-axis synchronous reactance.

S_{tan} = slope of tangent to no-load saturation curve at point whose ordinate is E_p.

S_{sec} = slope of secant through the same point and the origin.

S_{ag} = slope of air-gap line.

The *reciprocal of the short-circuit ratio* (Chapter XII, p. 128) is often used as an approximate value of the equivalent reactance of turbo-generators, especially when operated underexcited.

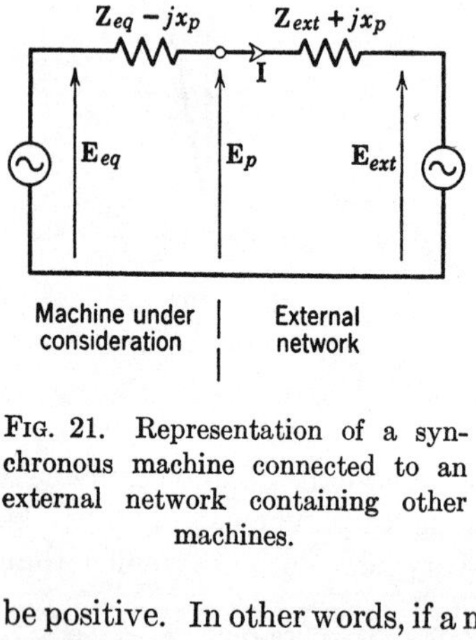

The internal voltage $\mathbf{E}_{eq}$ is simply the voltage required behind x_{eq} to give the actual initial conditions at the terminals of the machine.

The angular position δ_{eq} of voltage $\mathbf{E}_{eq}$ is not the same as the angular position δ of the rotor of the machine. However, if δ is advanced, δ_{eq} is also advanced; and if δ is retarded, δ_{eq} is also retarded. Hence, the algebraic sign of $dP/d\delta_{eq}$ is the same as that of $dP/d\delta$, and a valid criterion for stability is that $dP/d\delta_{eq}$

Fig. 21. Representation of a synchronous machine connected to an external network containing other machines.

be positive. In other words, if a machine is represented by its equivalent synchronous reactance and equivalent excitation voltage, it may be tested for stability by advancing the phase of its equivalent excitation voltage $\mathbf{E}_{eq}$ and noting whether or not its power output increases.

Example 8

Determine the correct value of equivalent synchronous reactance of the generator of Example 7 when it is operating at its power limit under the

EXAMPLE 8   291

conditions of that example. Compare this value of reactance with the minimum, maximum, and average values computed from eqs. 49, 50, and 51 and with the reciprocal of the short-circuit ratio.

Solution. *Conditions at pullout.* From Fig. 18 at the maximum of the curve of P_a versus δ,

$$\delta \approx 99°, \qquad P_a = 1.24, \qquad \text{and} \qquad P_b = 1.01$$

From eq. *m* of Example 7, with $\delta = 99°$,

$$(sZE_p)^2 = 1.62$$

and from Fig. 17 at abscissa 1.62,

$$sZ = 1.46$$

Hence

$$E_p = \frac{\sqrt{(sZE_p)^2}}{sZ} = \frac{\sqrt{1.62}}{1.46} = 0.874$$

The power transmitted from a point where the voltage is $E_p\underline{/\delta_p}$ through an impedance $Z_c\underline{/90° - \alpha_c}$ to a point where the voltage is $V\underline{/0}$ is, by analogy to eq. *a* of Example 7,

$$P_a = \frac{E_p V}{Z_c} \sin (\delta_p - \alpha_c) + \frac{E_p^2 r}{Z_c^2} \tag{a}$$

Substitution of numerical values gives

$$1.24 = \frac{0.874 \times 1.00}{0.553} \sin (\delta_p - 11.9°) + \frac{(0.874)^2 \times 0.114}{(0.553)^2}$$

$$= 1.58 \sin (\delta_p - 11.9°) + 0.285$$

$$0.955 = 1.58 \sin (\delta_p - 11.9°)$$

$$0.604 = \sin (\delta_p - 11.9°)$$

$$\delta_p - 11.9° = 37.2°$$

$$\delta_p = 49.1°$$

$$\mathbf{E}_p = E_p\underline{/\delta_p} = 0.874\underline{/49.1°} = 0.575 + j0.660$$

The current is

$$\mathbf{I} = \frac{\mathbf{E}_p - \mathbf{V}}{\mathbf{Z}_c} = \frac{0.575 + j0.660 - 1.000}{0.553\underline{/78.1°}}$$

$$= \frac{-0.425 + j0.660}{0.553\underline{/78.1°}} = \frac{0.783\underline{/122.8°}}{0.553\underline{/78.1°}}$$

$$= 1.42\underline{/44.7°} = 1.01 + j1.00$$

The power delivered to the infinite bus is

$$P_b = V \times \text{Re }(\mathbf{I}) = 1.00 \times 1.01 = 1.01$$

which agrees with the value read from the curve.

The copper loss in the circuit is

$$I^2 r = (1.42)^2 \times 0.114 = 0.23$$

Hence the air-gap power of the generator is

$$P_a = P_b + I^2 r = 1.01 + 0.23 = 1.24$$

This value agrees with the value read from the curve and used in the foregoing calculations.

Determination of equivalent reactance. At the point of pullout, $dP_a/d\delta = 0$. The equivalent reactance is the constant value of reactance which, backed by the constant voltage E_{eq}, will give $dP_a/d\delta_{eq} = 0$ (where δ_{eq} is the angle by which E_{eq} leads V) with the conditions deduced above. This reactance may be found graphically by means of a Clarke diagram, constructed somewhat differently from the way described before, because the power at pullout is now known and the reactance is sought, whereas previously the reverse was true. Another difference to be taken into account is that in the present example the condition considered is that of maximum power at the sending end of the circuit instead of at the receiving end. The angular separation for this condition is $\delta_{eq} = 180° - \theta_{12}$.

The construction of the Clarke diagram is shown in Fig. 22. From point O as origin, the following vectors are drawn to scale:

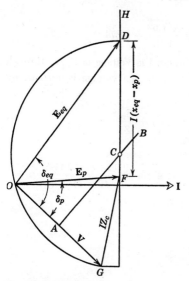

FIG. 22. Determination of equivalent reactance from Clarke diagram, E_p and the power limit being known (Example 8).

$$\mathbf{V} = 1.000 + j0$$

$$\mathbf{E}_p = 0.575 + j0.660$$

$$\mathbf{I} = 1.01 + j1.00$$

From point F, the tip of vector $\mathbf{E}_p$, a line FH is drawn perpendicular to $\mathbf{I}$. Line AB, the perpendicular bisector of $\mathbf{V}$, is then drawn, intersecting line FH at point C. With C as center and radius CO, a circular arc is drawn intersecting FH at point D. Length FD, which represents $I(x_{eq} - x_p)$, is measured and is found to be 1.00 unit of voltage. Hence

$$x_{eq} - x_p = \frac{I(x_{eq} - x_p)}{I} = \frac{1.00}{1.42} = 0.705 \text{ per unit}$$

$$x_{eq} = 0.705 + x_p = 0.705 + 0.105 = 0.810 \text{ per unit}$$

EXAMPLE 8 293

Minimum, maximum, and average values of equivalent reactance. In Fig. 16 at $E_p = 0.874$, the slope of the tangent to the open-circuit characteristic is

$$S_{tan} = \frac{1.30 - 0.27}{1.67 - 0} = \frac{1.03}{1.67} = 0.62$$

and the slope of the secant at the same point is

$$S_{sec} = \frac{0.874}{0.96} = 0.91$$

The slope of the air-gap line is

$$S_{ag} = 1.00$$

By eq. 49, the minimum value of equivalent synchronous reactance is

$$x_{eq(min)} = 0.105 + (0.970 - 0.105) \times 0.62/1.00$$
$$= 0.105 + 0.865 \times 0.62$$
$$= 0.105 + 0.535 = 0.64$$

By eq. 50, the maximum value is

$$x_{eq(max)} = 0.105 + 0.865 \times 0.91/1.00$$
$$= 0.105 + 0.786 = 0.891$$
$$= 0.89$$

By eq. 51, the average value is

$$x_{eq(avg)} = 0.105 + 0.865\sqrt{0.62 \times 0.91}/1.00$$
$$= 0.105 + 0.650 = 0.755$$
$$= 0.76$$

Equivalent reactance as reciprocal of short-circuit ratio. From Fig. 16, the excitation for unit short-circuit current is 0.96 per unit and that for unit open-circuit voltage is 1.20 per unit. Hence

$$x_{eq} = \frac{1}{\text{S.C.R.}} = \frac{0.96}{1.20} = 0.80 \text{ per unit}$$

Conclusions. The following synchronous reactances were found:

Unsaturated value	0.97 per unit
Equivalent values	
Minimum	0.64
Average	0.76
Maximum	0.89
1/S.C.R.	0.80
Actual	0.81

The actual value for the conditions of this problem is very close to the reciprocal of the short-circuit ratio and does not differ greatly from the average value.

Representation of loads. Loads, as well as synchronous machines, have nonlinear characteristics although for convenience they are usually represented by constant impedances. The impedances are given such values that at normal voltage they consume the same active and reactive power as the actual load does. The advantages

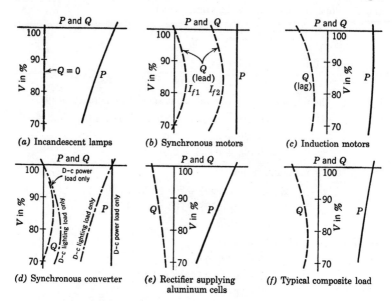

(a) Incandescent lamps   (b) Synchronous motors   (c) Induction motors

(d) Synchronous converter   (e) Rectifier supplying   (f) Typical composite load
                           aluminum cells

FIG. 23.   Active power P and reactive power Q as functions of voltage V for different kinds of load.

of using constant impedances to represent loads are that on the calculating board the load units need not be readjusted while a machine is being tested for stability, and in paper calculation the network, including loads, can be reduced to the simplest form and the equations of power previously derived can be used.

In the accurate determination of steady-state stability and stability limits, the nonlinearity of loads should be taken into account under some circumstances (see next section). The characteristics of loads may be represented advantageously by curves of active power against voltage and of reactive power against voltage. The shapes of these curves vary with the kind of load.

For a *constant-impedance load*, both active and reactive power vary as the square of the voltage; hence the curves are parabolas.

The power taken by *incandescent lamps* varies as a power of the voltage between 1.5 and 1.6. (The resistance of metal filaments increases with temperature.) The reactive power is zero. See Fig. 23a.

The active power taken by *synchronous motors* is practically independent of voltage unless the voltage drops so low that the motor pulls out of step. The reactive power varies with voltage, becoming more leading as the voltage decreases. See Fig. 23b. The exact reactive-power characteristic may be obtained from a synchronous-machine chart.[5]

The active power taken by *induction motors* is nearly independent of voltage because the slip is small. The reactive power varies with voltage, however. See Fig. 23c. The principal component of reactive power, due to the exciting current, decreases with a decrease of voltage; another component, due to load current, increases with a decrease of voltage.

The power taken by *synchronous converters and rectifiers* depends upon the nature of the d-c. load. For d-c. lighting load, the power varies with the voltage as it does for a-c. lighting load. For d-c. motor load, the power is nearly constant. The reactive power of a synchronous converter varies like that of a synchronous motor. The reactive power of a rectifier is more like that of a constant inductive impedance. See Fig. 23d and e.

It is not feasible to take into account individually many small loads. Usually the entire load on a substation or in a large load area is treated as a unit. Such a load consists mainly of the several kinds of load mentioned above, combined in proportions which differ according to whether the load area is predominantly residential, commercial, or industrial, and also according to the time of day. A typical segregation of daytime loads might be as follows:

Induction motors	60%
Synchronous motors*	10%
Lighting and heating	30%

The characteristics of a composite load may be found by adding the values of active power of the different kinds of load at a particular value of voltage to obtain the total active power at this voltage, and by similarly adding the components of reactive power to obtain the total reactive power. The losses of the distribution feeders and transformers may be included also. The characteristics of a typical composite load are shown in Fig. 23f.

The most important feature of the curves of active and reactive

*Large synchronous motors can be treated as individual machines if that appears desirable.

power against voltage are their *slopes* at normal voltage. In most cases the initial load voltages may be assumed to be normal when a test of stability is being made, regardless of the initial loads and of the substation bus voltages. Most power systems have feeder-voltage regulators which hold the voltages at the individual loads nearly constant. However, when a test for stability is made by means of a small increment of angle and load, the feeder-voltage regulators are assumed not to work. This assumption is consistent with the usual assumption that generator-voltage regulators work too slowly to affect stability. Hence the slopes dP/dV and dQ/dV at $V = 100\%$ suffice to determine the action of the load during the test for stability.

If the power of a load varies as the k'th power of the voltage ($P = KV^k$), then

$$\frac{dP}{dV} = k\,\frac{P}{V} \qquad [52]$$

For constant impedance, $k = 2$; for constant current, $k = 1$; and for constant power, $k = 0$. A similar relation holds for reactive power. For any curves of P and Q against V, the slopes at normal value of voltage may be expressed by a dimensionless quantity k as in eq. 52.

Effect of loads. Heffron[31] has made an analytical study of the effect of a shunt load on the steady-state stability of a system consisting of a finite machine connected through a reactance of 0.4 per unit to an infinite bus. The load is at unity power factor and has any one of three characteristics: $k = 0.5$, 1.0, or 2.0 (eq. 52), and either of two magnitudes: 1 or 5 times the rating of the finite machine. It is connected at a point such that the reactance between the load and the finite machine is either 0.1 or 0.3 per unit. The results of his study show that the effect of the load on the steady-state stability limit is negligible unless the load is large (5 per unit) compared to the generator rating and electrically close to the generator ($x = 0.1$ per unit). If the load is heavy and close, it has a stabilizing effect if $k = 1$ (constant current), and an even greater stabilizing effect if $k = 2$ (constant resistance), but it has the contrary effect if $k = 0.5$ (intermediate between constant current and constant power). The effect of heavy, close load on the stability limit ranges from a 40% increase to a 15% reduction. These results indicate that it is not worth while to take load characteristics into account except for heavy loads electrically close to the generator being tested for stability.

Crary has presented an analytical method of finding the synchronizing power of any machine of a system of any number of machines and composite loads, taking into account the slopes of the load characteristics (see Ref. 9 or Chapter 4 of Ref. 20).

On a calculating board the impedance of loads may be adjusted manually as the voltage varies in order to give the proper variation of P and Q.

Graphical methods are also available for taking into account load characteristics as well as saturation of synchronous machines. Some of these methods are described in the next section.

Graphical methods. By the use of graphical methods it is possible to take into account the nonlinear characteristics of loads and of synchronous machines while checking the steady-state stability of a system or while finding its steady-state stability limit. In these graphical methods the power system is figuratively cut in two at some point at which the power flow is of interest. Each half of the system has certain relations between active power, reactive power, and voltage (all measured at the point of observation). These relations are determined for appropriate initial conditions and constant field currents in all synchronous machines.

If there is more than one synchronous machine in the same part of the system, the division of power between the several machines can be determined according to whichever of the three assumptions previously discussed under "Multimachine system" is deemed most appropriate. Synchronous condensers, however, should be assumed to take no active power except when the stability of a condenser itself is being checked.

The relations between voltage, power, and reactive power for each half of the system can be plotted in any of three different ways:

1. Reactive power may be plotted against active power for constant voltage, and a family of such curves may be drawn for different values of voltage (see Fig. 24).

2. Voltage may be plotted against reactive power for constant active power, and a family of such curves may be drawn for different values of active power (see Fig. 25).

3. Voltage may be plotted against active power for constant reactive power, and a family of such curves may be drawn for different values of reactive power (see Fig. 26).

When the two parts of the system which were cut apart are rejoined, the voltages of the two parts at the junction point are equal, and the output of active and reactive power from one part equals the input of active and reactive power, respectively, to the other part. Sets of values of voltage, active power, and reactive power which satisfy both parts of the system can be found by superposing the graphs for one part upon the graphs of the same type for the other part. Thus, if the first type of plot listed above (reactive power versus active power)

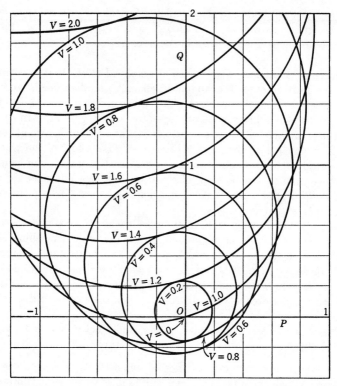

Fig. 24. Loci of constant voltage V in the complex power plane, $P + jQ$, for a circuit consisting of constant e.m.f. $E = 1$ in series with constant impedance $Z = 1 \underline{/75°}$.

is used, the intersection of the curve for the sending system for 100% voltage and the curve for the receiving system for the same value of voltage is one point which satisfies both parts. Another such point is the intersection of the two curves for 90% voltage, and so on for other values of voltage. See Fig. 27. A curve drawn through these points (a curve of reactive power versus active power) is a characteristic of the sending and receiving systems combined. Each point on the curve is associated with a definite value of voltage. Hence the information

given by the curve could be replotted as active power against voltage
(Fig. 28) or as reactive power against voltage.

Similar information can be obtained by superposition of plots of the
second or third types. From plots of the second type, a composite
curve of voltage versus reactive power is obtained. The information

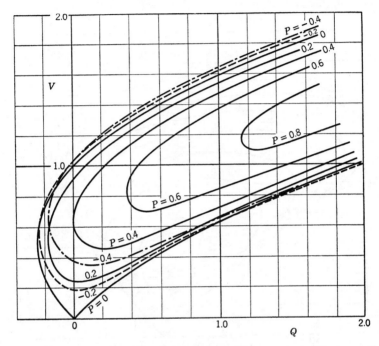

FIG. 25. Voltage V as a function of reactive power Q for constant active power P.
These curves are drawn for the same circuit as the curves of Fig. 24.

can be replotted as voltage versus active power or as reactive power
versus active power. From plots of the third type, a composite curve
of voltage versus active power is obtained. The results can be replotted as voltage versus reactive power or as reactive power versus
active power.

It is also possible to visualize (though not practical to plot) the
characteristics of each half of the system as a surface in three-dimensional coordinates of active power, reactive power, and voltage. Each
of the three types of families of curves for each half of the system
results from intersections of the surface with a set of planes parallel
to one of the coordinate planes and the projection of the intersections

onto that plane. The common characteristic of the two halves of the system is the three-dimensional curve resulting from the intersection of the two surfaces. This curve can be projected onto any one of the three coordinate planes as a two-dimensional curve.

Of the three two-dimensional curves which satisfy both halves of the system, those of voltage against active power (Fig. 28) and of reactive

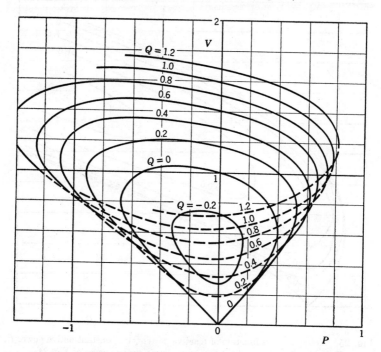

FIG. 26. Voltage V as a function of active power P for constant reactive power Q. These curves are drawn for the same circuit as the curves of Figs. 24 and 25.

power against active power (Fig. 27) are most useful. From either of these curves the value of *maximum power* of either sign can be read.*
This is the *power limit* at the point of observation *for constant field currents in the synchronous machines* and for the assumed division of power between machines of each group. This power limit may or may not be a stability limit. Suppose, for illustration, that the point of observation lies between a synchronous generator and a static-impedance load. In this case there will be a maximum power but no

*In practice only part of the curve need be constructed, depending upon the assumed direction of power flow.

question of loss of synchronism. Again, suppose that the point of observation lies between a synchronous generator and a combination of a static-impedance or composite load and a large synchronous motor or condenser. The critical point on the curve as regards stability may lie on one side or the other of the point of maximum power.

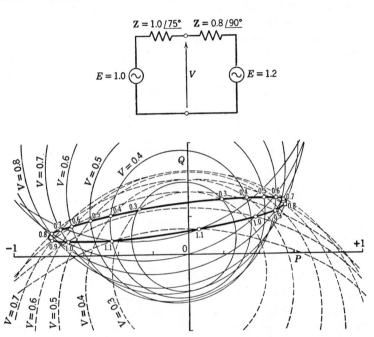

FIG. 27. Curve of reactive power Q versus active power P that satisfies the parts of the circuit on both sides of the point of observation. Points on this curve are obtained from the intersections of the loci of Fig. 24 for the left part of the circuit with similar loci for the right part of the circuit and equal voltage.

Check for stability of synchronous machines. In order to check whether a power system is stable or unstable at some particular operating condition, the point of observation should be taken in turn between each synchronous machine and the remainder of the system. According to the conservative criterion of steady-state stability, previously discussed, a machine is stable if its synchronizing power $dP/d\delta$ is positive. In order that the curves of power P against voltage V or reactive power Q may be used in this connection, an alternative criterion for stability will be formulated. It is found that as the angular separation between a machine and the remaining machines is increased in either direction, the terminal voltage of the machine decreases. At the condition of maximum power not only does $dP/d\delta = 0$ but also $dP/dV = 0$ and $dP/dQ = 0$. If the machine is operating *stably*, the voltage V is *higher* than it is at maximum power; whereas, if the machine is *unstable*, the voltage is *lower* than at maximum power. (The alternative criterion for stability is not expressed in terms of the sign of the slope dP/dV because this depends upon whether the machine being examined is operating as a motor or as a generator.) Thus it is possible to check the stability of each synchronous machine by finding

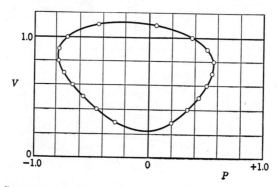

FIG. 28. Curve of voltage V versus active power P that satisfies the parts of the circuit on both sides of the point of observation.

a curve (such as that of Fig. 28) of active power against voltage at the terminals of the machine (with constant field currents) and noting whether at the initial operating condition the voltage is higher or lower than it is at maximum power. A curve of active power versus reactive power can be used in similar fashion if values of voltage are marked on it (Fig. 27).

Synchronous condensers are checked for stability in the same manner as synchronous motors.

Induction machines. The stability of an induction machine may be checked by the same procedure as for synchronous machines. In case of the induction machine there is no question regarding loss of synchronism. Nevertheless, if an induction motor cannot develop as much torque as required by its shaft load, it will "break down" and come to rest. This condition is called instability. It may occur because of low voltage. In checking for stability the assumption is made that the induction motor operates stably at any slip less than the slip associated with maximum power. Actually the motor may operate stably at greater slips provided the slope of the curve of motor torque (or power) against slip is greater than the slope of the curve of load torque against slip. Hence the use of the same criterion for induction machines as for synchronous machines is conservative.

If all machines of a system are stable, the system is stable.

Stability limit. In order to find the steady-state stability limit graphically, the load carried by a particular machine or line is increased, the values of bus voltage and the division of power among machines being adjusted in accordance with established or proposed operating procedure. Then, keeping the field currents constant, the stability of each machine is checked as described above. These steps are repeated as many times as necessary. The stability limit is reached when, in the check for stability, maximum power of any machine occurs at the initial voltage (or reactive power).

Preparation of charts. The general principles of graphical methods of examining steady-state stability have been discussed, but more needs to be said on ways of preparing the charts that are used.

Charts are required for the separate components of the power system, such as synchronous machines, transmission lines, transformers, and loads. In addition, methods are needed for deriving the characteristics of a part of the system consisting of two or more of these components.

Transmission lines. Evans and Sels charts[4] are used in many problems dealing with transmission lines with or without terminal transformers. They are applicable to any linear circuit having a pair of input terminals and a pair of output terminals. The sending chart has rectangular coordinates Q_S and P_S, the reactive and active power input to the sending end of the line. In these coordinates are drawn circular loci representing constant magnitudes of sending-end voltage V_S and receiving-end voltage V_R, with varying phase difference between V_S and V_R. A family of such circles is drawn either for the same value of V_S and different values of V_R or for the same value of V_R and different values of V_S. In the sending chart for constant V_S (shown in Fig. 29) the circles for various values of V_R are concentric, and radial lines may be drawn which are the loci of constant phase angle between V_S and V_R. In the sending chart for constant V_R (shown in Fig. 30) the circles for various values of V_S are eccentric and intersect one another.

The receiving charts (Figs. 31 and 32) differ from the sending charts in that the rectangular coordinates are Q_R and P_R, the reactive and active power output at the receiving end, instead of Q_S and P_S. The circles may be drawn either for the same value of V_R and different

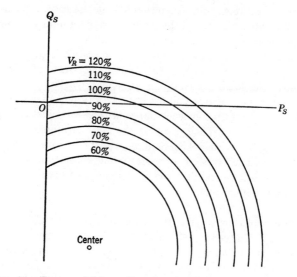

Fig. 29.   Evans and Sels sending chart for constant sending voltage.

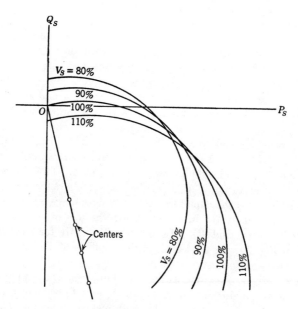

Fig. 30.   Evans and Sels sending chart for constant receiving voltage.

values of V_S, in which case they are concentric (Fig. 31), or they may be drawn for the same value of V_S and different values of V_R, in which case they are eccentric (Fig. 32).

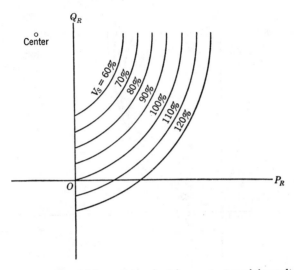

FIG. 31. Evans and Sels receiving chart for constant receiving voltage.

Briefly stated, the theory of these charts is as follows:

To derive the receiving charts, the sending voltage may be expressed in terms of the receiving voltage and current and the general circuit constants, thus:

$$\mathbf{V}_S = \mathbf{A}\mathbf{V}_R + \mathbf{B}\mathbf{I}_R \qquad [53]$$

which, solved for $\mathbf{I}_R$, becomes:

$$\mathbf{I}_R = -\frac{\mathbf{A}}{\mathbf{B}}\mathbf{V}_R + \frac{1}{\mathbf{B}}\mathbf{V}_S \qquad [54]$$

The receiving-end vector power is

$$P_R + jQ_R = \bar{\mathbf{V}}_R\mathbf{I}_R = -\frac{\mathbf{A}}{\mathbf{B}}V_R^2 + \frac{1}{\mathbf{B}}V_R V_S\underline{/\delta} \qquad [55]$$

Here δ is the angle by which $\mathbf{V}_S$ leads $\mathbf{V}_R$. For constant V_R and V_S and varying δ, this equation represents a circle in the P_R–Q_R plane. The position of the center is given by the first term and the moving radius by the second term. This is but one circle of the family of circles on the receiving chart, others being obtained by giving new values to either V_R or V_S. In the latter case, the position of the center is unchanged; in the former case, the centers lie on the same straight line at various distances from the origin.

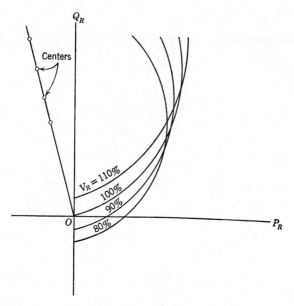

Fig. 32. Evans and Sels receiving chart for constant sending voltage.

The sending charts are derived in a similar manner. The receiving voltage, in terms of the sending voltage and current and the general circuit constants, is:

$$\mathbf{V}_R = \mathbf{D}\mathbf{V}_S - \mathbf{B}\mathbf{I}_S \qquad [56]$$

Solve for $\mathbf{I}_S$, obtaining:

$$\mathbf{I}_S = \frac{\mathbf{D}}{\mathbf{B}}\mathbf{V}_S - \frac{1}{\mathbf{B}}\mathbf{V}_R \qquad [57]$$

The sending-end vector power is:

$$P_S + jQ_S = \bar{\mathbf{V}}_S\mathbf{I}_S = \frac{\mathbf{D}}{\mathbf{B}}V_S{}^2 - \frac{1}{\mathbf{B}}V_RV_S\underline{/-\delta} \qquad [58]$$

This equation represents a circle in the P_S–Q_S plane. Again the position of the center is given by the first term. It is on the opposite side of the origin from the center of the receiving-chart circle. The second term represents the moving radius. As δ increases, this sending circle is traversed clockwise, whereas the receiving circle was traversed counterclockwise.

The theory, construction, and use of the charts are explained in greater detail in Ref. 4.

Synchronous machines. A useful form of synchronous-machine chart is similar to the Evans and Sels receiving chart. The rectangular coordinates of the generator chart are active and reactive power output. In these coordinates are drawn loci for each of which both the field current and either the terminal voltage or the voltage E_p behind Potier reactance are constant. The latter alternative has the advantage that for constant E_p the saturation is constant; hence, as previously shown for a nonsalient-pole machine, the saturated values of excitation voltage E_f/s and of reactance corresponding to armature reaction x_m/s are constant. Consequently, the locus for constant values of E_f and E_p is a circle, which is easily drawn. By assigning various values to E_f on the one hand or to E_p on the other hand, one or the other of the two types of receiving charts is obtained. For checking the stability of a synchronous machine graphically, the chart for constant E_f (corresponding to constant field current) is used. A family of such charts may be prepared for different values of E_p.

In the chart for a salient-pole machine, the loci of constant E_f and E_p are not circles, but are curves that can be constructed from the vector diagram (Fig. 64 of Chapter XII).

If a chart is desired having loci for constant terminal voltage instead of for constant E_p, it can be derived as explained below for tandem combinations.

Tandem combination of synchronous machine and transmission line. Suppose that a plot of Q_R versus P_R is desired for various constant values of V_R at the receiving end of a transmission line, to the sending end of which is connected a synchronous generator operated at constant field current. The Potier reactance of the generator may be included in either the generator chart or the transmission-line chart. In either event the voltage at the junction point will be referred to as V_S in what follows.

In order to obtain the desired composite chart, the generator chart for the given value of field current and the transmission-line sending chart for some particular value of V_R are superposed. The intersection of each curve on the generator chart for a particular value of V_S with the curve on the transmission-line chart for the same value of V_S is recorded. These points are then transferred from the sending chart to the receiving chart for the same value of V_R by noting the values of V_S and of angle between V_S and V_R. The result is a curve of Q_R against P_R for the particular value of V_R. The process is then repeated for other values of V_R, resulting in a family of curves.

Parallel combination of machine, or machine and line, with load. The load characteristics, discussed in an earlier section of this chapter, are plotted as curves of P versus V and of Q versus V. For a given voltage V, the active power of a parallel combination is equal to the sum of the active powers of the two parallel circuits; likewise for the reactive power. Hence each curve of Q versus P for a machine, or machine and line, at a particular value of V is simply shifted vertically by the Q of the load and horizontally by the P of the load at the same value of V, with no change in the shape of the curve. Each curve for a different value of V is shifted by different amounts.

Parallel combination of two or more machines with or without lines and loads. As in any parallel combination, the P and Q of the combination at any particular value of V equal the sums of the P's and Q's, respectively, of the several parallel branches at the same value of V. However, these sums are not uniquely determined by the voltage V because for each machine there are an infinite number of pairs of values of P and Q, represented by points on a curve, and any pair for one machine can be added to any pair for another machine. Therefore, one of the assumptions previously considered on division of power must be chosen. If it is assumed that the phase angles between excitation voltages of the various machines in the group are constant, then corresponding to any point on the curve for one machine there is a certain point on the curve for each other machine where the phase difference between machines has the required value. If, on the other hand, it is assumed that all machines but one in the group have constant power outputs, then various points are taken on the curve for the one machine whose output varies, but fixed points are used for the others.

By means of tandem and parallel combinations, the characteristics of almost any network on one side of the point of observation can be derived. The superposition of the characteristics of one side upon those of the other side leads, as already explained, to a composite characteristic by means of which the steady-state stability of a system can be examined.

In practice the entire characteristics need not be plotted, but only that part of them in the vicinity of the operating point.

Résumé. In order accurately to take into account the nonlinear characteristics of machines and of loads, graphical methods consisting of superposition of charts can be used for determining whether or not a system is stable in the steady state. However, because of the immense amount of labor required in the graphical method and because of the fact that steady-state stability limits usually are not needed with exactness, approximate methods are generally used in which loads are represented by constant impedances and synchronous machines, by constant reactances and voltages. The reactances of the machines theoretically should be the proper equivalent reactances for the prevailing degree of saturation, external circuit, and change of angle. Because of the difficulty of determining the correct value of equivalent reactance for each condition, however, approximate values are generally used. The steady-state stability of a multimachine linear system is checked most easily by use of an a-c. calculating board. The system is stable if $dP/d\delta$ is positive for each machine. The steady-state stability limit of a two-machine linear system is readily found by means of the Clarke diagram.

Steady-state stability with automatic voltage regulators. Whereas automatic voltage regulators with dead band do not raise the steady-state stability limit appreciably above that obtainable with close manual control of excitation, properly designed excitation systems with regulators of the continuously acting type can raise the limit considerably.

A voltage regulator attempts to maintain the terminal voltage of its machine constant, but it cannot succeed completely because of insufficient amplification, limits or "ceilings," and delays in the excitation system. It may be of interest, however, to consider the effect of a perfect excitation system which would maintain constant terminal voltage. We will consider three cases: (1) two equal finite round-rotor machines, (2) one finite round-rotor machine connected directly to an infinite bus, and (3) the same machine connected through external reactance to the infinite bus.

Two finite machines. (See Fig. 33.) The power transferred from one machine to the other is given by

$$P = \frac{E_1 E_2}{x_1 + x_2} \sin \delta \qquad [59]$$

where E_1 and E_2 are the excitation voltages of the two machines, δ is the angle between these voltages, and x_1 and x_2 are the equivalent synchronous reactances of the machines. As is well known, maximum power occurs, for constant excitation, at $\delta = 90°$. If we take $x_1 = x_2 = 1$ and make the excitation voltages $E_1 = E_2 = \sqrt{2}$, so as to give rated terminal voltage at rated current (Fig. 34), the power is

$$P = \sin \delta \qquad [60]$$

and has the maximum value 1 at $\delta = 90°$, as shown in Fig. 35 by the "unregulated" curve.

If the excitations are controlled so as always to maintain unit terminal voltage, the required excitation voltages are (see Fig. 36):

$$E_1 = E_2 = \frac{1}{\cos (\delta/2)} \qquad [61]$$

and the power is

$$P = \frac{\sin \delta}{2 \cos^2 (\delta/2)} = \tan \frac{\delta}{2} \qquad [62]$$

which is plotted as the "regulated" curve in Fig. 35. Here the power increases beyond $\delta = 90°$, becoming infinite at $\delta = 180°$. Of course, the excitation voltages and armature current would also become infinite, which is obviously impossible.

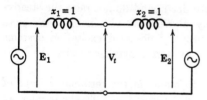

FIG. 33.   Two-machine system.

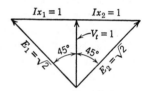

FIG. 34.   Voltage vector diagram of two equal finite machines at $\delta = 90°$. $V_t = 1$ and $I = 1$.

One machine and infinite bus. If the machine is connected directly to the infinite bus, the terminal voltage is constant, even without a regulator, and the regulator may be used to keep the power factor constant, say, at unity. Equation 59 then is valid with $x_1 = 1$, $x_2 = 0$, and $E_2 = 1$. For the unregulated condition, let $E_1 = \sqrt{2}$, as before. Then

$$P = \frac{\sqrt{2} \times 1}{1 + 0} \sin \delta = \sqrt{2} \sin \delta \qquad [63]$$

With regulation of power factor, $E_1 = 1/\cos \delta$, and

$$P = \frac{\sin \delta}{\cos \delta} = \tan \delta \qquad [64]$$

These results are plotted in Fig. 37.

One machine, line, and infinite bus. Let the machine reactance $= 1$, line reactance $= 1$, and voltage of infinite bus $= 1$. For the case without regulation, let the excitation voltage E_1 be such as to produce

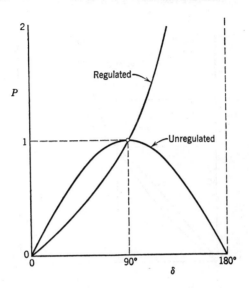

Fig. 35. Power-angle curves of two equal finite machines.

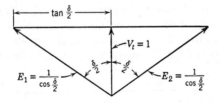

Fig. 36. Voltage vector diagram of two equal finite machines with V_t maintained constant at $\delta > 90°$.

unit terminal voltage at unit current. From the vector diagram (Fig. 38), it is determined that $E_1 = \sqrt{3}$. Then, by eq. 59, the power is

$$P = \frac{\sqrt{3} \times 1}{2} \sin \delta = 0.866 \sin \delta \qquad [65]$$

and has the maximum value of 0.866 at $\delta = 90°$, as shown by the "unregulated" curve of Fig. 39. For the case with regulation, let the terminal voltage be kept at 1.

$$P = \frac{1 \times 1}{1} \sin \alpha = \sin \alpha \qquad [66]$$

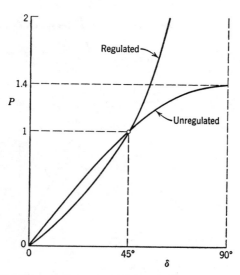

Fig. 37. Power-angle curves of finite machine and infinite bus.

where α is the angle between the two fixed voltages V_t and E_2. Now the power has the maximum value 1 at $\alpha = 90°$. The corresponding value of δ, found from the vector diagram of Fig. 40, is 116.6°. The "regulated" curve of Fig. 39 shows this power as a function of δ.

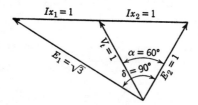

Fig. 38. Vector diagram of finite machine connected through reactance to an infinite bus: $\delta = 90°$.

It is apparent from the foregoing calculations that, even with excitation which could maintain the desired terminal voltage or power factor exactly, the obtainable increase of power limit would vary considerably with the type of power system, being infinite for two of the three cases considered but only 15% for the third case.

The power systems which show more increase in steady-state power limit due to an ideal excitation system also show more increase due to an actual excitation system, although, of course, the increase is less with an actual than with an ideal excitation system.

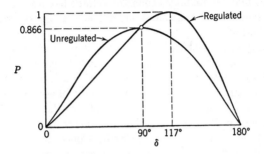

Fig. 39. Power-angle curves of finite machine connected through reactance to infinite bus.

One of the most favorable cases, that of two machines (generator and motor) connected together without external reactance, is encountered in electrical ship propulsion, and here the use of automatic voltage regulators has effected a considerable economy in the size of

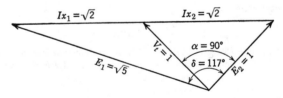

Fig. 40. Vector diagram of finite machine connected through reactance to an infinite bus: $\alpha = 90°$.

machines required. The cases encountered in long-distance power transmission, in which there is a substantial amount of reactance between the points of controlled voltage, are less favorable as to the amount of increase of power limit attainable by voltage regulators.

Actual excitation systems are unable to hold constant voltage at the generator terminals or other external points; as a rule, they are unable even to hold constant voltage behind transient reactance, in attempting which they are aided by the long transient time constant. Roughly speaking, the excitation system can increase the steady-state power limit to a value corresponding to constant voltage behind a reactance which is intermediate (usually about halfway) between transient reactance and equivalent synchronous reactance. Hence steady-state stability with automatic regulators, like transient stability, is promoted by low transient reactance of the machines.

The use of series-wound main exciters can, as explained in Chapter XIII, be made to maintain constant voltage behind transient reactance, this reactance being somewhat augmented by the reactance of the series-field winding.

The steady-state stability of power systems having continuously acting generator voltage regulators is analyzed by methods similar to those used for analyzing servomechanisms. Such analysis is beyond the scope of this book. The general theory of servomechanisms is treated in many books. The application of this theory to the calculation of the steady-state stability limits of power systems with voltage regulators is limited to a few articles by Concordia.[19,24,26] His calculations on excitation systems show increases in the steady-state stability limit, resulting from the use of continuously acting voltage regulators, of the order of 30% to 60% for two machines connected without external reactance.

Rothe[32] states that the steady-state stability limit of a steam-turbine generator of low short-circuit ratio, equipped with a continuously acting voltage regulator, is roughly equal to that of a generator of short-circuit ratio twice as great having a noncontinuously acting voltage regulator.

REFERENCES

1. EDITH CLARKE, "Steady-State Stability in Transmission Systems: Calculation by Means of Equivalent Circuits or Circle Diagrams," *A.I.E.E. Trans.*, vol. 45, pp. 22–41, February, 1926. Disc., pp. 80–94.

2. EDITH CLARKE, closing discussion of Ref. 1.

3. H. V. PUTMAN, "Synchronizing Power in Synchronous Machines Under Steady and Transient Conditions," *A.I.E.E. Trans.*, vol. 45, pp. 1116–24, September, 1926. Disc., pp. 1124–30.

4. O. G. C. DAHL, *Electric Circuits — Theory and Applications*, Vol. I, "Short-Circuit Calculations and Steady-State Theory," McGraw-Hill Book Co., New York, 1st edition, 1928. Chapter X, "Transmission-Line Charts,"

5. Same, Chapter XI, "Synchronous-Machine Charts."

6. R. A. HENTZ and J. W. JONES, "Stability Experiences with Conowingo Hydroelectric Station," *A.I.E.E. Trans.*, vol. 51, pp. 375–84, June, 1932. Disc., p. 384. Abstract in *Elec. Eng.*, vol. 51, pp. 95–102, February, 1932.

7. H. B. DWIGHT, "Adjusted Synchronous Reactance and Its Relation to Stability," *Gen. Elec. Rev.*, vol. 35, pp. 609–14, December, 1932.

8. EDITH CLARKE and R. G. LORRAINE, "Power Limits of Synchronous Machines," *A.I.E.E. Trans.*, vol. 53, pp. 1802–9, 1934; also in *Elec. Eng.*, vol. 52, pp. 780–7, November, 1933.

9. S. B. Crary, "Steady-State Stability of Composite Systems," *A.I.E.E. Trans.*, vol. 53, pp. 1809–14, 1934; also in *Elec. Eng.*, vol. 52, pp. 787–92, November, 1933. Appendix V. Disc., *Elec. Eng.*, vol. 54, p. 477, March; p. 594, April, 1934.

10. S. B. Crary, L. A. March, and L. P. Shildneck, "Equivalent Reactance of Synchronous Machines," *Elec. Eng.*, vol. 53, pp. 124–32, January, 1934. Disc., pp. 484–8, March; 603–7, April.

11. L. A. Kilgore, discussion of Ref. 10, p. 488.

12. Charles Kingsley, Jr., "Saturated Synchronous Reactance," *Elec. Eng.*, vol. 54, pp. 300–5, March, 1935. Disc., pp. 1111–3, October, 1935.

13. Sterling Beckwith, "Steady-State Solution of Saturated Circuits," *Elec. Eng.*, vol. 54, pp. 728–34, July, 1935.

14. O. G. C. Dahl, *Electric Power Circuits — Theory and Applications*, Vol. II, "Power System Stability," McGraw-Hill Book Co., Inc., New York, 1938. Chapters II through X.

15. Charles F. Dalziel, "Static Power Limits of Synchronous Machines," *A.I.E.E. Trans.*, vol. 58, pp. 93–101, March, 1939. Disc., pp. 101–2.

16. Edith Clarke and S. B. Crary, "Stability Limitations of Long-Distance A-C Power-Transmission Systems," *A.I.E.E. Trans.*, vol. 60, pp. 1051–9, 1941. Disc., pp. 1299–1303.

17. *Electrical Transmission and Distribution Reference Book*, by Central Station Engineers of the Westinghouse Electric & Manufacturing Co., East Pittsburgh, Pa., 1st edition, 1942. Chapter 8, "Power-System Stability — Basic Elements of Theory and Application," by R. D. Evans, pp. 175, 182–3, 185–8, 189–90, 195, 198, 200, 208.

18. John Grzybowski Holm, "Stability Study of A-C Power-Transmission Systems," *A.I.E.E. Trans.*, vol. 61, pp. 893–905, 1942. Disc., pp. 1046–8.

19. C. Concordia, "Steady-State Stability of Synchronous Machines as Affected by Voltage-Regulator Characteristics," *A.I.E.E. Trans.*, vol. 63, pp. 215–20, May, 1944. Disc., pp. 489–90.

20. Selden B. Crary, *Power System Stability*, Vol. I, "Steady State Stability," John Wiley & Sons, Inc., New York, 1945.

21. C. Concordia, S. B. Crary, and F. J. Maginniss, "Long-Distance Power Transmission as Influenced by Excitation Systems," *A.I.E.E. Trans.*, vol. 65, pp. 974–87, 1946. Disc., pp. 1175–6.

22. G. Darrieus, "Long-Distance Transmission of Energy and the Artificial Stabilization of Alternating-Current Systems," *C.I.G.R.E.*, 1946, Report 110.

23. W. Frey, "Artificial Stability of Synchronous Machines Employed for Long-Distance Power Transmission," *C.I.G.R.E.*, 1946, Report 317.

24. C. Concordia, "Steady-State Stability of Synchronous Machines as Affected by Angle-Regulator Characteristics," *A.I.E.E. Trans.*, vol. 67, part I, pp. 687–90, 1948.

25. A. J. Gibbons and E. B. Powell, "The Influence of Design and Operational Practice on the Stability of Large Metropolitan Cable Systems," *C.I.G.R.E.*, 1948, Report 318.

26. C. Concordia, "Effect of Buck-Boost Voltage Regulator on Steady-State Power Limit," *A.I.E.E. Trans.*, vol. 69, part I, pp. 380–4, 1950. Disc., pp. 384–5.

27. W. G. Heffron and R. A. Phillips, "Effect of a Modern Amplidyne Voltage Regulator on Underexcited Operation of Large Turbine Generators," *A.I.E.E. Trans.*, vol. 71, part III, pp. 692–7, August, 1952. Disc., pp. 697 and 1134–5.

28. E. Friedlander, "Control Scheme for Improved Alternator Stability on Low Excitation," *C.I.G.R.E.*, 1952, Report 321.

29. CH. LAVANCHY, "A New Solution for the Regulation of Counter-Excitation Synchronous Compensators," *C.I.G.R.E.*, 1952, Report 331.

30. J. M. DYER, "Shunt Inductors Solve Problems of Unstable Operation," *Elec. Light and Power*, vol. 31, no. 2, pp. 92–4, February, 1953.

31. W. G. HEFFRON, JR., "A Simplified Approach to Steady-State Stability Limits," *A.I.E.E. Trans.*, vol. 73, part III, pp. 39–44, February, 1954.

32. F. S. ROTHE, "The Effect of Generator Voltage Regulators on Stability and Line Charging Capacity," *C.I.G.R.E.*, 1954, Report 321.

PROBLEMS ON CHAPTER XV

1. It has been proposed to raise the steady-state stability limit of a two-machine power system by interposing between the machines a bank of quadrature-boost transformers which would introduce a phase shift of the proper sign to decrease the net angular displacement between the two machines for a given value of transmitted power. Analyze the feasibility of this proposal.

2. Find the steady-state power limit of two synchronous machines connected through external series reactance of 1.0 unit. The internal reactance of the generator is 0.6 unit and that of the motor, 0.7 unit. The terminal voltages are held at 1.1 and 1.0 units, respectively. Plot curves of power versus δ, the angle between internal voltages, (a) with constant field currents that give the specified terminal voltages at particular values of power and (b) with the terminal voltages held at the specified values.

3. Find the equation of curve E of Fig. 3, Example 1.

4. Solve Prob. 2 by constructing Clarke diagrams.

5. Find the transfer reactance between $\mathbf{E}_1$ and $\mathbf{E}_2$ in the circuit of Fig. 7 and show that the maximum power of that circuit is the same as the maximum power of the circuit of Fig. 8 with equivalent e.m.f.'s and reactances as defined by eqs. 5 to 8.

6. Discuss the effect of parallel resonance between x_1 and x_s or between x_2 and x_r in the circuits of Figs. 7 and 8.

7. Draw power-angle curves and discuss the stability of two machines connected through resistance and enough series capacitive reactance to neutralize the inductive reactances of the machines themselves.

8. Draw the power-angle curve of a salient-pole synchronous condenser operating with reversed excitation.

9. Find the steady-state stability limit of two identical salient-pole synchronous machines, one operating as a generator, the other as a motor. Each machine has direct-axis synchronous reactance of 1.0 per unit and quadrature-axis synchronous reactance of 0.5 per unit. The machines are connected through an external reactance of 1.0 per unit. The field currents are adjusted to maintain terminal voltages of 1.0 per unit at each machine. Neglect resistance and saturation. What would be the error due to neglecting saliency?

INDEX

CATALOGUE OF DOVER BOOKS

ENGINEERING AND TECHNOLOGY

General and mathematical

ENGINEERING MATHEMATICS, Kenneth S. Miller. A text for graduate students of engineering to strengthen their mathematical background in differential equations, etc. Mathematical steps very explicitly indicated. Contents: Determinants and Matrices, Integrals, Linear Differential Equations, Fourier Series and Integrals, Laplace Transform, Network Theory, Random Function . . . all vital requisites for advanced modern engineering studies. Unabridged republication. Appendices: Borel Sets; Riemann-Stieltjes Integral; Fourier Series and Integrals. Index. References at Chapter Ends. xii + 417pp. 6 x 8½. S1121 Paperbound **$2.00**

MATHEMATICAL ENGINEERING ANALYSIS, Rufus Oldenburger. A book designed to assist the research engineer and scientist in making the transition from physical engineering situations to the corresponding mathematics. Scores of common practical situations found in all major fields of physics are supplied with their correct mathematical formulations—applications to automobile springs and shock absorbers, clocks, throttle torque of diesel engines, resistance networks, capacitors, transmission lines, microphones, neon tubes, gasoline engines, refrigeration cycles, etc. Each section reviews basic principles of underlying various fields: mechanics of rigid bodies, electricity and magnetism, heat, elasticity, fluid mechanics, and aerodynamics. Comprehensive and eminently useful. Index. 169 problems, answers. 200 photos and diagrams. xiv + 426pp. 5⅜ x 8½. S919 Paperbound **$2.50**

MATHEMATICS OF MODERN ENGINEERING, E. G. Keller and R. E. Doherty. Written for the Advanced Course in Engineering of the General Electric Corporation, deals with the engineering use of determinants, tensors, the Heaviside operational calculus, dyadics, the calculus of variations, etc. Presents underlying principles fully, but purpose is to teach engineers to deal with modern engineering problems, and emphasis is on the perennial engineering attack of set-up and solve. Indexes. Over 185 figures and tables. Hundreds of exercises, problems, and worked-out examples. References. Two volume set. Total of xxxiii + 623pp. 5⅜ x 8.
S734 Vol I Paperbound **$1.85**
S735 Vol II Paperbound **$1.85**
The set **$3.70**

MATHEMATICAL METHODS FOR SCIENTISTS AND ENGINEERS, L. P. Smith. For scientists and engineers, as well as advanced math students. Full investigation of methods and practical description of conditions under which each should be used. Elements of real functions, differential and integral calculus, space geometry, theory of residues, vector and tensor analysis, series of Bessel functions, etc. Each method illustrated by completely-worked-out examples, mostly from scientific literature. 368 graded unsolved problems. 100 diagrams. x + 453pp. 5⅝ x 8⅜. S220 Paperbound **$2.00**

THEORY OF FUNCTIONS AS APPLIED TO ENGINEERING PROBLEMS, edited by R. Rothe, F. Ollendorff, and K. Pohlhausen. A series of lectures given at the Berlin Institute of Technology that shows the specific applications of function theory in electrical and allied fields of engineering. Six lectures provide the elements of function theory in a simple and practical form, covering complex quantities and variables, integration in the complex plane, residue theorems, etc. Then 5 lectures show the exact uses of this powerful mathematical tool, with full discussions of problem methods. Index. Bibliography. 108 figures. x + 189pp. 5⅜ x 8.
S733 Paperbound **$1.35**

Aerodynamics and hydrodynamics

AIRPLANE STRUCTURAL ANALYSIS AND DESIGN, E. E. Sechler and L. G. Dunn. Systematic authoritative book which summarizes a large amount of theoretical and experimental work on structural analysis and design. Strong on classical subsonic material still basic to much aeronautic design . . . remains a highly useful source of information. Covers such areas as layout of the airplane, applied and design loads, stress-strain relationships for stable structures, truss and frame analysis, the problem of instability, the ultimate strength of stiffened flat sheet, analysis of cylindrical structures, wings and control surfaces, fuselage analysis, engine mounts, landing gears, etc. Originally published as part of the CALCIT Aeronautical Series. 256 illustrations. 47 study problems. Indexes. xi + 420pp. 5⅜ x 8½.
S1043 Paperbound **$2.25**

FUNDAMENTALS OF HYDRO- AND AEROMECHANICS, L. Prandtl and O. G. Tietjens. The well-known standard work based upon Prandtl's lectures at Goettingen. Wherever possible hydrodynamics theory is referred to practical considerations in hydraulics, with the view of unifying theory and experience. Presentation is extremely clear and though primarily physical, mathematical proofs are rigorous and use vector analysis to a considerable extent. An Engineering Society Monograph, 1934. 186 figures. Index. xvi + 270pp. 5⅜ x 8.
S374 Paperbound **$1.85**

FLUID MECHANICS FOR HYDRAULIC ENGINEERS, H. Rouse. Standard work that gives a coherent picture of fluid mechanics from the point of view of the hydraulic engineer. Based on courses given to civil and mechanical engineering students at Columbia and the California Institute of Technology, this work covers every basic principle, method, equation, or theory of interest to the hydraulic engineer. Much of the material, diagrams, charts, etc., in this self-contained text are not duplicated elsewhere. Covers irrotational motion, conformal mapping, problems in laminar motion, fluid turbulence, flow around immersed bodies, transportation of sediment, general charcteristics of wave phenomena, gravity waves in open channels, etc. Index. Appendix of physical properties of common fluids. Frontispiece + 245 figures and photographs. xvi + 422pp. 5⅜ x 8.   S729 Paperbound **$2.25**

WATERHAMMER ANALYSIS, John Parmakian. Valuable exposition of the graphical method of solving waterhammer problems by Assistant Chief Designing Engineer, U.S. Bureau of Reclamation. Discussions of rigid and elastic water column theory, velocity of waterhammer waves, theory of graphical waterhammer analysis for gate operation, closings, openings, rapid and slow movements, etc., waterhammer in pump discharge caused by power failure, waterhammer analysis for compound pipes, and numerous related problems. "With a concise and lucid style, clear printing, adequate bibliography and graphs for approximate solutions at the project stage, it fills a vacant place in waterhammer literature," WATER POWER. 43 problems. Bibliography. Index. 113 illustrations. xiv + 161pp. 5⅜ x 8½.
                                                                  S1061 Paperbound **$1.65**

AERODYNAMIC THEORY: A GENERAL REVIEW OF PROGRESS, William F. Durand, editor-in-chief. A monumental joint effort by the world's leading authorities prepared under a grant of the Guggenheim Fund for the Promotion of Aeronautics. Intended to provide the student and aeronautic designer with the theoretical and experimental background of aeronautics. Never equalled for breadth, depth, reliability. Contains discussions of special mathematical topics not usually taught in the engineering or technical courses. Also: an extended two-part treatise on Fluid Mechanics, discussions of aerodynamics of perfect fluids, analyses of experiments with wind tunnels, applied airfoil theory, the non-lifting system of the airplane, the air propeller, hydrodynamics of boats and floats, the aerodynamics of cooling, etc. Contributing experts include Munk, Giacomelli, Prandtl, Toussaint, Von Karman, Klemperer, among others. Unabridged republication. 6 volumes bound as 3. Total of 1,012 figures, 12 plates. Total of 2,186pp. Bibliographies. Notes. Indices. 5⅜ x 8.
                                                      S328-S330 Paperbound The Set **$13.50**

APPLIED HYDRO- AND AEROMECHANICS, L. Prandtl and O. G. Tietjens. Presents, for the most part, methods which will be valuable to engineers. Covers flow in pipes, boundary layers, airfoil theory, entry conditions, turbulent flow in pipes, and the boundary layer, determining drag from measurements of pressure and velocity, etc. "Will be welcomed by all students of aerodynamics," NATURE. Unabridged, unaltered. An Engineering Society Monograph, 1934. Index. 226 figures, 28 photographic plates illustrating flow patterns. xvi + 311pp. 5⅜ x 8.
                                                                    S375 Paperbound **$2.00**

SUPERSONIC AERODYNAMICS, E. R. C. Miles. Valuable theoretical introduction to the supersonic domain, with emphasis on mathematical tools and principles, for practicing aerodynamicists and advanced students in aeronautical engineering. Covers fundamental theory, divergence theorem and principles of circulation, compressible flow and Helmholtz laws, the Prandtl-Busemann graphic method for 2-dimensional flow, oblique shock waves, the Taylor-Maccoll method for cones in supersonic flow, the Chaplygin method for 2-dimensional flow, etc. Problems range from practical engineering problems to development of theoretical results. "Rendered outstanding by the unprecedented scope of its contents . . . has undoubtedly filled a vital gap," AERONAUTICAL ENGINEERING REVIEW. Index. 173 problems, answers. 106 diagrams. 7 tables. xii + 255pp. 5⅜ x 8.   S214 Paperbound **$1.45**

HYDRAULIC TRANSIENTS, G. R. Rich. The best text in hydraulics ever printed in English . . . by one of America's foremost engineers (former Chief Design Engineer for T.V.A.). Provides a transition from the basic differential equations of hydraulic transient theory to the arithmetic intergration computation required by practicing engineers. Sections cover Water Hammer, Turbine Speed Regulation, Stability of Governing, Water-Hammer Pressures in Pump Discharge Lines, The Differential and Restricted Orifice Surge Tanks, The Normalized Surge Tank Charts of Calame and Gaden, Navigation Locks, Surges in Power Canals—Tidal Harmonics, etc. Revised and enlarged. Author's prefaces. Index. xiv + 409pp. 5⅜ x 8½.
                                                                    S116 Paperbound **$2.50**

HYDRAULICS AND ITS APPLICATIONS, A. H. Gibson. Excellent comprehensive textbook for the student and thorough practical manual for the professional worker, a work of great stature in its area. Half the book is devoted to theory and half to applications and practical problems met in the field. Covers modes of motion of a fluid, critical velocity, viscous flow, eddy formation, Bernoulli's theorem, flow in converging passages, vortex motion, form of effluent streams, notches and weirs, skin friction, losses at valves and elbows, siphons, erosion of channels, jet propulsion, waves of oscillation, and over 100 similar topics. Final chapters (nearly 400 pages) cover more than 100 kinds of hydraulic machinery: Pelton wheel, speed regulators, the hydraulic ram, surge tanks, the scoop wheel, the Venturi meter, etc. A special chapter treats methods of testing theoretical hypotheses: scale models of rivers, tidal estuaries, siphon spillways, etc. 5th revised and enlarged (1952) edition. Index. Appendix. 427 photographs and diagrams. 95 examples, answers. xv + 813pp. 6 x 9.
                                                                    S791 Clothbound **$8.00**

FLUID MECHANICS THROUGH WORKED EXAMPLES, D. R. L. Smith and J. Houghton. Advanced text covering principles and applications to practical situations. Each chapter begins with concise summaries of fundamental ideas. 163 fully worked out examples applying principles outlined in the text. 275 other problems, with answers. Contents: The Pressure of Liquids on Surfaces; Floating Bodies; Flow Under Constant Head in Pipes; Circulation; Vorticity; The Potential Function; Laminar Flow and Lubrication; Impact of Jets; Hydraulic Turbines; Centrifugal and Reciprocating Pumps; Compressible Fluids; and many other items. Total of 438 examples. 250 line illustrations. 340pp. Index. 6 x 8⅞.　S981 Clothbound **$6.00**

THEORY OF SHIP MOTIONS, S. N. Blagoveshchensky. The only detailed text in English in a rapidly developing branch of engineering and physics, it is the work of one of the world's foremost authorities—Blagoveshchensky of Leningrad Shipbuilding Institute. A senior-level treatment written primarily for engineering students, but also of great importance to naval architects, designers, contractors, researchers in hydrodynamics, and other students. No mathematics beyond ordinary differential equations is required for understanding the text. Translated by T. & L. Strelkoff, under editorship of Louis Landweber, Iowa Institute of Hydraulic Research, under auspices of Office of Naval Research. Bibliography. Index. 231 diagrams and illustrations. Total of 649pp. 5⅜ x 8½.　Vol. I: S234 Paperbound **$2.00**
Vol. II: S235 Paperbound **$2.00**

THEORY OF FLIGHT, Richard von Mises. Remains almost unsurpassed as balanced, well-written account of fundamental fluid dynamics, and situations in which air compressibility effects are unimportant. Stressing equally theory and practice, avoiding formidable mathematical structure, it conveys a full understanding of physical phenomena and mathematical concepts. Contains perhaps the best introduction to general theory of stability. "Outstanding," Scientific, Medical, and Technical Books. New introduction by K. H. Hohenemser. Bibliographical, historical notes. Index. 408 illustrations. xvi + 620pp. 5⅜ x 8⅜.　S541 Paperbound **$3.50**

THEORY OF WING SECTIONS, I. H. Abbott, A. E. von Doenhoff. Concise compilation of subsonic aerodynamic characteristics of modern NASA wing sections, with description of their geometry, associated theory. Primarily reference work for engineers, students, it gives methods, data for using wing-section data to predict characteristics. Particularly valuable: chapters on thin wings, airfoils; complete summary of NACA's experimental observations, system of construction families of airfoils. 350pp. of tables on Basic Thickness Forms, Mean Lines, Airfoil Ordinates, Aerodynamic Characteristics of Wing Sections. Index. Bibliography. 191 illustrations. Appendix. 705pp. 5⅜ x 8.　S558 Paperbound **$3.25**

WEIGHT-STRENGTH ANALYSIS OF AIRCRAFT STRUCTURES, F. R. Shanley. Scientifically sound methods of analyzing and predicting the structural weight of aircraft and missiles. Deals directly with forces and the distances over which they must be transmitted, making it possible to develop methods by which the minimum structural weight can be determined for any material and conditions of loading. Weight equations for wing and fuselage structures. Includes author's original papers on inelastic buckling and creep buckling. "Particularly successful in presenting his analytical methods for investigating various optimum design principles," AERONAUTICAL ENGINEERING REVIEW. Enlarged bibliography. Index. 199 figures. xiv + 404pp. 5⅝ x 8⅜.　S660 Paperbound **$2.50**

Electricity

TWO-DIMENSIONAL FIELDS IN ELECTRICAL ENGINEERING, L. V. Bewley. A useful selection of typical engineering problems of interest to practicing electrical engineers. Introduces senior students to the methods and procedures of mathematical physics. Discusses theory of functions of a complex variable, two-dimensional fields of flow, general theorems of mathematical physics and their applications, conformal mapping or transformation, method of images, freehand flux plotting, etc. New preface by the author. Appendix by W. F. Kiltner. Index. Bibliography at chapter ends. xiv + 204pp. 5⅜ x 8½.　S1118 Paperbound **$1.50**

FLUX LINKAGES AND ELECTROMAGNETIC INDUCTION, L. V. Bewley. A brief, clear book which shows proper uses and corrects misconceptions of Faraday's law of electromagnetic induction in specific problems. Contents: Circuits; Turns, and Flux Linkages; Substitution of Circuits; Electromagnetic Induction; General Criteria for Electromagnetic Induction; Applications and Paradoxes; Theorem of Constant Flux Linkages. New Section: Rectangular Coil in a Varying Uniform Medium. Valuable supplement to class texts for engineering students. Corrected, enlarged edition. New preface. Bibliography in notes. 49 figures. xi + 106pp. 5⅜ x 8.　S1103 Paperbound **$1.25**

INDUCTANCE CALCULATIONS: WORKING FORMULAS AND TABLES, Frederick W. Grover. An invaluable book to everyone in electrical engineering. Provides simple single formulas to cover all the more important cases of inductance. The approach involves only those parameters that naturally enter into each situation, while extensive tables are given to permit easy interpolations. Will save the engineer and student countless hours and enable them to obtain accurate answers with minimal effort. Corrected republication of 1946 edition. 58 tables. 97 completely worked out examples. 66 figures. xiv + 286pp. 5⅜ x 8½.　S974 Paperbound **$1.85**

GASEOUS CONDUCTORS: THEORY AND ENGINEERING APPLICATIONS, J. D. Cobine. An indispensable text and reference to gaseous conduction phenomena, with the engineering viewpoint prevailing throughout. Studies the kinetic theory of gases, ionization, emission phenomena; gas breakdown, spark characteristics, glow, and discharges; engineering applications in circuit interrupters, rectifiers, light sources, etc. Separate detailed treatment of high pressure arcs (Suits); low pressure arcs (Langmuir and Tonks). Much more. "Well organized, clear, straightforward," Tonks, Review of Scientific Instruments. Index. Bibliography. 83 practice problems. 7 appendices. Over 600 figures. 58 tables. xx + 606pp. 5⅜ x 8.
S442 Paperbound **$3.25**

INTRODUCTION TO THE STATISTICAL DYNAMICS OF AUTOMATIC CONTROL SYSTEMS, V. V. Solodovnikov. First English publication of text-reference covering important branch of automatic control systems—random signals; in its original edition, this was the first comprehensive treatment. Examines frequency characteristics, transfer functions, stationary random processes, determination of minimum mean-squared error, of transfer function for a finite period of observation, much more. Translation edited by J. B. Thomas, L. A. Zadeh. Index. Bibliography. Appendix. xxii + 308pp. 5⅜ x 8.
S420 Paperbound **$2.35**

TENSORS FOR CIRCUITS, Gabriel Kron. A boldly original method of analyzing engineering problems, at center of sharp discussion since first introduced, now definitely proved useful in such areas as electrical and structural networks on automatic computers. Encompasses a great variety of specific problems by means of a relatively few symbolic equations. "Power and flexibility . . . becoming more widely recognized," Nature. Formerly "A Short Course in Tensor Analysis." New introduction by B. Hoffmann. Index. Over 800 diagrams. xix + 250pp. 5⅜ x 8.
S534 Paperbound **$2.00**

SELECTED PAPERS ON SEMICONDUCTOR MICROWAVE ELECTRONICS, edited by Sumner N. Levine and Richard R. Kurzrok. An invaluable collection of important papers dealing with one of the most remarkable developments in solid-state electronics—the use of the p-n junction to achieve amplification and frequency conversion of microwave frequencies. Contents: General Survey (3 introductory papers by W. E. Danielson, R. N. Hall, and M. Tenzer); General Theory of Nonlinear Elements (3 articles by A. van der Ziel, H. E. Rowe, and Manley and Rowe); Device Fabrication and Characterization (3 pieces by Bakanowski, Cranna, and Uhlir, by McCotter, Walker and Fortini, and by S. T. Eng); Parametric Amplifiers and Frequency Multipliers (13 articles by Uhlir, Heffner and Wade, Matthaei, P. K. Tien, van der Ziel, Engelbrecht, Currie and Gould, Uenohara, Leeson and Weinreb, and others); and Tunnel Diodes (4 papers by L. Esaki, H. S. Sommers, Jr., M. E. Hines, and Yariv and Cook). Introduction. 295 Figures. xiii + 286pp. 6½ x 9¼.
S1126 Paperbound **$2.50**

THE PRINCIPLES OF ELECTROMAGNETISM APPLIED TO ELECTRICAL MACHINES, B. Hague. A concise, but complete, summary of the basic principles of the magnetic field and its applications, with particular reference to the kind of phenomena which occur in electrical machines. Part I: General Theory—magnetic field of a current, electromagnetic field passing from air to iron, mechanical forces on linear conductors, etc. Part II: Application of theory to the solution of electromechanical problems—the magnetic field and mechanical forces in non-salient pole machinery, the field within slots and between salient poles, and the work of Rogowski, Roth, and Strutt. Formery titled "Electromagnetic Problems in Electrical Engineering." 2 appendices. Index. Bibliography in notes. 115 figures. xiv + 359pp. 5⅜ x 8½.
S246 Paperbound **$2.25**

Mechanical engineering

DESIGN AND USE OF INSTRUMENTS AND ACCURATE MECHANISM, T. N. Whitehead. For the instrument designer, engineer; how to combine necessary mathematical abstractions with independent observation of actual facts. Partial contents: instruments & their parts, theory of errors, systematic errors, probability, short period errors, erratic errors, design precision, kinematic, semikinematic design, stiffness, planning of an instrument, human factor, etc. Index. 85 photos, diagrams. xii + 288pp. 5⅜ x 8.
S270 Paperbound **$2.00**

A TREATISE ON GYROSTATICS AND ROTATIONAL MOTION: THEORY AND APPLICATIONS, Andrew Gray. Most detailed, thorough book in English, generally considered definitive study. Many problems of all sorts in full detail, or step-by-step summary. Classical problems of Bour, Lottner, etc.; later ones of great physical interest. Vibrating systems of gyrostats, earth as a top, calculation of path of axis of a top by elliptic integrals, motion of unsymmetrical top, much more. Index. 160 illus. 550pp. 5⅜ x 8.
S589 Paperbound **$2.75**

MECHANICS OF THE GYROSCOPE, THE DYNAMICS OF ROTATION, R. F. Deimel, Professor of Mechanical Engineering at Stevens Institute of Technology. Elementary general treatment of dynamics of rotation, with special application of gyroscopic phenomena. No knowledge of vectors needed. Velocity of a moving curve, acceleration to a point, general equations of motion, gyroscopic horizon, free gyro, motion of discs, the damped gyro, 103 similar topics. Exercises. 75 figures. 208pp. 5⅜ x 8.
S66 Paperbound **$1.75**

STRENGTH OF MATERIALS, J. P. Den Hartog. Distinguished text prepared for M.I.T. course, ideal as introduction, refresher, reference, or self-study text. Full clear treatment of elementary material (tension, torsion, bending, compound stresses, deflection of beams, etc.), plus much advanced material on engineering methods of great practical value: full treatment of the Mohr circle, lucid elementary discussions of the theory of the center of shear and the "Myosotis" method of calculating beam deflections, reinforced concrete, plastic deformations, photoelasticity, etc. In all sections, both general principles and concrete applications are given. Index. 186 figures (160 others in problem section). 350 problems, all with answers. List of formulas. viii + 323pp. 5⅜ x 8. **S755 Paperbound $2.00**

PHOTOELASTICITY: PRINCIPLES AND METHODS, H. T. Jessop, F. C. Harris. For the engineer, for specific problems of stress analysis. Latest time-saving methods of checking calculations in 2-dimensional design problems, new techniques for stresses in 3 dimensions, and lucid description of optical systems used in practical photoelasticity. Useful suggestions and hints based on on-the-job experience included. Partial contents: strained and stress-strain relations, circular disc under thrust along diameter, rectangular block with square hole under vertical thrust, simply supported rectangular beam under central concentrated load, etc. Theory held to minimum, no advanced mathematical training needed. Index. 164 illustrations. viii + 184pp. 6⅛ x 9¼. **S720 Paperbound $2.00**

APPLIED ELASTICITY, J. Prescott. Provides the engineer with the theory of elasticity usually lacking in books on strength of materials, yet concentrates on those portions useful for immediate application. Develops every important type of elasticity problem from theoretical principles. Covers analysis of stress, relations between stress and strain, the empirical basis of elasticity, thin rods under tension or thrust, Saint Venant's theory, transverse oscillations of thin rods, stability of thin plates, cylinders with thin walls, vibrations of rotating disks, elastic bodies in contact, etc. "Excellent and important contribution to the subject, not merely in the old matter which he has presented in new and refreshing form, but also in the many original investigations here published for the first time," NATURE. Index. 3 Appendixes. vi + 672pp. 5⅜ x 8. **S726 Paperbound $3.25**

APPLIED MECHANICS FOR ENGINEERS, Sir Charles Inglis, F.R.S. A representative survey of the many and varied engineering questions which can be answered by statics and dynamics. The author, one of first and foremost adherents of "structural dynamics," presents distinctive illustrative examples and clear, concise statement of principles—directing the discussion at methodology and specific problems. Covers fundamental principles of rigid-body statics, graphic solutions of static problems, theory of taut wires, stresses in frameworks, particle dynamics, kinematics, simple harmonic motion and harmonic analysis, two-dimensional rigid dynamics, etc. 437 illustrations. xii + 404pp. 5⅜ x 8½. **S1119 Paperbound $2.50**

THEORY OF MACHINES THROUGH WORKED EXAMPLES, G. H. Ryder. Practical mechanical engineering textbook for graduates and advanced undergraduates, as well as a good reference work for practicing engineers. Partial contents: Mechanisms, Velocity and Acceleration (including discussion of Klein's Construction for Piston Acceleration), Cams, Geometry of Gears, Clutches and Bearings, Belt and Rope Drives, Brakes, Inertia Forces and Couples, General Dynamical Problems, Gyroscopes, Linear and Angular Vibrations, Torsional Vibrations, Transverse Vibrations and Whirling Speeds (Chapters on vibrations considerably enlarged from previous editions). Over 300 problems, many fully worked out. Index. 195 line illustrations. Revised and enlarged edition. viii + 280pp. 5⅝ x 8¾. **S980 Clothbound $5.00**

THE KINEMATICS OF MACHINERY: OUTLINES OF A THEORY OF MACHINES, Franz Reuleaux. The classic work in the kinematics of machinery. The present thinking about the subject has all been shaped in great measure by the fundamental principles stated here by Reuleaux almost 90 years ago. While some details have naturally been superseded, his basic viewpoint has endured; hence, the book is still an excellent text for basic courses in kinematics and a standard reference work for active workers in the field. Covers such topics as: the nature of the machine problem, phoronomic propositions, pairs of elements, incomplete kinematic chains, kinematic notation and analysis, analyses of chamber-crank trains, chamber-wheel trains, constructive elements of machinery, complete machines, etc., with main focus on controlled movement in mechanisms. Unabridged republication of original edition, translated by Alexander B. Kennedy. New introduction for this edition by E. S. Ferguson. Index. 451 illustrations. xxiv + 622pp. 5⅜ x 8½. **S1124 Paperbound $3.00**

ANALYTICAL MECHANICS OF GEARS, Earle Buckingham. Provides a solid foundation upon which logical design practices and design data can be constructed. Originally arising out of investigations of the ASME Special Research Committee on Worm Gears and the Strength of Gears, the book covers conjugate gear-tooth action, the nature of the contact, and resulting gear-tooth profiles of: spur, internal, helical, spiral, worm, bevel, and hypoid or skew bevel gears. Also: frictional heat of operation and its dissipation, friction losses, etc., dynamic loads in operation, and related matters. Familiarity with this book is still regarded as a necessary prerequisite to work in modern gear manufacturing. 263 figures. 103 tables. Index. x + 546pp. 5⅜ x 8½. **S1073 Paperbound $2.75**

Optical design, lighting

THE SCIENTIFIC BASIS OF ILLUMINATING ENGINEERING, Parry Moon, Professor of Electrical Engineering, M.I.T. Basic, comprehensive study. Complete coverage of the fundamental theoretical principles together with the elements of design, vision, and color with which the lighting engineer must be familiar. Valuable as a text as well as a reference source to the practicing engineer. Partial contents: Spectroradiometric Curve, Luminous Flux, Radiation from Gaseous-Conduction Sources, Radiation from Incandescent Sources, Incandescent Lamps, Measurement of Light, Illumination from Point Sources and Surface Sources, Elements of Lighting Design. 7 Appendices. Unabridged and corrected republication, with additions. New preface containing conversion tables of radiometric and photometric concepts. Index. 707-item bibliography. 92-item bibliography of author's articles. 183 problems. xxiii + 608pp. 5⅜ x 8½. **S242 Paperbound $3.25**

OPTICS AND OPTICAL INSTRUMENTS: AN INTRODUCTION WITH SPECIAL REFERENCE TO PRACTICAL APPLICATIONS, B. K. Johnson. An invaluable guide to basic practical applications of optical principles, which shows how to set up inexpensive working models of each of the four main types of optical instruments—telescopes, microscopes, photographic lenses, optical projecting systems. Explains in detail the most important experiments for determining their accuracy, resolving power, angular field of view, amounts of aberration, all other necessary facts about the instruments. Formerly "Practical Optics." Index. 234 diagrams. Appendix. 224pp. 5⅜ x 8. **S642 Paperbound $1.75**

APPLIED OPTICS AND OPTICAL DESIGN, A. E. Conrady. With publication of vol. 2, standard work for designers in optics is now complete for first time. Only work of its kind in English; only detailed work for practical designer and self-taught. Requires, for bulk of work, no math above trig. Step-by-step exposition, from fundamental concepts of geometrical, physical optics, to systematic study, design, of almost all types of optical systems. Vol. 1: all ordinary ray-tracing methods; primary aberrations; necessary higher aberration for design of telescopes, low-power microscopes, photographic equipment. Vol. 2: (Completed from author's notes by R. Kingslake, Dir. Optical Design, Eastman Kodak.) Special attention to high-power microscope, anastigmatic photographic objectives. "An indispensable work," J., Optical Soc. of Amer. "As a practical guide this book has no rival," Transactions, Optical Soc. Index. Bibliography. 193 diagrams. 852pp. 6⅛ x 9¼. **Vol. 1 S366 Paperbound $3.50**
Vol. 2 S612 Paperbound $2.95

Miscellaneous

THE MEASUREMENT OF POWER SPECTRA FROM THE POINT OF VIEW OF COMMUNICATIONS ENGINEERING, R. B. Blackman, J. W. Tukey. This pathfinding work, reprinted from the "Bell System Technical Journal," explains various ways of getting practically useful answers in the measurement of power spectra, using results from both transmission theory and the theory of statistical estimation. Treats: Autocovariance Functions and Power Spectra; Direct Analog Computation; Distortion, Noise, Heterodyne Filtering and Pre-whitening; Aliasing; Rejection Filtering and Separation; Smoothing and Decimation Procedures; Very Low Frequencies; Transversal Filtering; much more. An appendix reviews fundamental Fourier techniques. Index of notation. Glossary of terms. 24 figures. XII tables. Bibliography. General index. 192pp. 5⅜ x 8. **S507 Paperbound $1.85**

CALCULUS REFRESHER FOR TECHNICAL MEN, A. Albert Klaf. This book is unique in English as a refresher for engineers, technicians, students who either wish to brush up their calculus or to clear up uncertainties. It is not an ordinary text, but an examination of most important aspects of integral and differential calculus in terms of the 756 questions most likely to occur to the technical reader. The first part of this book covers simple differential calculus, with constants, variables, functions, increments, derivatives, differentiation, logarithms, curvature of curves, and similar topics. The second part covers fundamental ideas of integration, inspection, substitution, transformation, reduction, areas and volumes, mean value, successive and partial integration, double and triple integration. Practical aspects are stressed rather than theoretical. A 50-page section illustrates the application of calculus to specific problems of civil and nautical engineering, electricity, stress and strain, elasticity, industrial engineering, and similar fields.—756 questions answered. 566 problems, mostly answered. 36 pages of useful constants, formulae for ready reference. Index. v + 431pp. 5⅜ x 8. **T370 Paperbound $2.00**

METHODS IN EXTERIOR BALLISTICS, Forest Ray Moulton. Probably the best introduction to the mathematics of projectile motion. The ballistics theories propounded were coordinated with extensive proving ground and wind tunnel experiments conducted by the author and others for the U.S. Army. Broad in scope and clear in exposition, it gives the beginnings of the theory used for modern-day projectile, long-range missile, and satellite motion. Six main divisions: Differential Equations of Translatory Motion of a projectile; Gravity and the Resistance Function; Numerical Solution of Differential Equations; Theory of Differential Variations; Validity of Method of Numerical Integration; and Motion of a Rotating Projectile. Formerly titled: "New Methods in Exterior Ballistics." Index. 38 diagrams. viii + 259pp. 5⅜ x 8½. **S232 Paperbound $1.75**

BOOKS EXPLAINING SCIENCE AND MATHEMATICS

General

WHAT IS SCIENCE?, Norman Campbell. This excellent introduction explains scientific method, role of mathematics, types of scientific laws. Contents: 2 aspects of science, science & nature, laws of science, discovery of laws, explanation of laws, measurement & numerical laws, applications of science. 192pp. 5⅜ x 8.
S43 Paperbound **$1.25**

THE COMMON SENSE OF THE EXACT SCIENCES, W. K. Clifford. Introduction by James Newman, edited by Karl Pearson. For 70 years this has been a guide to classical scientific and mathematical thought. Explains with unusual clarity basic concepts, such as extension of meaning of symbols, characteristics of surface boundaries, properties of plane figures, vectors, Cartesian method of determining position, etc. Long preface by Bertrand Russell. Bibliography of Clifford. Corrected, 130 diagrams redrawn. 249pp. 5⅜ x 8.
T61 Paperbound **$1.60**

SCIENCE THEORY AND MAN, Erwin Schrödinger. This is a complete and unabridged reissue of SCIENCE AND THE HUMAN TEMPERAMENT plus an additional essay: "What is an Elementary Particle?" Nobel laureate Schrödinger discusses such topics as nature of scientific method, the nature of science, chance and determinism, science and society, conceptual models for physical entities, elementary particles and wave mechanics. Presentation is popular and may be followed by most people with little or no scientific training. "Fine practical preparation for a time when laws of nature, human institutions . . . are undergoing a critical examination without parallel," Waldemar Kaempffert, N. Y. TIMES. 192pp. 5⅜ x 8.
T428 Paperbound **$1.35**

FADS AND FALLACIES IN THE NAME OF SCIENCE, Martin Gardner. Examines various cults, quack systems, frauds, delusions which at various times have masqueraded as science. Accounts of hollow-earth fanatics like Symmes; Velikovsky and wandering planets; Hoerbiger; Bellamy and the theory of multiple moons; Charles Fort; dowsing, pseudoscientific methods for finding water, ores, oil. Sections on naturopathy, iridiagnosis, zone therapy, food fads, etc. Analytical accounts of Wilhelm Reich and orgone sex energy; L. Ron Hubbard and Dianetics; A. Korzybski and General Semantics; many others. Brought up to date to include Bridey Murphy, others. Not just a collection of anecdotes, but a fair, reasoned appraisal of eccentric theory. Formerly titled IN THE NAME OF SCIENCE. Preface. Index. x + 384pp. 5⅜ x 8.
T394 Paperbound **$1.50**

A DOVER SCIENCE SAMPLER, edited by George Barkin. 64-page book, sturdily bound, containing excerpts from over 20 Dover books, explaining science. Edwin Hubble, George Sarton, Ernst Mach, A. d'Abro, Galileo, Newton, others, discussing island universes, scientific truth, biological phenomena, stability in bridges, etc. Copies limited; no more than 1 to a customer.
FREE

POPULAR SCIENTIFIC LECTURES, Hermann von Helmholtz. Helmholtz was a superb expositor as well as a scientist of genius in many areas. The seven essays in this volume are models of clarity, and even today they rank among the best general descriptions of their subjects ever written. "The Physiological Causes of Harmony in Music" was the first significant physiological explanation of musical consonance and dissonance. Two essays, "On the Interaction of Natural Forces" and "On the Conservation of Force," were of great importance in the history of science, for they firmly established the principle of the conservation of energy. Other lectures include "On the Relation of Optics to Painting," "On Recent Progress in the Theory of Vision," "On Goethe's Scientific Researches," and "On the Origin and Significance of Geometrical Axioms." Selected and edited with an introduction by Professor Morris Kline. xii + 286pp. 5⅜ x 8½.
T799 Paperbound **$1.45**

BOOKS EXPLAINING SCIENCE AND MATHEMATICS

Physics

CONCERNING THE NATURE OF THINGS, Sir William Bragg. Christmas lectures delivered at the Royal Society by Nobel laureate. Why a spinning ball travels in a curved track; how uranium is transmuted to lead, etc. Partial contents: atoms, gases, liquids, crystals, metals, etc. No scientific background needed; wonderful for intelligent child. 32pp. of photos, 57 figures. xii + 232pp. 5⅜ x 8.
T31 Paperbound **$1.50**

THE RESTLESS UNIVERSE, Max Born. New enlarged version of this remarkably readable account by a Nobel laureate. Moving from sub-atomic particles to universe, the author explains in very simple terms the latest theories of wave mechanics. Partial contents: air and its relatives, electrons & ions, waves & particles, electronic structure of the atom, nuclear physics. Nearly 1000 illustrations, including 7 animated sequences. 325pp. 6 x 9.
T412 Paperbound **$2.00**

FROM EUCLID TO EDDINGTON: A STUDY OF THE CONCEPTIONS OF THE EXTERNAL WORLD, Sir Edmund Whittaker. A foremost British scientist traces the development of theories of natural philosophy from the western rediscovery of Euclid to Eddington, Einstein, Dirac, etc. The inadequacy of classical physics is contrasted with present day attempts to understand the physical world through relativity, non-Euclidean geometry, space curvature, wave mechanics, etc. 5 major divisions of examination: Space; Time and Movement; the Concepts of Classical Physics; the Concepts of Quantum Mechanics; the Eddington Universe. 212pp. 5⅜ x 8. T491 Paperbound **$1.35**

PHYSICS, THE PIONEER SCIENCE, L. W. Taylor. First thorough text to place all important physical phenomena in cultural-historical framework; remains best work of its kind. Exposition of physical laws, theories· developed chronologically, with great historical, illustrative experiments diagrammed, described, worked out mathematically. Excellent physics text for self-study as well as class work. Vol. 1: Heat, Sound: motion, acceleration, gravitation, conservation of energy, heat engines, rotation, heat, mechanical energy, etc. 211 illus. 407pp. 5⅜ x 8. Vol. 2: Light, Electricity: images, lenses, prisms, magnetism, Ohm's law, dynamos, telegraph, quantum theory, decline of mechanical view of nature, etc. Bibliography. 13 table appendix. Index. 551 illus. 2 color plates. 508pp. 5⅜ x 8.
Vol. 1 S565 Paperbound **$2.25**
Vol. 2 S566 Paperbound **$2.25**
The set **$4.50**

A SURVEY OF PHYSICAL THEORY, Max Planck. One of the greatest scientists of all time, creator of the quantum revolution in physics, writes in non-technical terms of his own discoveries and those of other outstanding creators of modern physics. Planck wrote this book when science had just crossed the threshold of the new physics, and he communicates the excitement felt then as he discusses electromagnetic theories, statistical methods, evolution of the concept of light, a step-by-step description of how he developed his own momentous theory, and many more of the basic ideas behind modern physics. Formerly "A Survey of Physics." Bibliography. Index. 128pp. 5⅜ x 8. S650 Paperbound **$1.15**

THE ATOMIC NUCLEUS, M. Korsunsky. The only non-technical comprehensive account of the atomic nucleus in English. For college physics students, etc. Chapters cover: Radioactivity, the Nuclear Model of the Atom, the Mass of Atomic Nuclei, the Disintegration of Atomic Nuclei, the Discovery of the Positron, the Artificial Transformation of Atomic Nuclei, Artificial Radioactivity, Mesons, the Neutrino, the Structure of Atomic Nuclei and Forces Acting Between Nuclear Particles, Nuclear Fission, Chain Reaction, Peaceful Uses, Thermocluear Reactions. Slightly abridged edition. Translated by G. Yankovsky. 65 figures. Appendix includes 45 photographic illustrations. 413 pp. 5⅜ x 8. S1052 Paperbound **$2.00**

PRINCIPLES OF MECHANICS SIMPLY EXPLAINED, Morton Mott-Smith. Excellent, highly readable introduction to the theories and discoveries of classical physics. Ideal for the layman who desires a foundation which will enable him to understand and appreciate contemporary developments in the physical sciences. Discusses: Density, The Law of Gravitation, Mass and Weight, Action and Reaction, Kinetic and Potential Energy, The Law of Inertia, Effects of Acceleration, The Independence of Motions, Galileo and the New Science of Dynamics, Newton and the New Cosmos, The Conservation of Momentum, and other topics. Revised edition of "This Mechanical World." Illustrated by E. Kosa, Jr. Bibliography and Chronology. Index. xiv + 171pp. 5⅜ x 8½. T1067 Paperbound **$1.35**

THE CONCEPT OF ENERGY SIMPLY EXPLAINED, Morton Mott-Smith. Elementary, non-technical exposition which traces the story of man's conquest of energy, with particular emphasis on the developments during the nineteenth century and the first three decades of our own century. Discusses man's earlier efforts to harness energy, more recent experiments and discoveries relating to the steam engine, the engine indicator, the motive power of heat, the principle of excluded perpetual motion, the bases of the conservation of energy, the concept of entropy, the internal combustion engine, mechanical refrigeration, and many other related topics. Also much biographical material. Index. Bibliography. 33 illustrations. ix + 215pp. 5⅜ x 8½. T1071 Paperbound **$1.25**

HEAT AND ITS WORKINGS, Morton Mott-Smith. One of the best elementary introductions to the theory and attributes of heat, covering such matters as the laws governing the effect of heat on solids, liquids and gases, the methods by which heat is measured, the conversion of a substance from one form to another through heating and cooling, evaporation, the effects of pressure on boiling and freezing points, and the three ways in which heat is transmitted (conduction, convection, radiation). Also brief notes on major experiments and discoveries. Concise, but complete, it presents all the essential facts about the subject in readable style. Will give the layman and beginning student a first-rate background in this major topic in physics. Index. Bibliography. 50 illustrations. x + 165pp. 5⅜ x 8½. T978 Paperbound **$1.15**

THE STORY OF ATOMIC THEORY AND ATOMIC ENERGY, J. G. Feinberg. Wider range of facts on physical theory, cultural implications, than any other similar source. Completely non-technical. Begins with first atomic theory, 600 B.C., goes through A-bomb, developments to 1959. Avogadro, Rutherford, Bohr, Einstein, radioactive decay, binding energy, radiation danger, future benefits of nuclear power, dozens of other topics, told in lively, related, informal manner. Particular stress on European atomic research. "Deserves special mention . . . authoritative," Saturday Review. Formerly "The Atom Story." New chapter to 1959. Index. 34 illustrations. 251pp. 5⅜ x 8. T625 Paperbound **$1.60**

THE STRANGE STORY OF THE QUANTUM, AN ACCOUNT FOR THE GENERAL READER OF THE GROWTH OF IDEAS UNDERLYING OUR PRESENT ATOMIC KNOWLEDGE, B. Hoffmann. Presents lucidly and expertly, with barest amount of mathematics, the problems and theories which led to modern quantum physics. Dr. Hoffmann begins with the closing years of the 19th century, when certain trifling discrepancies were noticed, and with illuminating analogies and examples takes you through the brilliant concepts of Planck, Einstein, Pauli, de Broglie, Bohr, Schroedinger, Heisenberg, Dirac, Sommerfeld, Feynman, etc. This edition includes a new, long postscript carrying the story through 1958. "Of the books attempting an account of the history and contents of our modern atomic physics which have come to my attention, this is the best," H. Margenau, Yale University, in "American Journal of Physics." 32 tables and line illustrations. Index. 275pp. 5⅜ x 8.
T518 Paperbound **$1.75**

THE EVOLUTION OF SCIENTIFIC THOUGHT FROM NEWTON TO EINSTEIN, A. d'Abro. Einstein's special and general theories of relativity, with their historical implications, are analyzed in non-technical terms. Excellent accounts of the contributions of Newton, Riemann, Weyl, Planck, Eddington, Maxwell, Lorentz and others are treated in terms of space and time, equations of electromagnetics, finiteness of the universe, methodology of science. 21 diagrams. 482pp. 5⅜ x 8.
T2 Paperound **$2.25**

THE RISE OF THE NEW PHYSICS, A. d'Abro. A half-million word exposition, formerly titled THE DECLINE OF MECHANISM, for readers not versed in higher mathematics. The only thorough explanation, in everyday language, of the central core of modern mathematical physical theory, treating both classical and modern theoretical physics, and presenting in terms almost anyone can understand the equivalent of 5 years of study of mathematical physics. Scientifically impeccable coverage of mathematical-physical thought from the Newtonian system up through the electronic theories of Dirac and Heisenberg and Fermi's statistics. Combines both history and exposition; provides a broad yet unified and detailed view, with constant comparison of classical and modern views on phenomena and theories. "A must for anyone doing serious study in the physical sciences," JOURNAL OF THE FRANKLIN INSTITUTE. "Extraordinary faculty . . . to explain ideas and theories of theoretical physics in the language of daily life," ISIS. First part of set covers philosophy of science, drawing upon the practice of Newton, Maxwell, Poincaré, Einstein, others, discussing modes of thought, experiment, interpretations of causality, etc. In the second part, 100 pages explain grammar and vocabulary of mathematics, with discussions of functions, groups, series, Fourier series, etc. The remainder is devoted to concrete, detailed coverage of both classical and quantum physics, explaining such topics as analytic mechanics, Hamilton's principle, wave theory of light, electromagnetic waves, groups of transformations, thermodynamics, phase rule, Brownian movement, kinetics, special relativity, Planck's original quantum theory, Bohr's atom, Zeeman effect, Broglie's wave mechanics, Heisenberg's uncertainty, Eigen-values, matrices, scores of other important topics. Discoveries and theories are covered for such men as Alembert, Born, Cantor, Debye, Euler, Foucault, Galois, Gauss, Hadamard, Kelvin, Kepler, Laplace, Maxwell, Pauli, Rayleigh, Volterra, Weyl, Young, more than 180 others. Indexed. 97 illustrations. ix + 982pp. 5⅜ x 8.
T3 Volume 1, Paperbound **$2.25**
T4 Volume 2, Paperbound **$2.25**

SPINNING TOPS AND GYROSCOPIC MOTION, John Perry. Well-known classic of science still unsurpassed for lucid, accurate, delightful exposition. How quasi-rigidity is induced in flexible and fluid bodies by rapid motions; why gyrostat falls, top rises; nature and effect on climatic conditions of earth's precessional movement; effect of internal fluidity on rotating bodies, etc. Appendixes describe practical uses to which gyroscopes have been put in ships, compasses, monorail transportation. 62 figures. 128pp. 5⅜ x 8.
T416 Paperbound **$1.25**

THE UNIVERSE OF LIGHT, Sir William Bragg. No scientific training needed to read Nobel Prize winner's expansion of his Royal Institute Christmas Lectures. Insight into nature of light, methods and philosophy of science. Explains lenses, reflection, color, resonance, polarization, x-rays, the spectrum, Newton's work with prisms, Huygens' work with polarization, Crookes' with cathode ray, etc. Leads into clear statement of 2 major historical theories of light, corpuscle and wave. Dozens of experiments you can do. 199 illus., including 2 full-page color plates. 293pp. 5⅜ x 8.
S538 Paperbound **$1.85**

THE STORY OF X-RAYS FROM RÖNTGEN TO ISOTOPES, A. R. Bleich. Non-technical history of x-rays, their scientific explanation, their applications in medicine, industry, research, and art, and their effect on the individual and his descendants. Includes amusing early reactions to Röntgen's discovery, cancer therapy, detections of art and stamp forgeries, potential risks to patient and operator, etc. Illustrations show x-rays of flower structure, the gall bladder, gears with hidden defects, etc. Original Dover publication. Glossary. Bibliography. Index. 55 photos and figures. xiv + 186pp. 5⅜ x 8.
T662 Paperbound **$1.50**

ELECTRONS, ATOMS, METALS AND ALLOYS, Wm. Hume-Rothery. An introductory-level explanation of the application of the electronic theory to the structure and properties of metals and alloys, taking into account the new theoretical work done by mathematical physicists. Material presented in dialogue-form between an "Old Metallurgist" and a "Young Scientist." Their discussion falls into 4 main parts: the nature of an atom, the nature of a metal, the nature of an alloy, and the structure of the nucleus. They cover such topics as the hydrogen atom, electron waves, wave mechanics, Brillouin zones, co-valent bonds, radioactivity and natural disintegration, fundamental particles, structure and fission of the nucleus, etc. Revised, enlarged edition. 177 illustrations. Subject and name indexes. 407pp. 5⅜ x 8½.
S1046 Paperbound **$2.25**

CHEMISTRY AND PHYSICAL CHEMISTRY

ORGANIC CHEMISTRY, F. C. Whitmore. The entire subject of organic chemistry for the practicing chemist and the advanced student. Storehouse of facts, theories, processes found elsewhere only in specialized journals. Covers aliphatic compounds (500 pages on the properties and synthetic preparation of hydrocarbons, halides, proteins, ketones, etc.), alicyclic compounds, aromatic compounds, heterocyclic compounds, organophosphorus and organometallic compounds. Methods of synthetic preparation analyzed critically throughout. Includes much of biochemical interest. "The scope of this volume is astonishing," INDUSTRIAL AND ENGINEERING CHEMISTRY. 12,000-reference index. 2387-item bibliography. Total of x + 1005pp. 5⅜ x 8.
Two volume set. S700 Vol I Paperbound **$2.25**
S701 Vol II Paperbound **$2.25**
The set **$4.50**

THE MODERN THEORY OF MOLECULAR STRUCTURE, Bernard Pullman. A reasonably popular account of recent developments in atomic and molecular theory. Contents: The Wave Function and Wave Equations (history and bases of present theories of molecular structure); The Electronic Structure of Atoms (Description and classification of atomic wave functions, etc.); Diatomic Molecules; Non-Conjugated Polyatomic Molecules; Conjugated Polyatomic Molecules; The Structure of Complexes. Minimum of mathematical background needed. New translation by David Antin of "La Structure Moleculaire." Index. Bibliography. vii + 87pp. 5⅜ x 8½. S987 Paperbound **$1.00**

CATALYSIS AND CATALYSTS, Marcel Prettre, Director, Research Institute on Catalysis. This brief book, translated into English for the first time, is the finest summary of the principal modern concepts, methods, and results of catalysis. Ideal introduction for beginning chemistry and physics students. Chapters: Basic Definitions of Catalysis (true catalysis and generalization of the concept of catalysis); The Scientific Bases of Catalysis (Catalysis and chemical thermodynamics, catalysis and chemical kinetics); Homogeneous Catalysis (acid-base catalysis, etc.); Chain Reactions; Contact Masses; Heterogeneous Catalysis (Mechanisms of contact catalyses, etc.); and Industrial Applications (acids and fertilizers, petroleum and petroleum chemistry, rubber, plastics, synthetic resins, and fibers). Translated by David Antin. Index. vi + 88pp. 5⅜ x 8½. S998 Paperbound **$1.00**

POLAR MOLECULES, Pieter Debye. This work by Nobel laureate Debye offers a complete guide to fundamental electrostatic field relations, polarizability, molecular structure. Partial contents: electric intensity, displacement and force, polarization by orientation, molar polarization and molar refraction, halogen-hydrides, polar liquids, ionic saturation, dielectric constant, etc. Special chapter considers quantum theory. Indexed. 172pp. 5⅜ x 8. S64 Paperbound **$1.65**

THE ELECTRONIC THEORY OF ACIDS AND BASES, W. F. Luder and Saverio Zuffanti. The first full systematic presentation of the electronic theory of acids and bases—treating the theory and its ramifications in an uncomplicated manner. Chapters: Historical Background; Atomic Orbitals and Valence; The Electronic Theory of Acids and Bases; Electrophilic and Electrodotic Reagents; Acidic and Basic Radicals; Neutralization; Titrations with Indicators; Displacement; Catalysis; Acid Catalysis; Base Catalysis; Alkoxides and Catalysts; Conclusion. Required reading for all chemists. Second revised (1961) eidtion, with additional examples and references. 3 figures. 9 tables. Index. Bibliography xii + 165pp. 5⅜ x 8. S201 Paperbound **$1.50**

KINETIC THEORY OF LIQUIDS, J. Frenkel. Regarding the kinetic theory of liquids as a generalization and extension of the theory of solid bodies, this volume covers all types of arrangements of solids, thermal displacements of atoms, interstitial atoms and ions, orientational and rotational motion of molecules, and transition between states of matter. Mathematical theory is developed close to the physical subject matter. 216 bibliographical footnotes. 55 figures. xi + 485pp. 5⅜ x 8. S95 Paperbound **$2.55**

THE PRINCIPLES OF ELECTROCHEMISTRY, D. A. MacInnes. Basic equations for almost every subfield of electrochemistry from first principles, referring at all times to the soundest and most recent theories and results; unusually useful as text or as reference. Covers coulometers and Faraday's Law, electrolytic conductance, the Debye-Hueckel method for the theoretical calculation of activity coefficients, concentration cells, standard electrode potentials, thermodynamic ionization constants, pH, potentiometric titrations, irreversible phenomena, Planck's equation, and much more. "Excellent treatise," AMERICAN CHEMICAL SOCIETY JOURNAL. "Highly recommended," CHEMICAL AND METALLURGICAL ENGINEERING. 2 Indices. Appendix. 585-item bibliography. 137 figures. 94 tables. ii + 478pp. 5⅝ x 8⅜. S52 Paperbound **$2.45**

THE PHASE RULE AND ITS APPLICATION, Alexander Findlay. Covering chemical phenomena of 1, 2, 3, 4, and multiple component systems, this "standard work on the subject" (NATURE, London), has been completely revised and brought up to date by A. N. Campbell and N. O. Smith. Brand new material has been added on such matters as binary, tertiary liquid equilibria, solid solutions in ternary systems, quinary systems of salts and water. Completely revised to triangular coordinates in ternary systems, clarified graphic representation, solid models, etc. 9th revised edition. Author, subject indexes. 236 figures. 505 footnotes, mostly bibliographic. xii + 494pp. 5⅜ x 8. S91 Paperbound **$2.50**

THE SOLUBILITY OF NONELECTROLYTES, Joel H. Hildebrand and Robert L. Scott. The standard work on the subject; still indispensable as a reference source and for classroom work. Partial contents: The Ideal Solution (including Raoult's Law and Henry's Law, etc.); Nonideal Solutions; Intermolecular Forces; The Liquid State; Entropy of Athermal Mixing; Heat of Mixing; Polarity; Hydrogen Bonding; Specific Interactions; "Solvation" and "Association"; Systems of Three or More Components; Vapor Pressure of Binary Liquid Solutions; Mixtures of Gases; Solubility of Gases in Liquids; of Liquids in Liquids; of Solids in Liquids; Evaluation of Solubility Parameters; and other topics. Corrected republication of third (revised) edition. Appendices. Indexes. 138 figures. 111 tables. 1 photograph. iv + 488pp. 5⅜ x 8½.
$$\text{S1125 Paperbound } \mathbf{\$2.50}$$

TERNARY SYSTEMS: INTRODUCTION TO THE THEORY OF THREE COMPONENT SYSTEMS, G. Masing. Furnishes detailed discussion of representative types of 3-components systems, both in solid models (particularly metallic alloys) and isothermal models. Discusses mechanical mixture without compounds and without solid solutions; unbroken solid solution series; solid solutions with solubility breaks in two binary systems; iron-silicon-aluminum alloys; allotropic forms of iron in ternary system; other topics. Bibliography. Index. 166 illustrations. 178pp. 5⅝ x 8⅜.
$$\text{S631 Paperbound } \mathbf{\$1.50}$$

THE KINETIC THEORY OF GASES, Leonard B. Loeb, University of California. Comprehensive text and reference book which presents full coverage of basic theory and the important experiments and developments in the field for the student and investigator. Partial contents: The Mechanical Picture of a Perfect Gas, The Mean Free Path—Clausius' Deductions, Distribution of Molecular Velocities, discussions of theory of the problem of specific heats, the contributions of kinetic theory to our knowledge of electrical and magnetic properties of molecules and its application to the conduction of electricity in gases. New 14-page preface to Dover edition by the author. Name, subject indexes. Six appendices. 570-item bibliography. xxxvi + 687pp. 5⅜ x 8½.
$$\text{S942 Paperbound } \mathbf{\$3.50}$$

IONS IN SOLUTION, Ronald W. Gurney. A thorough and readable introduction covering all the fundamental principles and experiments in the field, by an internationally-known authority. Contains discussions of solvation energy, atomic and molecular ions, lattice energy, transferral of ions, interionic forces, cells and half-cells, transference of electrons, exchange forces, hydrogen ions, the electro-chemical series, and many other related topics. Indispensable to advanced undergraduates and graduate students in electrochemistry. Index. 45 illustrations. 15 tables. vii + 206pp. 5⅜ x 8½.
$$\text{S124 Paperbound } \mathbf{\$1.!5}$$

IONIC PROCESSES IN SOLUTION, Ronald W. Gurney. Lucid, comprehensive examination which brings together the approaches of electrochemistry, thermodynamics, statistical mechanics, electroacoustics, molecular physics, and quantum theory in the interpretation of the behavior of ionic solutions—the most important single work on the subject. More extensive and technical than the author's earlier work (IONS IN SOLUTION), it is a middle-level text for graduate students and researchers in electrochemistry. Covers such matters as Brownian motion in liquids, molecular ions in solution, heat of precipitation, entropy of solution, proton transfers, dissociation constant of nitric acid, viscosity of ionic solutions, etc. 78 illustrations. 47 tables. Name and subject index. ix + 275pp. 5⅜ x 8½.
$$\text{S134 Paperbound } \mathbf{\$1.85}$$

CRYSTALLOGRAPHIC DATA ON METAL AND ALLOY STRUCTURES, Compiled by A. Taylor and B. J. Kagle, Westinghouse Research Laboratories. Unique collection of the latest crystallographic data on alloys, compounds, and the elements, with lattice spacings expressed uniformly in absolute Angstrom units. Gathers together previously widely-scattered data from the Power Data File of the ATSM, structure reports, and the Landolt-Bornstein Tables, as well as from other original literature. 2300 different compounds listed in the first table, Alloys and Intermetallic Compounds, with much vital information on each. Also listings for nearly 700 Borides, Carbides, Hydrides, Oxides, Nitrides. Also all the necessary data on the crystal structure of 77 elements. vii + 263pp. 5⅜ x 8.
$$\text{S1013 Paperbound } \mathbf{\$2.25}$$

MATHEMATICAL CRYSTALLOGRAPHY AND THE THEORY OF GROUPS OF MOVEMENTS, Harold Hilton. Classic account of the mathematical theory of crystallography, particularly the geometrical theory of crystal-structure based on the work of Bravais, Jordan, Sohncke, Federow, Schoenflies, and Barlow. Partial contents: The Stereographic Projection, Properties Common to Symmetrical and Asymmetrical Crystals, The Theory of Groups, Coordinates of Equivalent Points, Crystallographic Axes and Axial Ratios, The Forms and Growth of Crystals, Lattices and Translations, The Structure-Theory, Infinite Groups of Movements, Triclinic and Monoclinic Groups, Orthorhombic Groups, etc. Index. 188 figures. xii + 262pp. 5⅜ x 8½.
$$\text{S1058 Paperbound } \mathbf{\$2.00}$$

CLASSICS IN THE THEORY OF CHEMICAL COMBINATIONS. Edited by O. T. Benfey. Vol. I of the Classics of Science Series, G. Holton, Harvard University, General Editor. This book is a collection of papers representing the major chapters in the development of the valence concept in chemistry. Includes essays by Wöhler and Liebig, Laurent, Williamson, Frankland, Kekulé and Couper, and two by van't Hoff and le Bel, which mark the first extension of the valence concept beyond its purely numerical character. Introduction and epilogue by Prof. Benfey. Index. 9 illustrations. New translation of Kekulé paper by Benfey. xiv + 191pp. 5⅜ x 8½.
$$\text{S1066 Paperbound } \mathbf{\$1.85}$$